To:

Harvey W. Attra
B.S. P.E. 1954

Thanks for your support

James B. Hoyman

# COMMITMENT
# TO EXCELLENCE

## ONE HUNDRED YEARS OF
## ENGINEERING EDUCATION AT
## THE UNIVERSITY OF TEXAS AT AUSTIN

# COMMITMENT TO EXCELLENCE

ONE HUNDRED YEARS OF ENGINEERING EDUCATION AT
THE UNIVERSITY OF TEXAS AT AUSTIN

By Richard B. McCaslin
and Dean Earnest F. Gloyna, P.E.

1986
THE ENGINEERING FOUNDATION OF
THE COLLEGE OF ENGINEERING
THE UNIVERSITY OF TEXAS AT AUSTIN

ISBN 0-9617692-0-3

Cover and interior design by Barbara Jezek
Typeset by G&S Typesetters, Inc.
Printed in the United States of America
by The Whitley Company
Photograph for frontispiece by
Walter Barnes Studio

# TABLE OF CONTENTS

*Letter from President William H. Cunningham,*                    ix
*The University of Texas at Austin*

PREFACE                                                           xi

ACKNOWLEDGEMENTS                                                  xiii

INTRODUCTION:                                                     1
*The Development of a Model for*
*Engineering Education in Texas*

FIFTY YEARS ON FORTY ACRES:                                       13
*Dean Thomas U. Taylor and the*
*College of Engineering, 1888–1936*

MEN OF INGENUITY:                                                 39
*Dean Willis R. Woolrich and the*
*College of Engineering, 1936–1958*

AN EXPERIMENT WITH ENGINEERING SCIENCE:                           63
*Dean William W. Hagerty and the*
*College of Engineering, 1958–1963*

THE DRIVE FOR TEACHING EXCELLENCE:                                85
*Dean John J. McKetta, Jr., and the*
*College of Engineering, 1963–1969*

TOWARD A POSITION OF ACADEMIC EXCELLENCE:                105
    *Dean Earnest F. Gloyna and the*
    *College of Engineering, 1970–*

ENGINEERING LEADERSHIP THROUGH RESEARCH:                 145
    *The College of Engineering*
    *and the State of Texas*

THE CHILDREN OF ALEC:                                    185
    *Student Life and Tradition in*
    *the College of Engineering*

EDUCATION FOR TECHNOLOGICAL LEADERSHIP:                  209
    *A Look to the Future*

EPILOGUE:                                                217
    *A Challenge for the Future*

NOTES                                                    219

APPENDIX                                                 247

INDEX                                                    305

This seal of the College of Engineering adorns the T. U. Taylor Hall of Engineering, completed in 1933. [College of Engineering, The University of Texas at Austin]

# THE UNIVERSITY OF TEXAS SYSTEM

*Board of Regents*

On behalf of The University of Texas at Austin, I am pleased to present this history of the College of Engineering. When the founders of The University laid the cornerstone in 1882, they could hardly have anticipated its century of evolution from a small public university in a rural society to an internationally recognized graduate research institution in a highly urbanized state that contains three of the nation's most populous cities. Today The University fulfills the constitutional mandate to be a university of the first class.

The College of Engineering has been an important element in that development. Through education and research, its talented and devoted faculty have moved forward each year toward national and international eminence. The strong leadership and distinguished contributions of its alumni have made them superb examples for all young Texans.

As The University enters its second century, we can be sure that society in the information age will expect even more of higher education and will redefine "first class" in ever-escalating standards. The College of Engineering will meet the challenges of tomorrow as it has those of the past, through a continuing commitment to excellence. This record of those who brought the College to greatness will provide future generations with a model for even greater achievements.

William H. Cunningham
President
The University of Texas at Austin
July 15, 1986

# PREFACE

The evolution of the College of Engineering of The University of Texas at Austin represents a commitment to excellence through more than a century of engineering education and research. This book commemorates the sesquicentennial of Texas and the outstanding contributions of the College to the state. Within these pages, an attempt has been made to chronicle the achievements of those individuals who facilitated the development of the College into an institution of international academic prominence.

The primary objectives of this project were to document as many historical highlights as possible, present some of the current initiatives, and provide some perspectives on the future. The introduction discusses engineering education and the difficulties associated with a struggling young institution. Five chapters are devoted to a narrative of the College during nearly one hundred years of development from 1888 to 1986. The life and times of engineering education during the tenure of deans Thomas U. Taylor, Willis R. Woolrich, William W. Hagerty, John J. McKetta, Jr., and Earnest F. Gloyna illustrate various stages in the academic growth of The University, now known as The University of Texas at Austin. Because of the contemporary improvement in the quality of engineering education and the emergence of a strong graduate program at The University, a separate chapter is included on engineering leadership through research. Student life deserves a special niche in an academic documentary; a final chapter is devoted to a brief review of the camaraderie and traditions established in the last century. A look to the future seemed to be a fitting conclusion. World–class aspirations for academic excellence begin with the dreams and plans of the faculty, both past and present. A wealth of tabular data and extensive notations, possibly of value only to future historians, is appended to the text.

The leadership of the engineering faculty in the classroom and in the laboratory has served as a model for the many alumni of the College. The number of teachers and their students who have been recognized with the highest honors of their chosen profession is enormous because both continue to address the demands of society. No less important are the contributions of those unsung legions of University–educated engineers who perform heroically every day in academia, government, and the business community. It is for all the "children of Alec," the patron saint of the College of Engineering, that this book is intended.

# ACKNOWLEDGMENTS

This undertaking would not have been possible without the aid of numerous staff, faculty, and alumni of the College. Former deans Hagerty and McKetta graciously consented to be interviewed, as well as assistant dean emeritus John A. Focht. The information supplied by associate deans Charles A. Sorber, Thomas W. Kennedy, and Herbert H. Woodson filled many crucial gaps in the narrative. On the dean's staff, Paul F. McClure, W. Thomas Reeder, and Linda M. Williams provided much of the data for the appendices, which were typed by Esther R. Moore and Frances V. Croy. Graphs to present this material in a more visually appealing fashion were created by Claire W. Kirkpatrick and Iris Schoenrock. Jack G. Lawrence and Lisa DeFalco patiently transcribed thirty–six taped interviews. Student assistants Stuart M. Crane and Jeff W. Glaser sifted through endless catalogs and University publications in order to ensure the thoroughness of this record. Barbara L. Cummings, Priscilla Faris-Eyman, and student assistant Rebecca L. Petersen handled the extra burden of correspondence with their usual cheerful efficiency. Jill M. Mayfield, as publications coordinator, participated in the first faltering steps of this project, but it was her successor, Patricia E. Cunningham, who brought all of the disparate elements together and made them a book. The manuscript was immeasurably improved through the copy editing skills of Alison Tartt, Austin freelance editor. The staff of the Barker Texas History Center deserve special mention for their patient compliance with our demands.

Alphabetically by department, faculty who deserve special mention for the effort they devoted to this project are: Lyle G. Clark, Linda J. Hayes, J. Parker Lamb, Jr., Victor G. Szebehely, and Byron D. Tapley of Aerospace Engineering and Engineering Mechanics; William A. Cunningham, Thomas F. Edgar, Donald R. Paul, Howard F. Rase, Robert S. Schechter, James E. Stice, and Eugene

H. Wissler of Chemical Engineering; Raymond F. Dawson, Franklin B. Johnson, Joe O. Ledbetter, Joseph F. Malina, Jr., Lymon C. Reese, and J. Neils Thompson of Civil Engineering; James D. McFarland of Drawing; William C. Deusterhoeft, Alfred H. LaGrone, Edward J. Powers, Jr., Harold W. Smith, and Archie W. Straiton of Electrical Engineering; Margaret R. Baker, Carl J. Eckhardt, Jr., Leonardt F. Kreisle, H. Grady Rylander, Jr., Byron E. Short, and Delbert Tesar of Mechanical Engineering; and Ben H. Caudle, Myron H. Dorfman, Larry W. Lake, Augusto L. Podio, and Gary A. Pope of Petroleum Engineering. Margaret N. Maxey, the faculty director of the Clint W. Murchison, Sr., Chair of Free Enterprise, generously donated time and materials. Former professor George H. Fancher of Petroleum Engineering devoted extra time and attention to this project. David S. Evans, of the Department of Astronomy, provided some perspective on the electrical engineering research effort in conjunction with the McDonald Observatory.

Among the alumni, a particular note of thanks goes to the former chairmen of the Engineering Foundation Advisory Council who replied to our questionnaire. Although at times puzzled by our interest in the past because their gaze is fixed irrevocably on the future, they nevertheless provided important pieces for solving the historical riddle. These loyal alumni include Louis A. Beecherl, William B. Franklin, John E. Kasch, Joe J. King, Paul D. Meek, William J. Murray, Jr., and Robert L. Parker, Sr. Alumnus John Hargis, who continues to work with the Equal Opportunity in Engineering program, supplied some insight on the experience of minority students in the College.

Finally, our wives deserve a personal note of gratitude for their support through this and many other projects. The position of dean for a vibrant academic institution such as the College requires two people; Agnes M. Gloyna has been a loyal supporter of the Dean and of the College for nearly forty years. In the hope that there may truly be life after graduate school for her wayward husband, Jana D. McCaslin patiently endured long nights alone while this and other manuscripts were prepared. To them this volume is dedicated.

# INTRODUCTION:

*The Development of a Model for*
*Engineering Education in Texas*

E ngineering education at The University of Texas at Austin began as a response to public demand for skilled technical leadership in an era of rapidly advancing technology. Modern engineering education, which had evolved slowly beginning in the seventeenth century in Europe, had taken on new life in the expanding United States, where the pace and character were set by the construction of canals, railroads, mining and steel enterprises, and later by electrical industries. The most pressing task in the nineteenth century was to produce "technical practitioners" to facilitate industrial development; much of the work rested not on scientific inquiry and research, but on practice, common sense, trial and error, and intuitive or informed engineering judgement.[1]

Until the late nineteenth century in the United States, as around the world, engineering education relied primarily on a system of apprenticeship. Texas, like the rest of the South, had to import educated engineers before the Civil War because the few schools that offered engineering degrees clustered in the industrially advanced North. The demand for education through a "university of the first class," however, received even greater support after 1865 in Texas as engineering schools multiplied in almost every state, North and South. The state constitution of 1876 codified public demand, and in 1883 Texas became one of the first states within the old Confederacy to provide an engineering curriculum based on the study of scientific theories and their application. The University of Texas incorporated a model developed through more than two centuries of structured engineering education, and added those features neccessary to provide for the technological needs of the region.

Formal engineering education originated in France during the late seventeenth century. Essentially a revival of Roman engineering, techniques

1

were refined to provide for military needs during an active period of road, bridge, and canal building. The Corps des Ponts et Chausées at Paris, responsible for the construction of bridges, roads, and other works for the army, was organized under the direct supervision of the king in 1716. D. C. Trudaine, a noted French engineer, founded a school to train draughtsmen for the Corps in 1747 that became the École des Ponts et Chausées by 1760, capably directed by Jean Randolphe Perronet. Revered as the "dean of French engineers," Perronet was an inventor as well as a builder of bridges and roads, and was recognized by election to the Royal Society, chartered by Charles II of England in 1662 as an "incubator" primarily for British scientists and architects but also for many Europeans distinguished in the pure and applied sciences. An École des Mines was also established by decree at about the same time, and the École Polytechnique opened in 1795, contributing to the spread of formal engineering education.[2]

The École des Ponts et Chausées and its contemporaries maintained an emphasis on teaching engineering skills by apprenticeship for military applications. The Industrial Revolution in Britain in the eighteenth century changed the focus for engineers, leading to the recognition of civil engineering as a separate profession. English innovations, unlike most French projects, developed from the commercial sector rather than being mandated from above, and consequently were of more use to the general population as they facilitated advances in textiles and hardware. The French were noted for their canals and roadways; the British, because of the emphasis on civilian industry, made great advances in mechanics, especially in the development of steam engines.

Civil engineering was the first branch of modern engineering to develop from the older military tradition, but other fields took root as the demand for technical expertise among civilians grew. Engineering as a discipline benefited from the development of mathematics as a tool; the initiation of scientific experimental studies into the forces of nature, which led to modern knowledge of the mechanics of liquids and solids; and the systemization of chemistry. The invention of the slide rule in 1622 by Englishman William Oughtred, using logarithms recently developed by John Napier, Henry Broggs, and Edmund Gunter, placed an invaluable tool in the hands of the new professionals alongside other implements for more accurate measurement.[3]

Civil engineering retained a strong element of the traditional arts of construction through the latter half of the eighteenth century. John Smeaton in 1750 became the first man in Europe to call himself a "civil engineer," to distinguish his vocation from that of the military engineer and the architect. Elected to the Royal Society in 1753, Smeaton regularly contributed articles on his investigations of methods to provide power for industry to the Society's journal, *Philosophical Transactions*. He built a five-sailed windmill at Leeds after a trip to Flanders and Holland to study their design, and in 1760 used a waterwheel to drive two pistons moving in cast–iron cylinders to provide air for a blast furnace belonging to John Roebuck, builder of the Carron Ironworks, which manufactured carronades in Scotland. Smeaton's work with waterwheels, which clearly demonstrated the advantage of an overshot design, was one of his most important contributions. Smeaton also experimented with early steam engines, improving the design of Thomas Newcomen's model until his own version, erected at Cronstadt Docks in Russia, had an overall thermal efficiency rating of 1.4. It was this very same engine that James Watt would perfect in 1786.[4]

Smeaton convened the Society of Civil Engineers for the first time on March 15, 1771, in the King's Head Tavern in Holborn. It was not the first engineering society, but it has become the most influential and enduring in the English–speaking world. Greatly influenced by the "almost transcendental ubiquity of Smeaton," many contemporaries referred to it as the "Smeatonian Society" and called its members "Smeatonians." The Society included such eminent names as James Watt among its subscribers, and conducted an active correspondence with French and American men of science. The organization expired in 1792 when Smeaton himself withdrew due to internal bickering, but revived in 1793 after his death. The continuing desire among professional engineers for productive association led to the creation of an assembly for younger men in 1818. Thomas Telford became president of the new club in 1820, directing its incorporation as the Institution of Civil Engineers in 1828. Smeaton's impetus for independent organization, like his Society, survived him, providing a model for future effort.[5]

The rise of engineering science in the nineteenth century forced a final distinction between architecture and civil engineering. New interests and techniques brought increasing complexity into the practice of engineering as quantitative procedure began to overshadow qualitative judgment. It soon became apparent that a more systematic education was required to facilitate entry into the profession and expedite the development of engineering as a discipline. The traditional method of apprenticeship could no longer provide the background needed to cope with the demands of society. The United States, a new nation open to experimentation, took the lead in providing a modern engineering curriculum as the older European nations clung stubbornly to the apprentice system.

Britain took the first step toward providing a modern engineering curriculum through the college classroom. A few simple courses on mechanics, mining, and hydrology were offered as early as 1796 at Cambridge University. King's College created the first department of engineering in England, issuing a prospectus for a curriculum on civil and mechanical engineering in 1838. University College founded the first chair in civil engineering in 1841, followed by the first chairs in mechanical engineering and machinery in 1846, the year the Institution of Mechanical Engineers originated in England. British engineering education, however, proceeded very slowly to the end of the century because a lack of coordination between it and the profession allowed the apprentice system to endure on a large scale, perpetuating the image of engineering as a trade and creating a wide gulf between industry and schools. The French model remained much more popular for the development of technical education in the United States.[6]

Engineering education reached its highest point of development in Germany before crossing the Atlantic. Great engineering advances were made from professorial chairs, not professional positions, in Germany. An early school teaching the practical skills of mining through apprenticeship had opened in the Frieberg area of Saxony in 1702, but after the end of the Napoleonic era a system of research–oriented institutions was created. The Universities of Berlin in 1810, Breslau in 1811, Bonn in 1818, and Munich in 1826 were supplemented by a growing number of technical secondary schools and military institutes. Their influence on the teaching methods of other European institutions and eventually schools in the United States was tremendous; the genesis of modern organized research can be found in the practices that gradually came into use during the late nineteenth century for graduate teaching in the universities of Europe, beginning with Germany. For the first time, research, especially engineering, was put on a production basis, with each student receiving an assignment on a portion of the problem, making his inquiry, and reporting his findings. Many of America's finest engineers in the nineteenth century, before such procedures for graduate education were generally adopted in the United States, attended German technical schools, which had taken the lead in engineering education from the French by the latter half of the nineteenth century.[7]

Engineering in the United States repeated the European pattern of evolution in emphasis from military to civilian in a much briefer span of time. As in Britain, France, and Germany, education "was more a reflection of the needs of the hour than a product of any comprehensive planning." Prior to the American Revolution, the few technical needs of the colonies were met by British officers, many of them trained at the Royal Military Academy, established in 1741. George Washington, who himself had some experience in surveying and construction, decried the "want of engineers" when he took command of the tiny Continental Army before Boston in 1775. Only the arrival of foreign volunteers such as Thaddeus Kosciuszko, a Pole educated at the Royal Military Academy in Poland and a school of artillery and military engineering in France, overcame the scarcity of engineers.[8]

The need for formally educated American engineers had been made painfully obvious during the Revolution, but twenty years would pass after the close of the war before Congress acted. The U. S. Military Academy at West Point became the first school of applied science in any English–speaking country when it opened in 1802. Public demand for technical leadership quickly outstripped the capacities of the tiny cadet corps graduating each year, only a few of which actually practiced engineering. Alden Partridge, dismissed as superintendent of West Point, opened the American Literary, Scientific, and Military Academy, now known as Norwich University, in 1819. Partridge modeled his courses after those taught at West Point and the leading French schools, as King's College in London would not offer a curriculum in engineering for nearly two decades. Stephen van Rensselaer opened the Rensselaer School, now the Rensselaer Polytechnic Institute, in 1824, and granted the first civil engineering degree in the United States in 1835. Until the middle of the nineteenth century almost all of the academically educated engineers in this country came from West Point or Rensselaer Polytechnic Institute.[9]

Rapid development of engineering education occurred in the United States following the informal marriage of science and engineering about the middle of the nineteenth century after a "flirtation" of several hundred years. Railroads lent unprecedented impetus to many technical disciplines beginning in 1830, particularly in the design and construction of roadbeds, bridges, and tunnels that had to be built quickly and to exacting specifications. Two railroad magnates, Abbott Lawrence and J. E. Sheffield, founded scientific engineering schools at Harvard and Yale respectively in 1847. Eliphalet North had established engineering as a subject at Union College in 1846, followed by Dartmouth College and the University of Michigan, which in 1847 was the first state school to offer course work on civil engineering. By the 1850s England was sending representatives to the United States to study its armories, especially the works of Colt and Springfield, to learn their manufacturing techniques. The Birmingham Small Arms Factory was outfitted with American machinery, and other innovations were copied. The first national professional engineering association in the United States, the American Society of Civil Engineers and Architects, developed from the Boston Society of Civil Engineers in 1852. In 1867 the group reorganized as the American Society of Civil Engineers, becoming the model for similar forums in other engineering fields.[10]

The Massachusetts Institute of Technology, established in 1861, combined original research in applied science with diffusion of knowledge. It became a model for the Morrill Act of 1862, which gave federal support to higher education in a systematic manner for the first time. The Morrill Act facilitated a boom in the number of engineering schools, which began in response to the demand of wartime industry. "Of all the nineteenth century wars, that which began on 12 April 1861 . . . seems to have exerted the most intensely ripening effect on technology and engineering up to this time."[11] Steam–powered factories, railroads, bridges, balloons, telegraphs, and explosives were developed, useful for both the military and civilians. Institutions offering technical education almost tripled from six in 1852 to seventeen in 1870, then swelled five more times to eighty–five by 1880 after the Exposition in Philadelphia for the national centennial fired the public imagination. The typical engineering curriculum expanded from three years to a full four–year degree program, permitting incorporation of courses on mechanical, mining, and electrical engineering as well as civil. A beginning was made in graduate education: Yale awarded a doctorate in engineering in 1869, one of three before the turn of the century, and six schools granted master's degrees by 1890, the first in 1879. Advanced engineering studies, however, did not mature until after World War I.[12]

Many Southerners, because their region had been devastated by the Civil War, desired industrial progress even more than Northern manufacturers. The Union had benefited from the expertise of numerous experts such as Herman Haupt, rebuilder of the railroad system; James B. Eads, designer of thirty–two ironclad warships; and A. L. Holley, who purchased the rights to the Bessemer Steel process in 1863 and began the expansion of that industry. The Confederacy, on the other hand, suffered a dearth of engineering talent, in large part due to the lack of schools before the war. The South devoted great attention to development at one time, but under the influence of its cotton economy lagged behind in 1861. The first American state university chartered was the University of North Carolina in 1793; the first student enrolled was Hinton James, who became a civil engineer. James graduated in 1798 and later worked as an assistant to Chief Engineer Robert Fulton in his navigation work. The first canal to be completed within the United States was the Santee Canal, 22 miles long, built in South Carolina between 1793 and 1800. The first railroad in the United States, "and doubtless in the world," to be built from the first as a steam railroad throughout, was the South Carolina Railroad, 136 miles in length, completed in 1834.[13]

These few projects centered on transporting cotton to market, and were constructed by engineers imported from the North. Their success sparked little interest compared with the eye–opening experience of total defeat. At least nine schools in the South taught a course in engineering before 1861, but none awarded a degree in the antebellum period. The singular exception to the dearth of engineering education in the South was the Virginia Military Institute, where Thomas Williamson, a graduate of West Point, delivered lectures on military engineering from 1840 to 1865. Texas Agricultural and Mechanical College in 1871 became only the second Southern school to grant an engineering diploma, just two years after the first was given by the University of Virginia, which had failed in its earlier attempt to establish a program in 1848. Like Texas A&M, however, most state universities in the South could not afford a complete engineering department, and by 1900 only The University of Texas, Vanderbilt University, Washington and Lee University, the University of Missouri, and Washington University in St. Louis had joined the University of Virginia in offering a full curriculum. Their small ranks were supplemented by a handful of land–grant colleges such as Texas A&M that offered courses of varying quality and utility.[14]

The effort for a university in Texas began with the movement to repudiate Mexican rule. The Declaration of Independence signed by the leaders of the rebellious colonists on March 2, 1836, condemned the government of Mexico for several shortcomings, most notably the failure to provide for public education in the state of Coahuila y Texas. Even before the final triumph of the Texan armies at the battle of San Jacinto, the constitution of the new Republic of Texas declared, "It shall be the duty of congress, as soon as circumstances will permit, to provide by law a general system of education."[15] With the final defeat of Santa Anna's army and the withdrawal of Mexican troops, the stage was set for the establishment of Texas education according to the principles established in this early charter.

The mandate for public education included a responsibility to found an institution of higher education. When the Congress of the Republic passed an act for the surveying of a permanent capital in Austin on January 14, 1839, they stipulated that a "sufficient number" of the "most eligible lots" should be put aside for government buildings, including a university. Less than two weeks later the legislators provided an endowment of land for both a system of public schools in Texas and two state universities. The President of the Republic was empowered to contract a surveyor to mark out fifty leagues of vacant land in Texas to be sold for funding the colleges.[16]

A site for a university in Austin was surveyed along with other "out" lots in accordance with an act of January 5, 1840. Lying on a hill covered in live oaks, the original "Forty Acres" lay fallow for over four decades as legislative debate and civil war prevented decisive action for a university. In 1862, believing the Union army would attack the state capital following their capture of Galveston, Confederate Major General John B. Magruder posted a battery on College Hill, ordering that all the trees be cut down. The denuded hill was an even starker reminder to the Texas legislators of their failure to fulfill the constitutional mandate for higher education.[17]

Some small steps to provide funds for higher education had been taken just prior to secession. The legislature set aside public land to be sold for an endowment, stipulating that the proceeds would go into a permanent university fund and would be used for no other purpose. Sales began slowly, but were encouraging enough that Governor Hardin R. Runnels signed a bill February 11, 1858, which provided for the establishment of a university in Texas. The solons supplemented their initial provision with one hundred thousand dollars in U. S. bonds and reserved every tenth section of railroad land for the planned institution. Railroads were just beginning to be built in Texas, but it was anticipated that the sale of these tracts, embracing some of the best farmland in the state, would provide a magnificent sum in the future.[18]

Passage of this bill renewed legislative debate over the nature of the university–to–be. Some diehards insisted on two state institutions of higher learning, usually one in the capital at Austin and one in their home district. Those who agreed on a single university argued over the site; although College Hill had been surveyed just blocks away, many legislators wanted the new school to be constructed far from the debilitating effects of Austin and the legislative chamber itself. Often their ultimate solution, too, was to build it at home, where their constituents could oversee the proper development of the school. Pragmatists pointed out that available funds could not provide for even a single university of good quality until the railroad lands were surveyed and that a system of public education in Texas had yet to be established.

All of these arguments persisted until the final establishment of The University of Texas in Austin in 1881, but the most heated arguments, which lasted well into the twentieth century, centered on the students who would be able to attend the school. State Representative John H. Burnett set the tone of future conflict in 1858 when he voted against a university, asking,

"Who, sir, is to be benefitted by this outlay? A privileged few, in the enjoyment of wealth and prosperity? Or the hard-working, bare-footed, woolhatted, copperas breeches, one gallowsed, double-fisted, road-working and tax-paying masses?" [19]

This plebeian fear that the state university would not be for the "common man" plagued future discussions of the institution in the political forum, hindering the efforts of well–meaning governors and legislators to provide additional appropriations for the struggling University of Texas in its early years of development.

The Civil War and the troubled period of Reconstruction in Texas halted efforts to establish a university. The issue was not forgotten, however, and the Constitution of 1876 reaffirmed the legislature's responsibility for education in the state. In addition to a system of public primary and secondary schools, the lawmakers were to provide for the construction "as soon as possible" of a "university of the first class," to be located by a popular election. Debate in the succeeding legislatures, however, soon degenerated into the all–

too–familiar arguments over the number of universities to be created, which towns could be on the ballot, who would be admitted, and how it would be funded.[20]

It fell to Governor Oran M. Roberts to oversee final passage of the bill firmly establishing The University of Texas. Roberts was an experienced politician with an illustrious career dating from the early days of Texas state-hood. He had an early pioneer's love for the state and the crusty zeal of an un-reconstructed rebel: Roberts served as president of the Secession Convention in 1861, took to the field as a brigadier general, and never stopped fighting for the advancement of Texas. If his state was to lead the New South, and even the nation, it needed a "first class" university, and Roberts was determined to get it. Several state senators approached the newly elected governor in his chamber at the Capitol, insisting the time was not ripe for a university. They concluded by saying it was meant for posterity to provide for higher education in Texas. Roberts leaped out of his chair, shouting that he was posterity incarnate and that the legislature would pass his bill without further delay. On March 30, 1881, Roberts signed the enabling legislation for The University of Texas.[21]

A popular referendum confirmed the site of The University in Austin, and on November 17, 1882, the cornerstone was laid amid great cere-mony. Plans called for the completion of the west wing of the Main Building by the summer of 1883, but a workman's strike delayed its opening until January 1884. In the meantime, classes were held in the temporary Capitol at the corner of Congress Avenue and Mesquite, now Eleventh, Street. Tuition was free, and attendance was good: 221 students, most of them from near Austin, registered for the first year.[22]

Concern for engineering education in Texas closely paralleled the course of debate over The University itself. Texas before it won its indepen-dence had little need for educated engineers; the most striking engineering achievement of the period under Spanish and Mexican rule was the system of acequias, which supplied water to the missions of San Antonio. All of these had been dug during the eighteenth century, and those that were still in use required little maintenance. The influx of hundreds of thousands of new immigrants, however, made necessary the construction of roads, canals, and bridges for transportation, as well as modern water and sewage systems. In 1852 construc-tion began on the first railroad in Texas: the Buffalo Bayou, Brazos, and Colo-rado. The real boom in railroad construction began after the Civil War; as it ended, the demand for paved roads began. The Alamo Portland and Roman Cement Works opened in 1880, the first such plant west of the Mississippi River. As the demands of the people of Texas became more immediate and more com-plex, sentiment grew for the establishment of a sound engineering curriculum in an institution of higher education within the state.[23]

Engineering education at The University of Texas at Austin al-most became a political casualty of the legislative debate on creating two state universities. In 1857 the House Committee on Education reported that a resolu-tion had been submitted to charter a school on the coast to teach "navigation and civil engineering," along with the "arts of ship–building and mechanics gener-ally." This institution would be a branch of the yet–to–be–established univer-sity. The committee members wisely rejected the proposal, pointing out that if a state university was to be constructed, then the "theory of the branches pro-posed" would of course be taught there. They did speak in the spirit of their time when they added, "The practical part of the branches of education sought . . . will have to be learned in the work–shop and on the high seas practically." Most educated people before the Civil War thought a university should not teach prac-tical trades, but they did accept that the scientific and mathematical principles that underlay engineering could be taught in the classroom. The act signed by Governor Runnels in 1858 provided for all manner of curricula, including the branches of applied mathematics of which engineering was a part.[24]

The first postbellum legislature recognized the increasing need for professional engineers taught in Texas. The state required a modern transpor-tation network, public sanitation systems, and reliable sources of power in order to develop. The legislators realized they could not continue to rely on attracting qualified engineers from the North, and not a few of them wished to prevent an influx of Yankee mechanics. They passed an act on November 12, 1866, which affirmed and expanded the law of 1858 in order to expedite the organization of a university in Texas. It became just another legislative casualty of Reconstruction politics, but it was the first to list "civil and military engineering and mechanics" among the subjects to be taught at the university, indicating the legislators' grow-ing recognition of engineering as a necessary discipline.[25]

The founding of Texas A&M in 1871 did not alleviate the demand for scientifically trained engineers in Texas. The new college was a land–grant institution that offered instruction primarily in agricultural techniques and the mechanics of engineering construction. Oscar H. Cooper, revered as a pioneer in public education in Texas, declared in the *Texas Journal of Education* in 1880 that the public demand for "higher degrees," particularly in civil engineering, avail-able from a university of the first class in Texas would soon be overwhelming. This new institution would train men in the scientific and mathematical prin-ciples of engineering, creating professionals who could meet the problems of a developing region with innovative ideas and designs.[26]

Powerful political voices joined in demanding that a scientific curriculum in civil engineering be offered from the inception of The University of Texas. State Senator Alexander W. Terrell, who guided the bill establishing The University through the legislature in 1881, scolded,

> "After forty years of independence and prosperity, where, today, are the distinguished linguists, mathematicians, geologists, civil en-gineers, or learned men of any sort, who have been educated in our state? There is not one . . . If water works, gas works, or manufactories are to be established in your towns, you must send abroad for educated brains to construct and operate them. If a railroad is to be built, its courses and grades must be determined by engineers educated abroad."[27]

Terrell noted that the establishment of a university that offered a curriculum in engineering would provide for growth in Texas.

A great deal of regional prejudice colors his words, but Terrell had put his finger on a dilemma for Texas: the almost complete lack of profes-sionally trained engineers from the state, and the disinclination of those "trained abroad" to relocate in Texas. Colonel Ashbel Smith, first chairman of the Board of Regents and a veteran of both Texas and Confederate battles and politics, insisted to his audience at the laying of the cornerstone for The University that a first–class institution of higher education must produce engineers. The old soldier warned, "The immense expansion of railroad building and other industrial works are presenting daily in large and increasing numbers, practical problems to be solved in engineering." The University of Texas, if properly provided for, would send forth "a corps of educated men" every year to every county and district of the state and to the nation beyond.[28]

When The University of Texas opened in the fall of 1883 it was organized into two departments. The Academic Department consisted of six schools, each the charge of one faculty member: Ancient Languages, Modern Languages, English and History, Philosophy, Mathematics, and Chemistry and Physics. The Law Department had two faculty members, including former governor Roberts. The first faculty was steeped in the traditions of the South; seven of the eight members were Confederate veterans, as were all eight regents. Their experiences had instilled in them a recognition of the need for engineering education, reinforced by the demands echoing across the state. They adopted as their role model the University of Virginia, which now offered a broad spectrum of courses in civil engineering, and from the beginning took care to provide for every aspect of the education of a truly professional engineer.[29]

The University offered a full curriculum leading to a degree in civil engineering, in keeping with the latest developments of the profession and of technical education. The American Society of Mechanical Engineers had just been organized in 1880, securing recognition of that vocation as a professional–level discipline. Early course work at The University included some elements of both civil and mechanical engineering. William L. Broun, head of the School of Mathematics, taught applied mathematics, for which the textbook was *Mechanique de l'Eéole Polytechnique*, and included practical instruction on surveying in his freshman course broadly titled Geometry, Algebra, and Trigonometry. All aspiring engineers were required to take a two–year "scientific course" of French and German taught by the The School of Modern Languages for the degree of Civil Engineer. All students were required to take more traditional course work embracing rhetoric, philosophy, history, and English. The fields of electrical and chemical engineering were still in the formative stages, so no advanced curricula were provided in the first catalog. After the creation of the American Institute of Electrical Engineers in 1884, however, haste was made to provide proper instruction in the School of Physics, directed by Alexander MacFarlane.[30]

The engineering curriculum at The University initially centered on one man, John W. Mallet, director of the School of Chemistry and "in charge of Physics." A native of Dublin, Ireland, Mallet was the son of a member of the Royal Society and frequently had assisted his father in early research on earthquakes in England. He obtained a doctoral degree in applied chemistry from the University of Gottingen in Germany, then joined the Royal Society himself. Almost as important as Mallet's academic qualifications to the first regents was his Civil War record: he had come to the United States in 1853, then had served the Confederacy as the superintendent of the Ordnance Laboratories. After the war, he taught first at Louisiana State University, then the University of Virginia, where one of his students was Thomas U. Taylor, who became the first dean of the College of Engineering at The University of Texas in 1906.[31]

Professor Mallet primarily taught chemistry, but included in his lectures material on plant design and industrial applications of chemical theory. Mallet's strength in engineering was his work on sanitation systems and the treatment and disposal of industrial waste. He was a noted speaker and several times a guest lecturer at some of the finest schools in the country. He came to Texas because of his son's fragile health; he believed the southwestern climate would sustain the child. Tragically, the boy died within a few months. Mallet finished the academic year, then left when it had become clear that the legislature was not willing to increase his salary. After his departure, The University's only full–time engineering student, William H. P. Hunnicutt, resigned and returned to work as a draughtsman.[32]

Mallet's resignation quickly turned into a boon for engineering education at The University. He was replaced by two professors, one each for chemistry and physics, plus an assistant instructor of mathematics and graphics, Alvin V. Lane. Lane held a degree in civil engineering from Vanderbilt and inherited from Mallet and Broun all technical instruction in engineering, along with his duties as the only instructor in applied mathematics and geometry.[33]

Lane was an "enthusiastic and inspiring teacher" who worked diligently to establish civil engineering at The University of Texas. An epidemic of dengue fever shrank enrollment during the second year of the school's existence, but Lane was undaunted. He actually had four full–time engineering students register, and labored to develop a professional curriculum around this small cadre. The Civil Engineer degree departed with Mallet, but Lane established a sound four–year outline of courses for his pupils, who would earn a bachelor of science degree with an engineering major. Classwork included instruction in all known methods of surveying, hands–on study of existing engineering structures and machinery, four years of drawing and related artwork, a healthy dose of mathematics, and two years devoted to the research and writing of a thesis. Lane donated his library and instruments for the students' use. The regents rewarded him for his efforts with a promotion to "Associate Professor of Mathematics in Charge of Engineering" in the summer of 1885.[34]

Encouraged, Lane redoubled his efforts, defining for the first time every course his engineering students should take. The curriculum included two years of French and German, four years of pure mathematics and three more of applied mathematics, three years of graphics and chemistry, two years of physics, and one year each of geology and rhetoric. Lane was keeping abreast of his discipline, for he also required a full year of instruction in electrical engineering, to be taught by MacFarlane of the School of Physics. The rather stiff regimen prescribed in the catalog tells only part of the story because, as Lane admitted in his last faculty report, most of the classes he actually taught on engineering do not appear. They were held at odd hours as the regular class schedule allowed. Lane was almost irrepressible: despite this exhausting daily routine he planned a curriculum for a five–year program leading to the professional degree of Civil Engineer.[35]

Through this short period the number of engineering students was steadily growing. Although certainly not directly comparable to the staggering increase in the enrollment of the College of Engineering at The University of Texas in the twentieth century, the growth was enough to attract the attention of the regents and the legislature and to bring some small extra appropriations for engineering in the University budget. Hunnicutt returned to school in 1885 and three years later became the first engineering student to graduate from The University. Enrollment jumped from four in 1884 to fifteen in 1885 and grew to eighteen before Lane resigned in 1888. Two of his pupils, James Nagle and David W. Spence, graduated the year after he left and became the first and second deans of the Department of Engineering at Texas A&M, directing the establishment of a more diverse curriculum at that institution.[36]

Engineering education in the first five years of The University of Texas rested entirely on the efforts of one man, as did most of the programs at the struggling young institution. Lane readily accepted the mantle of responsibility from Mallet, but was unable to really develop the curriculum beyond himself. Despite several windfall appropriations, the books on engineering in the library were still basically those he had donated, and the equipment available to the students was little more than the few simple tools necessary for plane surveying in the nineteenth century. Lane clearly saw that engineering at The University needed the status and acceptance of being a separate department, but was unable to make much progress in that direction on his own. He did establish a scientifically based engineering curriculum at The University, combining the techniques developed by many others in Europe and the United States to teach engineers who would lead in the economic development of Texas. Lane established a base on which to build, but his departure to enter the banking business in Dallas left the future course of engineering education at The University of Texas in doubt.[37]

# FIFTY YEARS ON FORTY ACRES:

*Dean Thomas U. Taylor and the College of Engineering, 1888–1936*

Engineering education had been included as an important element in the curriculum of The University of Texas when it opened in the fall of 1883 because the regents recognized the need for a superior, science–based technical course of study taught within the state to build for the future. Accordingly, they chose Thomas U. Taylor, a native of Texas, to succeed Alvin V. Lane in 1888. Engineering education at The University continued to be neglected by some as little more than the practical application of more established disciplines, such as applied mathematics, chemistry, and physics, but the curriculum gained greater acceptance, then establishment as an independent department through the work of Taylor, who was appointed dean of the School of Engineering in 1906. In his thirty years as dean, Taylor astutely surrounded himself with some of the best engineering talent available. This faculty confirmed Dean Taylor's judgment by developing the most esteemed institution of engineering education in the Southwest by the time of his retirement.

Dean Taylor earned his undergraduate degree in civil engineering from the University of Virginia in 1883. His early professional engineering experience lay in surveying, but he spent the first five years after his graduation teaching in Virginia, developing a command of trigonometry and its application to engineering that became his strongest asset as a teacher of applied mathematics and civil engineering. Initially appointed an adjunct professor of applied mathematics at The University of Texas in 1888, Taylor brought renewed energy to the engineering curriculum and greater recognition through his Texas streamflow studies for the U. S. Geological Survey and by his service as an expert consultant on various public works projects across the state. He also had the tremendous advantage of being personally acquainted with many of the politically powerful figures surrounding The University, including Oran M. Roberts and Oscar H. Cooper. Such assets would stand Taylor in good stead in his effort to develop a reputable program in engineering.[1]

Taylor, remembering the elegant campus of the University of Virginia, expressed great disappointment when he first visited the campus of his native state's premier institution of higher education. The University of Texas consisted only of the west wing of the Main Building, which would be completed in sections over the next decade. Called West Main, the existing structure had been designed by architect F. E. Ruffini and constructed by Abner Cook, who also built the Governor's Mansion and other palatial homes in Austin. The appearance of West Main, however, reflected the restrictions of a small budget. Built in the shape of a "T", West Main was 280 feet in length and 149 feet across its front. Few provisions had been made for aesthetics or modern conveniences, keeping the cost of construction to less than $59,000. Four stories high with 25 rooms, West Main literally brooded in Gothic darkness, scarcely alleviated by a sparse growth of ivy transplanted from an English graveyard. Funds being short, the regents had purchased coal stoves for the wintertime that barely warmed the classrooms, much less the 16-feet-wide halls on every floor. The only physical improvement in five years had been the erection of a fence to keep cows from grazing on the campus.[2]

Taylor's office was in the attic, the drawing room was on the third floor, and his lecture room, equipped with two benches and a white chalkboard, was in the basement. Because his primary assignment was as a teacher of applied mathematics, he conducted, in addition to all the engineering work, all freshman courses in mathematics and one class in sophomore mathematics. The faculty at The University was still small, counting only seventeen in all, and their close camaraderie sustained many through the first trying years. As if the hard work and many trials of his initial year were not enough, Taylor also nearly destroyed the University library. The water pressure in West Main was unreliable, and the faucet for the blueprint sink in the drawing room would sometimes be left open by mistake. Shortly after Taylor's arrival he left the water running all night long. The next morning water stood four inches deep on the second floor. Holes had to be punched in the ceiling of the first floor to drain the library, where many books had swelled to several times their normal size. Taylor's ability to make friends quickly served him well that day. The story of his first class in hydraulics became a great source of merriment in the early folklore of The University.[3]

Taylor quickly expanded on the base established by Lane. He retained the latter's emphasis on drawing, but added courses such as Collection and Distribution of Water, Drainage, and Sewage, Highways, Railroads, and Canals, and other classes designed to produce civil engineers who could solve the problems of rapidly developing Texas. At the end of the year Taylor submitted his report, requesting four hundred dollars in additional funds for books and equipment, more than Lane had ever received, and the immediate establishment of a separate school of engineering in the Academic Department.[4]

Taylor's request for a separate school was denied because Texas simply could not afford extra expenditures for The University. The euphoria of the first years had evaporated, leaving the grim realization that the institution was on the edge of financial ruin. The proponents of higher education in Texas had failed to provide adequately for The University. Because the Constitution of

Thomas U. Taylor was the first professor of engineering at The University of Texas at Austin, and served as the first Dean of Engineering from 1906 to 1936. [College of Engineering, The University of Texas at Austin]

1876 mandated separate funding for a state university, the legislators steadfastly refused to put aside money from the general revenue for its daily maintenance and ignored pleas for funds to expand its facilities. The harsh discovery that the Permanent Fund alone was not enough to support The University reversed earlier optimism; the inflexibility of the legislature in responding to the financial crisis stunted the growth of the institution. Less–accepted disciplines such as civil engineering suffered the most.

Financial optimism had accompanied efforts to build a university in Texas. Governor Elisha M. Pease, speaking for the bill to be passed in 1858, declared in November 1857 that "ample means" were available in the state treasury to found a university. Most of the original funding, however, was expended in efforts to defend the state during the Civil War. The remaining bonds of the first endowment were converted to Confederate warrants, which of course became worthless after 1865. Efforts to replenish the university coffers during Reconstruction were cast aside for more pressing matters. The Constitution of 1876 renewed hope by creating the Permanent University Fund. The "princely sum" of approximately $2.5 million had been amassed for a university in Texas by 1881. Lieutenant Governor Lawrence J. Storey congratulated the Texas Senate, asking, "What Texan's heart does not throb with delight as he contemplates the prosperity before us?"[5]

The University of Texas, when it opened its doors, controlled an Available Fund of a little more than $150,000 and an unspendable Permanent Fund of about $500,000, hardly enough to provide for sustained development. The year before Taylor came to Austin the operating budget of The University was less than $144,000, while Texas A&M's budget for the same year was over $500,000. Because the Constitution of 1876 had created a Permanent Fund for The University, that institution was expected to subsist entirely on the Available Fund generated from the bonds and lands of that endowment, while A&M reaped the benefits of the general revenues. To add insult to injury, the legislators repaid only $125,000 of the nearly $1 million "borrowed" since 1858 from the university endowment fund.[6]

Much of the public confidence in the finances of The University of Texas in the first few years stemmed from misconceptions about the landed endowment of the school. Both politicians and their constituents were slow to grasp the import of the Constitution of 1876 which withdrew the earlier grant of railroad sections, amounting to nearly three million acres of some of the best land in Texas, and replaced it with one million acres in isolated West Texas. A supplement of one million more acres of this arid land in 1883 only added to the problem. The land was almost worthless to Texas farmers and manufacturers alike, encompassing barren, rocky sections of the Trans–Pecos that "only a rattlesnake could love." Much of it had already been rejected as useless by the Texas and Pacific Railroad. Sale of these sections was virtually impossible, so the regents in 1884 requested that it be offered for livestock grazing leases only. The legislature did not give its permission until ten years later, by which time incalculable revenue for The University had been lost through mismanagement and laws that encouraged free grazing by forbidding the fencing of public lands.[7]

Engineering education at The University of Texas developed even more slowly than many other curricula because of an additional impedi-

ment. Many legislators were unwilling to believe the course work in civil engineering at The University was actually different than at Texas A&M. They
contended that the engineering program at Austin represented costly duplication and should be eliminated. In 1889, the legislature refused Taylor's request for
four hundred dollars to expand his course work, but granted the Department of
Engineering at A&M one thousand dollars from the general revenue. The private
interests which championed the engineering program at Bryan nearly succeeded; within a few years that department was better equipped than the one at
Austin, ironically affirming the arguments of those who wished to see the latter
eliminated. The establishment of an autonomous Department of Engineering at
The University in 1895, however, brought a tremendous increase in the number
of students and the quality of engineering education in Austin. Several faculty
left A&M after the turn of the century and accepted positions at The University.
The controversy did not rest until 1934, when the legislature expressed its wish
that funds for graduate work in engineering be concentrated at The University,
which had come to have the better research facilities and faculty.[8]

Taylor had twenty–one engineering students when he came to
The University in the fall of 1888. Despite the chronic shortage of financial support, after the first year he constantly worked for the establishment of an autonomous department. More courses on civil engineering were added, including
instruction in materials testing, highway and railroad construction, and mechanical drawing. Taylor fought to retain his requirement for four years of drawing classes, using the hours to teach a broad spectrum of engineering skills
under the guise of a previously accepted, and economical, course. Moreover,
these class hours could later be delegated to other engineering disciplines as the
faculty grew and the curriculum diversified.[9]

The central section of the Main Building was completed in 1891,
and Taylor moved to the attic of the new portion, which he shared with Professor
William J. Battle's collection of plaster casts of Greek statuary. There Taylor had a
lecture room, office, drawing room, and "testing room" together for the first
time. Equipment was still hard to come by—the small testing room held only two
antiquated "testing machines" and an unreliable one–cylinder engine that ran
on "manufactured gas"—but Taylor must have felt that progress was being
made. A course in sanitary engineering was added, and graduate work was
offered in bridge, hydraulic and sanitary, and railroad engineering. Ten undergraduates received a degree in Taylor's first five years, and several stayed through
a year of additional study.[10]

Taylor's efforts drew a great measure of attention and respect for
his discipline. He was promoted to associate professor in 1892. The four–year
civil engineering degree, discontinued in 1886, was offered once more in 1893,
supported by a "windfall appropriation" of four thousand dollars from the legislature, indicating their slowly growing acceptance of the engineering program at
The University of Texas. Taylor required each of his students to spend at least one
summer working in the field of engineering within the state, which imparted
needed practical experience and, at the same time, served the carefully planned
purpose of acquainting the public with the quality of the program at The
University.[11]

The legislative attitude had obviously shifted in favor of The University of Texas. The first appropriation of general revenue for the expenses of The University came under Governor James S. Hogg in 1891 and grew more generous every year. The time was obviously right for Taylor to repeat his earlier request for separate recognition and even to push for the establishment of an organized Department of Engineering. Faculty president Thomas D. Wooten led the charge. Directing his remarks at Hogg's successor, Governor Charles A. Culberson, Wooten lamented that "none of the great mechanical inventions" which had lent "such splendor to the achievements of this age and country" had originated within the state. Texas continued to rely on "the superior skill of foreign engineers and experts" to build its railroads, factories, and bridges.[12]

Wooten's florid rhetoric and Taylor's stubborn actions won the day. The Department of Engineering at The University of Texas was inaugurated on January 17, 1895, following Taylor's return from Cornell University, where he had earned his master's degree in civil engineering. Taylor remained the only full–time faculty member, but the catalog advertised four groups of courses leading to three undergraduate degrees: civil and sanitary options for civil engineering; a curricula in mining engineering; and course work for electrical engineering. The appropriation of two years before had been well spent: Taylor bragged that the engineering laboratory at The University was now "one of the most complete in the South." It boasted four cement–testing machines, the largest capable of exerting 100,000 pounds of pressure.[13]

The Department stumbled and almost fell coming out of the gate. The University adopted a new system of administration to be directed by an appointed president for the first time. George T. Winston accepted the job in 1896, much to Taylor's consternation. President Winston reduced the budget for applied sciences and mathematics, believing The University was not the proper place for such instruction. Taylor later claimed that Winston "did all he could to strangle our then infant department." The budget for engineering was cut in half, and a request to the legislature for funds for equipment to expand the electrical engineering program was stifled. As a consequence, the curricula in electrical and mining engineering were discontinued after the graduation of only one man in the former discipline. Enrollment dwindled as Taylor continued to conduct the course work of his department with the aid of an ever–changing roster of student assistants. The student engineers during this period adopted a motto which reflected their jaundiced view of the whole affair: "Pinch in everything, pinch pretty rough, stick it to everyone, been stuck enough." Winston's antipathy toward nontraditional disciplines affected many departments, not just Engineering; according to Taylor, his departure in 1899 "came as a relief to a large majority of the University community."[14]

The years under President Winston were not a complete loss for the Department of Engineering, however. Taylor awarded the first undergraduate degrees in civil and electrical engineering, and initiated a graduate program for a professional degree in civil engineering. Predictably, no one enrolled and the curriculum was discontinued after a few semesters. Most jobs available in Texas did not require advanced training beyond that which could be acquired working in the field. Many students did not remain in the Department through their senior year, opting instead for employment after a few years of basic instruction. Although response had proven inadequate to continue scheduling courses, the opportunity for graduate work in engineering remained open. The University held classes during the summer for the first time in 1898, and Taylor taught courses in trigonometry, physics, and infinitesimal calculus. Throughout his tenure at The University, however, Taylor consistently discouraged engineering students from attending summer school, preferring instead that they work to gain practical experience.[15]

Winston's departure and the arrival of William L. Prather put the Department on the right track again. Funds began to flow into the Engineering coffers, and a permanent member of the faculty was at last employed to aid Taylor, now a full professor. Edward C. H. Bantel was chosen by Taylor for his experience in railroad engineering, and by President Prather because he was a graduate of the now venerable Rensselaer Polytechnic Institute. Bantel remained through Taylor's retirement in 1936, and at the request of Dean Willis R. Woolrich served until his own departure in 1943. This meticulous and kindly gentleman instilled in his students a strong sense of ethics, and was loved in return for it. After the turn of the century, when the renewed support for the Department of Engineering effected visible improvement, new students began to flock to the Department until the increase in engineering enrollment outstripped that of The University as a whole.[16]

Mining engineering was revived at The University of Texas in 1900. Taylor reported "quite a number" of students stood in line to register for the classes. The course work in mining surveying, mineral laws, methods of ventilation, and management of a mining operation varied little during the existence of the school at The University. William B. Phillips, professor of field and economic geology, served as the director of the School of Mines until he left in 1905. Charles E. Rowe took over the program until it was discontinued in 1913, following the establishment of the State School of Mines and Metallurgy at El Paso, now a branch of The University of Texas.[17]

Taylor was jubilant over the new–found success of the Department of Engineering. In an article published in the *University Record* in July 1902 he crowed, "The State is now in the throes of the birth of a great industrial advance and Texas-trained men will be gladly received." Taylor predicted the "feverish demand" for his civil engineers would be matched by the demand for mining engineers and the graduates of his next project, the School of Electrical Engineering. Instruction in that discipline had been taught intermittently by the School of Physics, but in 1903 it opened under the Department of Engineering, taught by Professor Arthur C. Scott. The emphasis was on electrical power systems: power plant operation, transmission, and management of utility systems. Scott remained through 1911, then was succeeded by Professor Newton H. Brown, formerly chairman of the Department of Physics and Electrical Engineering at Texas A&M. Brown continued to stress the need for adequate electricity to supply both an increasing population and a developing industrial sector in the state.[18]

The Department of Engineering was now bursting the seams of its cramped quarters in the Main Building. Enrollment had increased from 18 in the fall of 1895 to 153 in the fall of 1903. Denny Parker, a former student assistant, later declared, "I think we occupied, at one time or another, every room in the main building but the matron's room and the girl's gymnasium." For a short time the Department enjoyed spacious quarters under the new auditorium, but surrendered the space to make more room for the library. Completion of the East Wing, which brought the number of classrooms to over one hundred, did little to alleviate the crowded situation. In 1903 the desperate engineers moved their drawing room from the fourth–floor attic, where broken panes permitted a "keen wind" to "freely make its presence known" in the winter, into the chamber formerly occupied by the girl's gymnasium. They had already lost the room in the basement which housed the tiny hydraulic laboratory; its equipment now cluttered the testing room in a useless jumble. By 1903 the Department was "like a stray cat . . . without fixed abode."[19]

The regents agreed that the engineers needed a new home and began a five–year campaign in 1899 to convince the legislature to supplement the Available Fund with enough to construct a building for the Department. An appropriation of $50,000 passed both chambers in 1903, but Governor William T. Lanham vetoed their largesse out of hand. President Prather called on Lanham just before Thanksgiving that year and persuaded him to make a present of the money for the engineers, as The University had toed the line on the budget as requested. Lanham acquiesced; the news, announced at the yearly engineering banquet, was met with cheerful pandemonium, led by Taylor himself. The Department moved into its new quarters in September 1904. Originally designed as a temporary structure, the building is now the oldest structure on The University of Texas at Austin campus.[20]

The new Engineering Building had enough classrooms, drawing rooms, and laboratories to last for years of expansion to come. The laboratory equipment, worth an estimated $314,000 in 1905, was the best in the Southwest. The materials laboratory held machinery for testing all types of construction material. The testing room for hydraulics was supplied by its own 120–foot water tower, feeding a labyrinth of standpipes, wheels, valves, and weirs. A separate cement laboratory was soon established, and a pair of steam engines was purchased to provide hands–on experience in that field. Perhaps the most spectacular rooms were occupied by the Electrical Engineering Laboratory. Five in all, they were filled with turbines, motors, alternators, generators, transformers, and a 430–bulb lampbank. Electricity came direct current from the Austin power plant, tapping into the building through a maze of conduits laid in a brick–lined tunnel 60 feet long under the main electrical testing room. Joseph W. Ramsay joined the Electrical Engineering faculty in 1911 and added a "telephony laboratory" to supplement his lectures on telecommunications.[21]

The regents made the Department of Engineering autonomous in 1906 and promoted Taylor to Dean of Engineering that January, thereby affirming an informal title he had held for years. By that time enrollment in the Department had once again doubled: 259 students matriculated in the fall of 1906. President David F. Houston actively supported the development of the engineering program, much as he had done at Texas A&M before coming to The University. Dean Taylor was again able to offer four curricula within three degree programs—highway and sanitation options for civil engineering; electrical engineering; and mining engineering—with an important difference: this time the classrooms were filled. Perhaps even more significant, many students in engi-

The Department of Engineering during the first ten years of its existence occupied at one time or another almost every room in "Old Main," the first classroom building at The University of Texas at Austin. [College of Engineering, The University of Texas at Austin]

Engineering students practice their surveying on the lawn of the first Engineering Building, completed in 1904, which is now the oldest building on campus. [Barker Texas History Center, The University of Texas at Austin]

neering now stayed through graduation as their chosen profession had become more complex and demanding.[22]

The Department could not support a doctoral program in those years, despite President Houston's campus-wide effort to develop advanced graduate programs. Taylor, Scott, and Rowe together were able to establish a stronger five–year curriculum leading to the professional degree of Civil or Electrical Engineer, but still did not require a graduate–level thesis. In an effort to foster academic uniformity, the four–year degree returned to the former designation of bachelor of science, with a major specified in civil, mining, or electrical engineering, or architecture. Dean Taylor toured the larger engineering schools in the Mississippi Valley in 1910; from this trip evolved both the guidelines for the new five–year professional degrees and the structure for a School of Architecture.[23]

A course in architectural drawing had been taught as early as 1903 by George A. Endress in what was loosely styled the School of Drawing. In the spring semester of 1906 the regents endorsed the School of Architectural Engineering and Drawing. This soon became the School of Architecture and Drawing, and finally in 1909 simply the School of Architecture. Courses in architectural engineering were retained as a structural option in the program. Hugo F. Kuehne, who had been a student assistant under Endress before earning a degree in architecture from MIT, became the first full-time faculty member in Architecture at The University of Texas. Those who enrolled got a healthy dose of engineering instruction along with practice in architectural illustration. Kuehne was replaced as chairman in 1912 by Frederic E. Giesecke, formerly the director of the Department of Architecture and Architectural Engineering at Texas A&M, who initiated graduate work in those disciplines at The University of Texas.[24]

The creation of the School of Architecture in 1910 temporarily orphaned the courses in mechanical drawing. Rowe, then chairman of the moribund program in Mining Engineering, assumed direction of the curriculum, renamed the School of Drawing, in 1911. Course work focused on the various methods and techniques of presenting all varieties of engineering designs, and students were expected to obtain a good working knowledge of almost every field in the discipline. Walter H. McNeill came in 1918, and the arrival of James D. McFarland in 1928 completed the faculty for the newly designated Department in the reorganized College of Engineering for the balance of Dean Taylor's tenure. Although the Department was never a degree–granting program, its curriculum served as a valuable adjunct to the more established fields of engineering. The central role played by the Department of Drawing is evidenced by the rise in enrollment even during the worst years of the Great Depression.[25]

Growth in the Department of Engineering was accompanied by an ongoing attempt to establish professional administration. The first formal meeting of the engineering faculty took place in Taylor's office shortly after his appointment as dean in January 1906. In order to facilitate development, chairmen were selected for each school beginning in 1911. Taylor chaired the School of Civil Engineering, Brown headed Electrical Engineering, Rowe held the top post in both Mining Engineering, which stopped accepting new students in 1910, and the School of Drawing, and Giesecke, when he arrived in 1912, became the chairman for the School of Architecture. Bantel became the first assistant dean in

1913. Every effort was made to put the Department on a professional basis, in-cluding providing funds for guest speakers of note to supplement the resident faculty.[26]

The engineering faculty under Dean Taylor labored to place their program at The University of Texas on a par with similar schools around the nation. Engineering education in the United States in the years prior to World War I underwent extensive renovation in an effort to meet the demands of indus-try. Dean Taylor later recalled the years under President Sidney E. Mezes, from 1908 to 1914, as the "Golden Age" of The University, a time of team work and united development across the campus. The bitter political battles of The Univer-sity with Governor James E. Ferguson after 1916 did not slow the growth of the engineering program, which benefitted from some immunity as an integral part of economic development in Texas.[27] The engineering faculty remained small, but they did expand the curricula as technology advanced. Dean Taylor's boast that "there are practically no options, no electives, no lines of least resistance, and no substitutions—nothing but the straight and narrow path of the grindstone of the beehive" well defines the prevailing attitude toward the needs of engineering education within the United States during the period.[28] The subjects that were offered met the needs of the state and the region, and the elementary changes made met the demands of industry in a nation that remained largely rural.

Dean Taylor acted as chairman of Civil Engineering through 1924, devoting much of his time to keeping his original discipline abreast of changing times with the aid of Bantel and Stanley P. Finch, a stern lecturer with a talent for structures. They made constant additions to the laboratory in the Engi-neering Building in an ongoing effort to provide practical experience, purchasing from a steel mill in the summer of 1914 a second–hand Riehle universal testing machine capable of exerting 400,000 pounds of pressure. The device was then the largest such machine in the Southwest, and remained the largest at The Uni-versity of Texas until 1978, when it was dismantled and stored. This machine and others of lesser capacity facilitated diversification of the civil engineering cur-riculum as the need arose. For example, Richard G. Tyler joined the faculty as the first specialist in highway engineering in 1916 and four years later developed the first Highway Engineers Short Course presented in Texas.[29]

The Civil Engineering faculty discussed creating a Municipal Group of classes to supplement the existing curricula in civil and sanitary engi-neering for the undergraduate degree in civil engineering, but discarded the idea after weeks of debate. The southwestern United States in the second decade of this century clearly did not need many engineers exclusively trained in city plan-ning and development. The region did require engineers proficient in roadway and bridge construction and maintenance, and so the faculty approved Tyler's proposal for developing a Highway Group. Their action came in response to the Good Roads movement which had been gaining momentum in Texas since the turn of the century. The Texas State Highway Department was created through a reorganization of existing agencies in 1917, following a mandate of the federal government that promised increased appropriations for highway construction to those states with an established bureaucracy. University alumnus George A. Suren became the first State Highway Engineer and University facilities were selected by officials to conduct vital research. The Civil Engineering faculty once more revamped their five–year program, adding new course work on highway and sanitary engineering to the curricula for the professional degree of Civil Engineer.[30]

The School of Mechanical Engineering became a separate program in 1914 under the chairmanship of Forrest E. Cardullo. He stepped down at the end of the year, leaving the direction of the program to Dean Taylor until the accession of Hal C. Weaver in 1916. An alumnus of the University of Michigan, Weaver directed mechanical engineering until his death in 1929, except for a year in the U. S. Army Signal Corps during World War I, when James A. Correll served as interim director. Many mechanical engineering courses had been offered as part of other curricula prior to the creation of a separate degree program, most notably as an adjunct to the classes in electrical engineering. Weaver switched to mechanical engineering from electrical engineering, but Correll remained in the latter discipline, lecturing on steam turbines. These two men renovated the University Power Plant, allowing laboratory work in mechanical engineering to move back to the campus from the Austin Manual Training School. Although the first bachelor's degree in mechanical engineering was awarded in 1914, and the faculty did establish a curriculum for a professional degree, the departure of Weaver and many students during World War I forestalled real development until after 1918. At the same time, the School of Electrical Engineering, alternately chaired by John M. Bryant and Correll through Taylor's tenure, offered additional courses on gasoline and electric engines and even thermodynamics as a supplement to classwork on power generation.[31]

Electrical engineering education in the United States just prior to World War I acquired a previously unobtained purposefulness. Advanced studies now included high–tension transmission of power, hydraulics and turbine–driven generating stations, fatigue of metals, electrochemistry, psychometrics, and refrigeration as a complement to basic thermodynamics. The School of Electrical Engineering at The University of Texas, in conjunction with the newer Schools of Mechanical and Chemical Engineering, strove to provide the most modern instruction in each field. Chairman Bryant actively worked with Ramsay and Correll to incorporate new developments into their curricula and was instrumental in the reorganization of the professional degree, Electrical Engineer, just one year after his arrival in 1914. The continued growth of the program in electrical engineering suffered little from the disruption of the war effort, ensuring a smooth progression of instruction on power generation and transmission through the end of Dean Taylor's tenure.[32]

Eugene P. Schoch chaired the School of Chemical Engineering at its establishment in 1917. The first to receive the undergraduate degree of Civil Engineer after its reinstatement in 1894, Schoch had gone on to earn a doctorate in chemistry from the University of Chicago while continuing to teach in Austin. A noted pioneer in bringing chemical industry to the South, Schoch won national recognition as the "Father of Chemical Engineering" within the region. He expanded his efforts in the field through a career at The University of Texas that spanned almost six decades.[33]

Schoch's interest in a program of Chemical Engineering grew from his experience as the chairman of the Division of Chemistry in the Bureau of Economic Geology and Technology, founded at The University of Texas in

1911. His work with the abundant mineral wealth of Texas led him to realize the critical lack of properly educated engineers who could take the lead in converting this raw material into useful commercial products. Schoch incorporated the little available literature on the subject in his classroom lectures, and talked with Taylor about establishing a program in chemical engineering. After the outbreak of World War I, when the need for such training became painfully obvious, Dean Taylor introduced a motion for a School of Chemical Engineering to the chairmen of the Department of Engineering. The regents approved their resolution for a new curriculum in October 1917.[34]

In 1917, the program in chemical engineering included course work for a bachelor of science in chemical engineering, but did not provide for graduate degrees. Basically a major in chemistry, the program added the classes in civil, electrical, and mechanical engineering that were essential for advanced industrial plant design, construction, and operation. As Schoch, soon promoted to professor of physical chemistry and chemical engineering, wrote, the chemical engineering curriculum began "practically full–fledged." All but one course had been taught regularly for many years. That class, and several later ones on advanced industrial chemistry, developed directly from Schoch's work in the Division of Chemistry. Industrial leaders and students alike welcomed the inno-

Engineering students attend a laboratory on steam turbines in 1913. John A. Focht, who later became an Assistant Dean of Engineering, is seated on the left. [College of Engineering, The University of Texas at Austin]

vative curricula and the chemical engineering program awarded its first degree in 1919.[35]

The chemical engineering program did not offer graduate courses during Taylor's tenure because of its hybrid structure. Direction was divided between the Department of Chemistry, which controlled its budget, and the Department, later College, of Engineering, which approved its curriculum and granted degrees. Schoch did stress the importance of graduate instruction from the beginning, but urged students to study elsewhere or to transfer into other fields of either chemistry or engineering for advanced academic work. Of the first one hundred to earn an undergraduate degree in chemical engineering from The University, thirty–eight later earned a master's, and twenty–three received a doctorate. Some continued to study with Schoch, who could provide some research facilities through the Bureau of Industrial Chemistry, which was established through a reorganization of the Division of Chemistry in 1925 and existed until Schoch's retirement in 1953. Not until after 1938, when Chemical Engineering became a Department of the College of Engineering, were specialized research laboratories built, leading to the expansion of the graduate program.[36]

All of the schools in the Department of Engineering advanced greatly in the years immediately prior to World War I, but the School of Architecture developed more rapidly than any other. Much of its success was due to its dynamic chairman, Frederic E. Giesecke. A native Texan, Giesecke earned a baccalaureate in engineering from Texas A&M in 1886 at the age of seventeen, and was a full professor in charge of the Department of Drawing at that institution by 1892. He received an undergraduate degree in architecture from the Massachusetts Institute of Technology in 1904, and served as college architect and teacher at A&M before coming to The University of Texas in 1912.[37]

Giesecke revamped the curriculum established by his predecessor, Hugo F. Kuehne, expanding existing coursework and creating new degree programs within the School of Architecture. One of the most important additions was the employment of Samuel E. Gideon, also an alumnus of MIT and Giesecke's assistant at Texas A&M, to teach architectural history and graphic design. Gideon developed a program emphasizing the use of fine arts in construction and design; the immediate result was the division of the Bachelor of Science degree into a Fine Arts Group and an Architectural Engineering Group in 1917. Within five years of his arrival, Giesecke and his staff had pushed the School of Architecture at The University into the mainstream of technical education.[38]

The United States declared war against the Central Powers on April 6, 1917. It quickly became apparent that American military strength suffered from a critical lack of technically trained manpower. The national government turned to the universities for aid in rapidly producing the necessary cadre of scientists and engineers for industry, along with aviators, mechanics, and radio operators for combat. The University of Texas, now enjoying a measure of national recognition, joined a handful of institutions chosen as sites for military training. Much of the reputation for the school had grown from the efforts of Dean Taylor and the Department of Engineering. The engineering faculty and students were equal to the task before them. The engineers compiled a notable record both on the battlefield and in the classroom, where the demands of wartime accelerated the development of all fields of engineering instruction. Techniques developed in the training facilities of the U. S. Army and Navy became important foundations for curriculum innovation after the war.

Dean Taylor and the Department of Engineering, like the rest of The University population, wholeheartedly supported the war effort. Taylor addressed the student body on April 17, 1917, insisting, "We must show our colors once and for all, and we must show the world that there is not a slacker on the Campus." He did not stop there: "Neutrality after our President has called to arms is absolutely impossible. If you are not with him, you are against him." Recalling that speech years later, Dean Taylor remembered with satisfaction that "with every power in my soul I urged the Engineers to go and join the colors." Speeches by Dean Taylor and others simply unified the strong support for the war already present across the campus; pacifists were "as scarce as water in the Sahara." In the spring of 1917, about 500 students left The University for officers' training camp, while more than 2,500 enlisted as ordinary soldiers. Thirty–eight faculty members resigned or requested leaves of absence to join the armed forces as combatants or instructors. Few of the warriors from The University saw active duty, but 75 died in the service of their country.[39]

There were 354 alumni of the Department of Engineering active in the armed services during World War I. Of these, 14 died. The first was Louis Jordan, a 1915 graduate of the School of Electrical Engineering, a beloved football hero, and the first graduate of The University of Texas to die in World War I. Among the 13 engineering faculty, 5—Bryant and Ramsey of Electrical Engineering, Weaver of Mechanical Engineering, Tyler of Civil Engineering, and Gideon of Architecture,—took a leave of absence for the balance of the war and served as instructors in the U. S. Army.[40]

Those who stayed in school during the war did not remain apart from the war effort. Soon after the United States joined the Allied Powers, the entire male enrollment of The University of Texas organized into three battalions, the largest cadet corps in the Southwest. The national government later enrolled them as regular units of Student Army Training Corps A, created as a source of nontechnical manpower, in the fall of 1918. New ranks of wooden shacks were built along Speedway to house young students preparing for war, and the campus soon looked more like a military base than a university. Even the faculty joined in the spirit: Taylor was a member of the military company formed by the academic staff, which regularly met to drill and review tactics. The armistice in November 1918 ended the Student Army Training Corps and the faculty company, but the Department of Engineering was instrumental in establishing a permanent unit of the new Reserve Officer Training Corps in 1919.[41]

The Department of Engineering supported the war effort not only with manpower, but also with a number of technical training programs. Old course work was updated and new curricula were created to meet the increasing demands of the armed services. The establishment of the School of Chemical Engineering in 1917 was in large part a response to a wartime need. The Department also offered a number of shortened, intensive courses to prepare military personnel for technical duty, including a six–week class on naval architecture.[42]

The most important efforts of the Department lay outside its ordinary curricula. The federal government established a number of special training camps at The University in 1917. Weaver directed the School of Automobile Mechanics based at nearby Camp Mabry until the close of the war. Walter L. Eyres, an instructor in electrical and mechanical engineering, joined S. Leroy Brown of the Department of Physics in conducting the Air School for Radio Operators at Penn Field, one mile south of St. Edward's University in Austin.[43]

The Department won even more national recognition through its conduct of the School of Military Aeronautics, situated on Little Campus. The air service was the least prepared branch of the military in 1917; in fact, it was virtually nonexistent. There was only one flying school in the country, at San Diego, and eight nominally serviceable aircraft, most of them damaged beyond repair after being used by General John Pershing in Mexico to pursue Francisco Villa in the punitive expedition of 1916. The greatest need of the U. S. Army as it entered World War I was competent flyers, navigators, and mechanics for the fleet of aircraft to be assembled for combat in Europe, but the existing training facilities were completely inadequate for the job.[44]

Immediately after the United States entered the war, the Council on National Defense appointed the National Advisory Committee for Aeronautics to create an air corps. Congress appropriated over $640 million to fund construction of training camps and employ instructors for the cadets. The plan of operation adopted was to train a small number of professors from American universities who had some technical background. These in turn would organize the ground training schools employing their fellow faculty members as staff. The federal government selected six universities; on April 23 the presidents of Cornell, Ohio State, Illinois, California, MIT, and The University of Texas met with the National Advisory Committee in Washington and agreed to each send three faculty members to the ground training school in Toronto for a short period of intensive instruction.[45]

Texas was a prime choice for flight operations because of its clear skies and good flying weather. The army established flight schools in San Antonio and ordered The University in Austin to conduct a ground training school, providing the new cadets with basic course work in airplane mechanics and operation. Following the meeting in Washington, President Robert E. Vinson chose Brown from Physics, Theophilus S. Painter from Zoology, and Bryant of the School of Electrical Engineering to organize the academic core of military instruction in Austin. They spent just three weeks in Toronto to learn the equivalent of three months in training, and saw an airplane in flight only once. Undaunted, they returned to Austin on May 21, 1917, having agreed on a general system of instruction.[46]

Bryant was relieved of all other teaching duties and placed in charge of a committee to make the necessary arrangements for the foundation of the U. S. Army Signal Corps' School of Military Aeronautics at The University of Texas. The Engineering Building served initially as the headquarters of the operation and the engineering faculty made up the bulk of the instructors as Brown and Painter moved on to other projects. Bryant became Dean of Instruction and lectured on the theory of flight, as did Gideon, while Weaver, Rowe and F. L. Whitney taught courses on engine design and maintenance. Whitney also instructed the cadets in meteorology, considered a subdiscipline of civil engineering, and basic astronomy. The National Committee on Aeronautics rewarded

Bryant's achievements by appointing him to direct part of the national program the following year. Weaver later assumed full control of the School of Automobile Mechanics and, like Bryant, served a dual role for the balance of the war.[47]

The courses taught by the engineering faculty for the School of Military Aeronautics in the Engineering Building and the Men's Gymnasium were only accelerated versions of regular classwork at first, but expanded as the instructors became more familiar with the material. Most of the equipment used was conceived and constructed by the engineers as the need arose. The center of activity became J Hall, where Weaver taught the basics of internal combustion engines and flight dynamics. After the School closed many of the engines used there were salvaged for the mechanical engineering laboratories and have since been stored in the basement of the Academic Center as part of a small collection on the history of aeronautics in Texas.[48]

The School of Military Aeronautics rapidly outgrew its home in the Engineering Building. The legislature had given the Old Blind Institute on Nineteenth Street to The University for a period of ten years in May 1917, and in July the School began moving onto Little Campus. George A. Endress, now serving as the supervising architect of The University, designed all of the new additions and directed the remodeling of existing structures. By September 1917 the School of Military Aeronautics was receiving 125 men per week; in January the number of new recruits reached 200 every seven days.[49]

The curriculum of the School of Military Aeronautics remained strictly ground work, with qualified cadets receiving flight instruction at Kelly Field in San Antonio or Fort Sill, Oklahoma. Nearly 6,000 cadets began their training in Austin; over 4,600 graduated. Along with the School of Automobile Mechanics, the School of Military Aeronautics provided over 7,000 highly trained men to the U. S. Army. Of these, 61 died before the war ended; most were lost in training accidents, but 16 were killed in action. Pilots initially trained in Austin received decorations from the United States, France, Italy and Great Britain for their meritorious service. The total budget for the project was only slightly more than $200,000, but the work of the engineering faculty had made it the most successful ground training school in the country. The last cadet left Austin in February 1919, but the equipment and courses developed in the crash program endured for several decades to come.[50]

The population of The University of Texas celebrated Armistice Day, November 11, 1918, with the same wild excitement that had characterized the opening of the war. Solemnity settled over the campus as a "service flag," bearing 3,100 blue stars for alumni in service and 85 gold stars for former students believed killed in action, was lowered while a lone bugler played taps. At the annual engineers' banquet in February 1919 the usual festivities were muted as Dean Taylor delivered a eulogy for the engineering alumni who had "Gone West."[51]

There were few recognized engineering colleges in the United States that were not the recipients of many thousands of dollars worth of valuable equipment after World War I. Dean Taylor obtained not only the engines and other supplies from the School of Military Aeronautics at Little Campus, but also successfully petitioned for the material left from the School of Automobile Mechanics at Camp Mabry. The greatest beneficiary of those windfalls was Mechanical Engineering, which found itself with more machinery than it had room in the laboratories. The entire Department profited from the campuswide flood of new students returning from the war. Enrollment in engineering swelled from 192 in the fall of 1917 to 588 only two years later. In honor of its new status, the Department of Engineering became the College of Engineering in 1921, and each school became a department in the administrative hierarchy.[52]

At the same time, following the advice of the Society for the Promotion of Engineering Education, virtually every engineering curriculum in major universities across the country underwent a thorough postwar revision. The Society had been established at the Congress of Engineers, held in conjunction with the World's Columbian Exposition at Chicago in 1893, when much attention had focused on the potential contributions of engineers well–grounded in scientific theories and their application. Within the new curricula, graduate study and research received heavy emphasis, spurred by a new demand for professional engineers in the flush times of the 1920s. Textbooks were revamped to include the great advances of technical knowledge gained during the war, and the content of courses taught in all fields of engineering, both graduate and undergraduate, developed new emphases on fundamental theories and processes.[53]

Dean Taylor joined the Society for the Promotion of Engineering Education (SPEE) before World War I and regularly attended the annual meetings. The University of Texas became the seventieth member institution of the SPEE in 1918. Taylor was appointed in 1921 to the organization's Association of Administrative Officers as a representative for the state schools, such as The University, which were not land–grant institutions. Taylor remained active in the SPEE for many years, working to keep his program abreast of their recommendations.[54]

Architecture remained one of the most dynamic departments in the College of Engineering during the 1920's. Much of its success again can be attributed to the increasing abilities of Giesecke, who continued as chairman while earning a doctoral degree in mechanical engineering from the University of Illinois. Working with Giesecke and Taylor, the faculty reorganized the curriculum in 1923 according to the standards of the American Association of Collegiate Schools of Architecture. After the organization of the Graduate School at The University of Texas, Architecture began offering a master of science degree in 1926. Undergraduate course work was constantly expanded, and in 1927 the catalog offered a degree in interior design for the first time. Giesecke returned to A&M in the fall of 1927 and was succeeded by Goldwin W. Goldsmith, president of the American Association of Collegiate Schools of Architecture.[55]

Walter T. Rolfe, a graduate of MIT, accompanied Goldsmith to The University of Texas in 1928, and with him continued a program of sound development through Goldsmith's retirement in 1935. The undergraduate programs in architecture and interior architecture, both incorporating many elements of the fine arts, were expanded to five–year curricula beginning in the fall of 1930. Enrollment steadily increased during the late 1920s and through the Great Depression. Rolfe succeeded Goldsmith as chairman in 1935, the same year that the department was initially accredited by the National Architect Accrediting Board.[56]

The phenomenal expansion of the School of Architecture and growing acceptance of it as a separate discipline as early as 1920 is evident in a report by the Curriculum Committee of the General Faculty in that year. It recommended to Dean Taylor that the Department of Engineering become two autonomous departments, Engineering and Architecture. The engineering faculty disagreed, so the School of Architecture, like the other schools within the Department of Engineering, became a department of the new College of Engineering in 1921. Architecture remained a component of the College until 1951, although it occupied quarters apart from the engineers after 1927.[57]

Mechanical Engineering developed strongly during the last two decades of Taylor's tenure, in large part due to the experiences of its chairman, Weaver, during World War I. Weaver emerged from the Schools of Military Aeronautics and Automobile Mechanics as a highly sought–after consulting engineer. He incorporated the material he developed during the war and in private industry into the curriculum of the School of Mechanical Engineering, which became a Department of the College. At his death in January 1929, the Department boasted instruction in engine mechanics, heating and ventilation, refrigeration, aeronautical engineering, machine design, and industrial methods and management. Howard E. Degler came to Austin from the University of Illinois in September 1930 as chairman of the Department of Mechanical Engineering.[58]

Highway engineering really came into its own as a subdiscipline of civil engineering during the late 1920s. Tyler's work had led to the adoption of a Highway Option and the refitting of the Materials Laboratory in the Engineering Building to test concrete and asphalt compounds. After Tyler's departure in 1920, however, Dean Taylor could employ only graduate assistants to teach on the subject, and so the program declined. The Highway Engineers Short Course had to be discontinued, but was later revived by Texas A&M. In 1922, Dean Taylor began recruiting John A. Focht, an alumnus of The University and a veteran of World War I who had won recognition for his construction of roads in Texas. Because the College of Engineering could not offer a salary comparable to that available through private enterprise, Dean Taylor's efforts were fruitless until the organization of the Graduate School brought additional appropriations for salary increases. Focht joined the College in 1926 as a full professor, putting highway engineering at The University back on its feet, teaching the first courses on soil mechanics in the Southwest, and succeeding Bantel as chairman of Civil Engineering in 1933. With faculty such as Banks L. McLaurin, noted for his work in hydraulics, Phil M. Ferguson, who soon won national recognition for his research in reinforced concrete, and Leland C. Barclay, whose talent lay in surveying, the Department of Civil Engineering in its teaching contributed directly to the growth of a cadre of engineering professionals in Texas.[59]

Not all of the innovations of the Department of Engineering from the experiences surrounding World War I were successes. Shortly after the armistice a national meeting of university engineering instructors was held in St. Louis to discuss curricula combining courses in engineering and business administration. Undergraduate students who completed the proposed five–year program would be awarded a degree in commercial engineering. Dean Taylor was not present at the original convocation, but he heard of the new idea and hastened to attend later meetings on the subject. The faculty of the College of

Engineering also liked the new approach, and in 1926 offered undergraduate degrees combining civil or electrical engineering with business administration, as well as a program in mechanical and industrial engineering. Student response was underwhelming, so the next year the faculty revised all three curricula, dropping business administration and adding work on public policy management to offer a new five–year program. They retitled the degrees to highlight the change: civil and utility, electrical and utility, or mechanical and utility engineering. In 1935 the last remaining five–year curricula, civil and utility engineering, was discontinued as a "dead failure" due to a lack of interest from both students and employers.[60]

Success in innovation far outweighed failure in the new College of Engineering, however. Three achievements during the 1920's exemplify the rapid expansion of the period: organization of the Graduate School and creation of the Departments of Aeronautical Engineering and Petroleum Production Engineering. These set the pace for the engineering faculty during the final decade of Dean Taylor's tenure at The University, and industry and public works in Texas have benefited greatly from the establishment of these divisions.

Dean Taylor gave the credit for establishing the Graduate School on a sound footing to Walter M. W. Splawn, president of The University from 1924 to 1926. The Board of Regents in 1910 had created a Graduate Council to oversee studies for the various advanced degrees offered by individual departments within The University, but it had effected little improvement. The Council had no authority to enforce standard requirements and no funds to sponsor research. The appointment of Henry W. Harper by President Mezes in 1913 infused a greater measure of strong leadership and cooperation into the program, but the supervision of graduate study at The University of Texas in truth continued to be at best a haphazard affair. The Graduate Council remained little more than an advisory organization until its abolition in 1925.[61]

The College of Engineering offered five–year professional curricula in civil, mechanical and electrical engineering for many years after World War I, but awarded no master's degrees until June 1922, when the faculty granted four in the fields of mechanical, architectural, and chemical engineering. The next year the College discontinued its policy of independence from the Graduate Council, casting its vote to join with the University administration to work for progress. The engineers did not have to wait long for improvement. Splawn began reorganizing graduate study almost immediately after his appointment, and in June 1925 established an official Graduate Faculty, with representatives from every division to ensure coordinated action. The College chose Taylor, Bryant, Giesecke, and Finch to attend. The Graduate Faculty exercised exclusive jurisdiction over all advanced degree programs at The University of Texas and worked to standardize the system. The master of science degree supplanted the professional certifications in engineering, and the Graduate Council enforced rigid requirements for admission, candidacy, and financial aid in the College as well as elsewhere on campus.[62]

The legislature appropriated $50,000 to fund eight new graduate professorships, which raised faculty salaries generally as the new investment generated more revenue for better undergraduate instruction. Increased funds also brought innovation in research and grand plans for developing more advanced degrees. Splawn renewed discussion of a doctoral program in engineering, but the College rejected the notion. Facilities were not yet adequate, and faculty members saw little market for such highly educated graduates even if they made the effort to upgrade existing course work. Engineering remained a minor option for the doctoral degree at The University of Texas for another decade.[63]

Alexander Vallance, formerly of the Department of Mechanical Engineering, taught the first classes for the nascent Department of Aeronautical Engineering in 1926. Bryant, the chairman of Electrical Engineering, met the next summer with Harry Guggenheim in New York to discuss possible financial support for the newly established program. Guggenheim had funded similar efforts at the University of Michigan, Stanford University, and the California Institute of Technology. He gave Bryant the required support, and in 1927 the Department of Aeronautical Engineering awarded its first degree. Interest in the field was great during the 1920s with the romance of the barnstormers and popular heroes such as Charles Lindbergh, but the Department became one of the first academic casualties of the Depression as enrollment declined and efforts to establish commercial airlines stalled. With the end of the Guggenheim Foundation sponsorship, the program ground to a halt and course listings were removed from the catalog.[64]

Much of the course work in the new Department had developed from Bryant and Weaver's work with the School of Military Aeronautics and the latter's expansion of earlier courses in the Department of Mechanical Engineering. The first three years of instruction for the new degree were identical to the classes for Mechanical Engineering, but in the final semesters classes in aeronautics were taught by Hyman J. Ettlinger, a member of the mathematics faculty who had taught similar courses in the School of Military Aeronautics. Weaver also instructed seniors in the details of aeronautical engine design and maintenance. His place was taken by Degler, the new chairman of Mechanical Engineering, in 1930, who added more instruction on structural analysis and flight mechanics. After the temporary suspension of the bachelor of science in aeronautical engineering in 1933, limited technical courses continued to be offered as electives by Vallance and Degler until the revival of the Department during World War II.[65]

Petroleum Production Engineering began as a cooperative effort. Professor Elias H. Sellards of the Bureau of Economic Geology organized the first classes in 1928. The curriculum blended elements of geology for oil prospecting and engineering for producing, transporting, and refining the product. A thorough understanding of the related areas of physics and chemistry were also necessary to solve the problems inherent in the composition of petroleum and natural gas. Sellards taught four courses the first year, and Schoch taught one on refinery design. The next year, professors Frederick B. Plummer of the Bureau and Brown of Physics joined the faculty. The College of Engineering sponsored the adoption of a formal curriculum in 1929, and the Department of Petroleum Production Engineering began the year after, with Plummer as chairman. Once formally organized, it expanded and grew more rapidly than anticipated, awarding two bachelor of science degrees in 1931.[66]

The great expansion of the College of Engineering in the 1920s rapidly overflowed the old Engineering Building and Power Plant. Dean Taylor as early as 1916 complained about the desperate lack of room, but the vigorous development of the next decade made the situation critical. He repeated his request for more space after World War I, when the flood of new students and equipment made lab work almost impossible, but his pleas for updated and larger facilities went largely unheeded. The departments of the College of Engineering, like many divisions of The University in that period, had to content themselves with "half a dozen scattered, flimsy, temporary, inconvenient, and highly combustible shacks" where "every addition, student or shack, simply makes matters worse." By the end of World War I these structures lined the eastern perimeter of the campus from the old Power Plant to the Law Building.[67]

Hopes were revived in 1920 when regent George W. Brackenridge bequeathed four hundred acres on Town Lake to The University as a site for a new campus. Plans included a spacious building for engineering. The Board of Regents recommended abandoning the Forty Acres for the new tracts, but the legislature refused to grant leave. Instead, Governor Pat M. Neff signed a bill on April 1, 1921, which provided the funds to purchase a large block of land north and east of the existing campus. Bryant, as chairman of the Engineering Faculty Building Committee, reported its selection of the block bounded by Waller Creek, Twenty–First Street, Speedway, and Twenty–Fourth Street as the future site for a complex of engineering buildings. It was the first move beyond the original Forty Acres, and the engineers would lead the way, but for the time being they would have to wait.[68]

The problem lay with the Permanent University Fund: plans at The University of Texas had once again exceeded the actual returns from investments set aside for development of the physical plant. Legislative appropriations for construction remained small, restricted by the Constitution of 1876 which appeared to forbid using the general revenue of the state for buildings to house The University. The Permanent University Fund depended on grazing leases for profits, which in 1925 amounted to less than $225,000. The aggregate from the Permanent University Fund did provide for some new construction, but many classes were held in temporary wooden buildings that sometimes leaked in bad weather and always posed a fire hazard.[69]

The successive governors of Texas in the first two decades of the twentieth century petitioned the legislature, but with little effect. Oscar B. Colquitt taunted the assembly in February 1913: "Our boasted University Fund . . . has retarded rather than developed the University." He pointed out that the buildings were "inadequate in every way . . . built piecemeal" whenever funding allowed. Governor Colquitt continued his attack throughout his term, informing the legislature in January 1915, "I want to report . . . that the wooden shacks on the University campus have been built over my protest." At one time, a fourth of the classes on campus were taught in pine-board temporary buildings whose ramshackle appearance earned the sardonic architectural label of "Shackeresque." The legislators were not to blame, however; they often appropriated general revenues for The University after the expenses of state government were met, although many legalists agreed that the constitution did restrain them from supplementing the Permanent University Fund directly.[70]

The situation suddenly reversed on May 28, 1923. That spring morning a meeting of the Railroad Commission was interrupted by the director of the Division of Oil and Gas, who announced that a "little wildcat well in Reagan County" with the unlikely name of Santa Rita "gave strong evidence" of an oil field on University land. For years geologists had believed that oil could not be found below salt beds, like those underneath The University's lands in West Texas, and had disregarded a report to the contrary by Professor Johann A. Udden, chief of the Bureau of Economic Geology and Technology and a member of the American Society of Mining and Metallurgical Engineers. The drillers of Santa Rita had forged ahead anyway, naming their rig for the patron saint of the impossible. The University would forever be in their debt for converting the arid lands of West Texas into a bonanza.[71]

Santa Rita produced only one hundred barrels a day, but a second hole nearby brought up five thousand barrels daily. Seventeen productive wells were bored in Reagan County by the end of the year, and by the next May seventy–five gushers had been drilled on University property. Oil royalties poured into the Permanent Fund, which increased from nearly $17,000 in 1923 to almost $4 million by 1925. Two hundred oil wells operated in the Big Lake field, where Santa Rita blew in, by December 1928, bringing over $250,000 each month into the Permanent University Fund.[72]

The regents argued with the courts over the disposition of their new–found wealth, but the money continued to flow in, and the differences soon were settled in favor of The University. The Commissioner of the General Land Office had been given the sole power in 1917 to dispose of oil and gas rights to University lands, and exercised that right for several years after Santa Rita. The regents succeeded in forcing the creation of the Board for Lease of University Lands, composed of the Commissioner and two regents. They failed in their attempt to direct the oil royalties into the Available Fund, but were able to begin borrowing against the Permanent University Fund, which by 1927 totaled over $7 million dollars.[73]

The discovery of oil on University land was by no means a panacea, and the benefits were delayed by court battles and profit schemes, but it did sweep away the shacks dotting the campus. The administration began to evaluate solutions to the cramped conditions, initially to the distress of the College of Engineering. The legislature donated the site of the old Blind Institute to The University permanently in 1924, and officials suggested that the College move there. The engineers already had their eye on the property just across Speedway, and were appalled at the notion of moving five blocks from the central campus. Dean Taylor took care to ensure that the reports of Robert L. White, the architect in charge of evaluating Little Campus, appeared unfavorable to the move. The buildings truly were outdated and completely unsuited to the needs of the engineers. A Building Committee of Weaver, Rowe, Finch, Correll, and Giesecke insisted to President William J. Battle that the proposed relocation would be unwise, and he acquiesced.[74]

Once the engineers had defeated the proposed move to Little Campus, they began pressing for a new, modern engineering building on the site they had chosen along Twenty–Fourth Street. Spiraling enrollment in all fields of engineering spurred them to accelerate their efforts. The departments of the College of Engineering were scattered across campus. Architecture squatted in

Brackenridge Hall, a former men's dormitory, and often had to schedule courses in the slowly disappearing shacks. Mechanical Engineering was crowded into the old Power Plant, spilling into a few temporary structures nearby. Classes in Civil Engineering and Drawing were often held in Old Main, the original home of The University. Its lines were still striking, but portions had been condemned as unsafe for occupation.[75]

The Mechanical Engineering Laboratory was the first building of The University of Texas to be constructed off of the original Forty Acres. Built on the southeast corner of Twenty–Fourth and Speedway, on Clark Field, where the University football team played its first games, the building cost approximately $230,000 to complete, and remained in use until 1982. Weaver supervised construction along with University architect White. The faculty of the Department of Mechanical Engineering moved into their new home in 1928, finding to their satisfaction that Weaver and White had included plenty of room for future growth.[76]

The regents secured four million dollars in 1931, through loans against the Permanent University Fund, for a building campaign. The nine structures planned included a new home for the College of Engineering and a separate facility for Architecture. The Engineering Building, completed in 1933, was the largest of the new buildings. All were built in the Spanish Renaissance style of brick and limestone with a red tile roof. Two wings of the new structure enveloped the Mechanical Engineering Laboratory, creating a spacious environment for all departments. The faculty in 1926 had estimated the cost of a building for them would be no more than $310,000; including the earlier laboratories, the total bill came to over $600,000.[77]

Dean Taylor and the College of Engineering were understandably proud of their new home. By 1933 standards it was a "first–class, modern fireproof building" with a reinforced concrete frame and steel sash throughout, brick facing, and terra cotta trim. A red tile roof covered the three–story portion, while a steel saw–tooth roof protected the shops. Inside were classrooms and laboratories for every field of engineering, with room to spare. All of the testing–room equipment had been refurbished and supplemented with the most up–to–date machinery the College could afford on its expanded budget. The entire complex adjoined the new power plant, affording easy access to valuable practical experience in mechanical and electrical engineering. Taylor and twenty alumni gathered in his office to dedicate the structure, saluting it with a round from a Brazilian hydraulic gun that blew out several windows.[78]

The new Architecture Building, also in the Spanish Renaissance style, was not as large or well–appointed as the Engineering Building, nor was it even half as expensive, costing less than $300,000. It contained ample room for the growing Department of Architecture, however, and was a welcome relief from the shacks and old Brackenridge Hall. For the first time in several decades the architects were united under one roof with modern facilities for instruction at all levels of the discipline. The architecture students sketched their own Rubicon on a long piece of butcher paper, marched across it, and carried it with them into their new home, symbolizing their determination to pursue an independent course in the future.[79]

The College of Engineering weathered the remaining years of the

Depression quite well in its new buildings. The hard times after the stock market collapse in 1929 did not decrease enrollment or delay growth, except in less–accepted fields such as aeronautical engineering, and even then the effect was fleeting. Many former students applied for admittance to the graduate program as jobs became hard to find. Budgets were cut, of course, and the most drastic action was the reduction of every University salary by one-fourth in 1933. It was a great hardship, but none of the engineering faculty resigned. Austin banks helped by accepting warrants, with which the state paid its employees in the hardest times, at face value from University staff. This scrip was nothing more than a draft against future tax revenues, and by accepting them without a discount the banks were, in effect, advancing loans at no interest to the faculty. All other state employees had to sell their vouchers at discounts up to one fourth of the face value.[80]

In 1936, Dean Taylor became one of the first faculty members claimed by The University's new mandatory retirement policy. He was placed on modified service and moved his office, albeit under protest, from the Engineering Building to the Architecture Building. There he remained active, teaching a course each semester, completing literary pieces on the history of Texas, his beloved native state, and acting as a senior consultant to firms that sought him out

T. U. Taylor Hall of Engineering, completed in 1933, was the first classroom building at The University of Texas at Austin constructed off of the original campus, known as the "Forty Acres." [Barker Texas History Center, The University of Texas at Austin]

until his death in 1941. The College under Dean Taylor had achieved remarkable goals in nearly five decades of leadership. Engineering enrollment had swelled from 19 in 1888 to 1,443 in the fall of 1936. The engineering budget grew from just 2,042 in fiscal year 1889 to $117,830 in research and salaries in 1936. Recognized programs in chemical, electrical, mechanical, mining, aeronautical and petroleum production engineering, as well as architecture, were all established under his supervision. Dean Taylor awarded over 1,700 diplomas in 19 degree programs during his tenure at The University of Texas.[81]

An old–fashioned man, Dean Taylor in 1938 recalled with pride, "I have tried to turn out Engineers that love God, hate the Devil, and tell the truth even if it cost them their jobs." Warming to his subject, he continued, "A Texas Engineer, as I have tried to train, is a man of inflexible integrity, high conceptions of civic duty, lofty devotions to accuracy and absolute devotion to the truth." Faculty and students under his strong leadership, however, had helped to inaugurate the modern era of industry in Texas. The value of manufactures, inflated by profits from oil, exceeded that of agriculture in 1921, beginning a dominance unbroken to the present time. Petroleum production increased from just a thousand barrels in 1896 to over five billion in 1937, the peak year for pre–World War II wells. Texas engineers built almost 21,000 miles of roads after the turn of the century, nearly all of it paved, foreshadowing the demise of railroads, which increased to nearly 17,000 total miles in the same period, as the primary mode of transport. More than 18,000 miles of high–tension electrical lines crisscrossed the state, and 392 companies serviced at least 500,000 telephones by 1936, the centennial of Texas independence. The future of public health held promise as over 400 enclosed sewer systems served 575 incorporated towns. University engineers aided in the development of their alma mater by installing new electric streetlights, laying waterlines, and constructing or refurbishing power plants, dormitories, laboratory, and classroom buildings.[82] Within the context of the industrial era, Dean Taylor left a loving legacy of integrity and labor to his native state and to The University of Texas.

# MEN OF INGENUITY:

*Dean Willis R. Woolrich and*
*the College of Engineering, 1936–1958*

T he engineering faculty selected Willis R. Woolrich to be Dean
Taylor's successor. Dean Taylor had provided capable leadership
for the College of Engineering during the boots and britches period of industrial
growth in the United States, instilling a sense of pride in hard work and a certain
rough-and-tumble eagerness for a challenge. Dean Woolrich introduced a new
sense of professionalism to the College with the assistance of both the senior
faculty members and new members from all over the country. Unlike his predecessor, Dean Woolrich was "an utterly noiseless and unassuming man," but contemporaries noted his commitment to winning a national reputation for the College was "immense." Recognizing that the engineering program was a "diamond
in the rough [which] had to be polished," Woolrich set high standards for himself, the faculty, and the students, contributing to the development of new industry in the state and to a brilliantly enhanced image of The University of
Texas.[1]

Dean Woolrich, probably more than his predecessor, recognized
that the future of engineering practice and education lay in professionalization
and certification, and directed his efforts toward that end. When he assumed
office in 1936, however, The University had not yet recovered from the desperate
financial straits of the Great Depression, and would soon be drawn into the
United States' effort to win World War II. Significant curriculum development
and research, his primary concerns, remained limited in scope until wartime
advances in science and technology brought renewed public interest in the profession of engineering. New faculty, increasing graduate and undergraduate enrollment, and unprecedented research funding from government and industrial
contracts effected much of the change originally envisioned by Dean Woolrich
when he arrived. Throughout his tenure, Woolrich also steadfastly maintained

the image of a gentleman, infusing that attitude into the students of the College of Engineering.

Dean Taylor resented his precipitous retirement, but cooperated with his successor to ensure a smooth transition of command. He hastened to assure Woolrich, "I am ready to cooperate with you in any way you may desire." The former dean elected to move out of the Engineering Building, taking an office in the Architecture Building, geographically as far away from his old quarters as he could be and still remain within the engineering complex at The University. Taylor retained his characteristic sense of humor throughout the affair; once settled in his "New Deal Den" in the Architecture Building, he notified Woolrich that the dean's office in the Engineering Building was "as bare as the Plains of Texas" and had been given "a thorough cleaning, a shave and a haircut," anticipating its new tenant. Taylor explained to his new neighbors on the West Mall, "when a new President enters the White House, the old one does not stay on." He politely attended the first engineering faculty meeting at which Dean Woolrich presided, but remained judiciously silent and never entered the Engineering Building again.[2]

The engineering faculty welcomed the new dean. Educated at the University of Wisconsin, Woolrich was internationally known for his success as director of the Agricultural Industries Research Division of the Tennessee Valley Authority (TVA) in Knoxville. His appointment as chief engineer of TVA followed seventeen years of research and teaching in the mechanical engineering department at the University of Tennessee, where he had been nationally recognized as Engineer of the Year in his chosen field many times. Always an activist for the recognition of engineering as a profession, Woolrich was instrumental in the development of the American Society of Mechanical Engineers and other important organizations, including the Engineering Council for Professional Development (ECPD). The faculty of the College of Engineering reviewed fourteen candidates, but realized Woolrich stood far above the rest in activity, reputation, and progressiveness.[3]

Dean Woolrich came to Texas because he knew the future of the engineering profession lay in the education of new engineers. The TVA project he directed was nearing completion, and the position in the College of Engineering offered a "wonderful opportunity" to once again be a catalyst for progress. The University of Texas was not known for its financial resources, but the College of Engineering won respect from Woolrich for the enthusiasm of the faculty and students and their willingness to push for broader recognition in their particular fields. He quickly grew to love the College as deeply as Taylor ever had, and like his predecessor labored to reshape it in his own image of progress and development.[4]

Dean Woolrich became increasingly active in making the engineer, especially an alumnus of The University, a professional in the eyes of the public. Through his personal example and insistent instruction, he changed the role model from builder to designer and the practice from vocation to profession. Dean Taylor had emphasized engineering as a useful practice, engaged in the construction of roads, dams, highways, and other public works; Woolrich now stressed new research, broadening the vistas open to the College of Engineering. The latter also remained more aware of appearances; although Dean

Willis R. Woolrich, pictured here second from the left, served as Dean of Engineering from 1936 to 1958. With him, from left to right, are Frank W. Jessen, Eldred W. Hough, and Harry H. Power of the Department of Petroleum Engineering. [Barker Texas History Center, The University of Texas at Austin]

Taylor believed the best method for dealing with a problem was to roll up his shirt sleeves and pitch in, Woolrich retained his genteel outlook and an emphasis on professional decorum, which meant he always remained impeccable and thoroughly conscious of the image he was trying to create. Dean Woolrich registered as a professional engineer and attended the annual conventions, and insisted the faculty do the same. He never stopped being a professional engineer, continuing his own research throughout his tenure.[5]

Dean Woolrich arrived in Texas at a crucial point in the drive for the registration of professional engineers. The Texas Section of the American Society of Civil Engineers, established in 1913, had become the first successful professional organization for engineers in the state, but had not made headway on the matter of licensing until the National Society of Professional Engineers organized in 1934. The Texas Society of Professional Engineers appeared two years later and formed a strong lobby for mandatory registration. It spearheaded a bill through the legislature in 1937, and on January 1, 1938, the Texas Engineering Registration Act took effect. Dean Taylor, in recognition of his contribution to engineering in Texas, became the first registered engineer. A host of others followed suit, especially in the technological boom that followed World War II.[6]

The new dean did not waste time in introducing his vision to the College of Engineering. He read a comprehensive plan for the growth of the institution at the faculty meeting of November 3, 1936, less than two months after his arrival. The most immediate goal was to cooperate with the ECPD to achieve full accreditation of all existing undergraduate curricula. The ECPD would not evaluate graduate programs, but the College under Dean Woolrich would work alone to improve postbaccalaureate study. The Graduate Studies Committee of the engineering faculty, formed several years before to consider creating a doctoral program, would have to produce a "definite recommendation" to be printed in the catalog, in addition to the report already submitted. To organize academic innovation and aid the students in selecting the proper degree program, Woolrich proposed the installation of a permanent advisory system. Last but certainly not least, new emphasis would be placed on modern research in tandem with other bureaus at The University of Texas and across the state. Results would be broadcast through an accelerated publication effort. Taylor had jovially warned Woolrich, "The opinion you will form of the Engineering Faculty on January 1, 1937, will not be the opinion you will have on January 1, 1939." The new dean would make sure of that prediction.[7]

Dean Woolrich believed that his most important contribution to the College of Engineering was obtaining accreditation for its undergraduate curricula, "thus insuring high quality in all its programs and instilling a desire to do significant research in all departments." The ECPD was the first organization responsible for reviewing engineering curricula in the United States. Created in 1933 through the cooperative effort of the original "founder organizations"—the American Society of Civil Engineers, American Institute of Electrical Engineers, American Society of Mechanical Engineers, American Institute of Chemical Engineers, and American Society of Mining and Metallurgical Engineers—together with the Society for the Promotion of Engineering Education (SPEE), the ECPD sent review committees by invitation to those institutions seeking accreditation. The goal was not standardization but assurance of a minimum standard of engineering education.[8]

The ECPD quickly won great respect for its remarkably successful operation, supplemented in 1942 by the timely creation of the Engineering College Research Association (ECRA), which assumed a similar responsibility to review research programs and promote engineering innovation. Dean Woolrich, who maintained an active interest in engineering curriculum development nationwide, served as the president of the ECRA for its first four years, making the Engineering Building at The University the initial headquarters of the organization. The ECRA merged with the SPEE in 1948; the joint effort became known as the American Society for Engineering Education (ASEE).[9]

The engineering faculty at The University of Texas invited the ECPD to review their program in the spring of 1937. The visitors approved five of the existing departments: Civil, Electrical, Mechanical, and Petroleum Engineering, Architecture, and the sanitary group offered by Civil Engineering. Chemical Engineering was not accredited; although the committee commented favorably on the work done by Eugene P. Schoch and his staff, the department remained an administrative hybrid separate from the engineering program, dividing its annual budget and governing council between the College of Engineering and the

Department of Chemistry in the College of Arts and Sciences. Aeronautical Engineering had been moribund for several years and so was passed over, too. The ECPD reviewers also initially denied accreditation to architectural engineering as an independent curriculum within the Department of Architecture, but remedied their oversight the next year.[10]

A. A. Potter, chairman of the ECPD visiting committee and dean of engineering at Purdue University, indicated many deficiencies in the College in his report. Dean Woolrich initiated reform at the engineering faculty meeting of November 3, 1937. He repeated his earlier position that curriculum development would be a group effort requiring new faculty and that academic inbreeding would be combatted by recruitment from across the United States. Potter had recommended more advanced work by the Bureau of Engineering Research and coordination of research efforts at The University through the Dean of Engineering with similar organizations within Texas. This advice echoed Woolrich's own plans. He had embraced the ECPD ideal of professionalization, insisting to the gathered faculty, "It is here to stay and is bringing order out of chaos in engineering recognition and education." He appointed several committees, telling them in no uncertain terms that he expected concrete results leading to definite progress.[11]

The groundwork for Dean Woolrich's reorganization of the College had been laid in 1934, when Taylor appointed a committee for curriculum development following the legislature's recommendation that postbaccalaureate work in engineering within the state be concentrated at The University of Texas. The committee raised admission standards and graduation requirements for the College, but its request for additional funds went unheeded. Dean Woolrich selected a new group; through the reform impetus of the ECPD they effected real change. The three optional degree programs in Civil Engineering—the structural, highway, and sanitary groups—were eliminated in 1938, as well as the general and technical options in Electrical Engineering. At the same time, Petroleum Production Engineering became Petroleum Engineering, a semantic change that indicated the mainstreaming of the program. Courses in hydrology, fluid mechanics, soil mechanics, thermodynamics, and aerial surveying were added to undergraduate curricula. Architecture retained a five–year syllabus containing all of the requirements for membership in the American Association of Collegiate Schools of Architecture, but cancelled its interior architecture program. That curriculum had never quite been accepted by the College and had become the academic step–child of the Department of Home Economics, which continued to offer a similar degree. These changes brought the College abreast of the latest developments in engineering education in the United States but increased the time required for earning a baccalaureate. Summer school courses, never quite accepted by Dean Taylor but demanded by the students for several years past, were scheduled to accommodate the broader curriculum; by 1939 it took four years and a summer to finish each degree program.[12]

The College of Engineering offered six master of science degrees when Dean Woolrich came in 1936: architectural, chemical, civil, electrical, mechanical, and petroleum production engineering. In addition, the Department of Architecture awarded its own master's in architecture. By 1941, the graduate program had expanded to include master of science degrees in sanitary, aeronautical, and communications engineering. Chemical Engineering, reorganized as a department within the College in 1938, initiated a graduate field course in chemical engineering practice, modeled after classes given at MIT. John Griswold, an MIT alumnus who in 1936 had become the first "outsider" to join the chemical engineering faculty, directed this program. Students worked with the staff of industrial plants, observing the operation of chemical processes and writing technical reports on their conclusions. The effort was discontinued due to greater industrial security restrictions after the outbreak of World War II. The addition of more faculty in all departments made possible the creation of new course work within existing degree programs, such as Raymond F. Dawson's classes on soil mechanics and J. Neils Thompson's courses on materials for construction.[13]

The first doctoral degrees in engineering at The University were awarded during Dean Woolrich's tenure as a direct result of the push for greater professionalization. As early as 1925 President Splawn had addressed the engineering faculty on the possibility of establishing a doctoral program, but they did not act on the idea. C. Read Granberry, from Electrical Engineering, spoke to his peers on the same topic in 1933 and the Graduate Studies Committee considered the proposition, but little came of it. Until 1943 only Chemical Engineering, as an extension of the Department of Chemistry, offered a doctor of philosophy degree to its graduate students.[14]

Dean Woolrich appointed a new committee in 1939, led by Stanley P. Finch, to produce some definite proposals. It reported in May 1940, asking for the adoption of a doctor of science degree to be awarded in civil, electrical, mechanical, petroleum, and chemical engineering, now taught wholly within the College of Engineering. The Graduate Faculty of The University dismissed the motion for a Doctor of Science, retaining the doctor of philosophy in chemical engineering and approving similar doctoral programs in electrical and mechanical engineering. The Departments of Petroleum and Civil Engineering were advised to upgrade their faculties and reapply. The first doctorate given by the College was a combined degree in chemical and mechanical engineering to Luis H. Bartlett, an associate of the Bureau of Engineering Research, in 1943.[15]

The strongest graduate program in engineering at The University before World War II was chemical engineering, but its divided administration hindered full development. Schoch had created the curriculum and remained the catalyst for its growth, stressing always the importance of postbaccalaureate education. He and Dean Woolrich petitioned President Homer P. Rainey for the separation of the chemical engineering program from Chemistry; temporary accommodations for budget and faculty members were made in 1938, and the final split came in 1940. The ECPD granted provisional accreditation in 1942 because the chaos accompanying the outbreak of the war made it impossible for a review board to visit campus, but in 1943 it awarded the new department full certification. By 1946 the Department of Chemical Engineering had granted over five hundred undergraduate and graduate degrees, including nearly half of the master's degrees and almost all of the doctorates awarded in the College of Engineering.[16]

The Departments of Chemical and Petroleum Engineering were the two largest in the College by 1940. Twenty–six percent of the enrollment in

The Chemical Engineering Building, completed in 1942, was later re-named in honor of Eugene P. Schoch, director of the Bureau of Indus-trial Chemistry from 1915 to 1953. [Collection of William A. Cunningham]

The Petroleum Engineering Building, similar in design to the E. P. Schoch Laboratory, was the first classroom building in the United States dedicated to the study of petroleum engineering at its com-pletion in 1942. [College of Engineering, The University of Texas at Austin]

engineering at The University of Texas since 1935 had been in Chemical Engineering, making it the fourth largest program in the United States, and the proportion of students in Petroleum Engineering was even higher. Both departments sorely needed new quarters, and plans were laid for separate buildings to be constructed for each. Schoch requested facilities totaling over forty thousand square feet at a cost of more than a half million dollars, but the chemical engineering building completed in 1942 which bears his name was only thirty–three thousand square feet, built at a cost of less than two hundred thousand dollars. Nevertheless, he must have been pleased, for it was much better than his cramped quarters in the Chemistry Building. The facility built for the Department of Petroleum Engineering in 1941, with the same basic floorplan as the Eugene P. Schoch Laboratories, was the first in the United States constructed specifically for petroleum engineering instruction. Designed to accommodate the undergraduate program and provide room for more graduate research, the new building was constructed on a scale befitting its location in the nation's largest oil–producing state. In their new home, the Petroleum Engineering faculty initiated many projects for curricula reform, including a system of visiting committees that was adopted by The University on the occasion of its seventy–fifth anniversary to provide for renewed direction in development.[17]

A major obstacle to the development of all academic programs in the College of Engineering, especially the graduate curricula, remained the Engineering Library. An "Engineering Graduate School Report" produced shortly after Woolrich's arrival at The University complained that the collection lagged far behind other schools across the country in the number of books, subscriptions to current periodicals, and financial support. While campaigning for a doctoral program in engineering, Dean Woolrich confessed, "Our limitation in offering the Doctor's is based primarily on inadequate technical library facilities." Development of the Engineering Library began on a small scale, limited by the post–Depression budget, then skyrocketed after the close of the war in 1945, when new funds and students poured into the College.[18]

The Engineering Library as a separate collection began with the occupation of the first Engineering Building in 1904. Cataloged books and works on related subjects were removed from the Main Library and shelved in the anteroom to the dean's office, and his secretary acted as part–time librarian. The collection could not be called a true library, and the engineering faculty constantly petitioned for an upgrading of the budget and facilities for books. Their efforts bore fruit in 1915 when the reading room in the old Engineering Building was converted into "a kind of baby library" and additional funds were appropriated for publications and a part–time librarian.[19]

The holdings remained small through the next two decades, and despite repeated requests the Engineering Library was not given a full–time librarian to keep the stacks open at night. Budgetary sleight–of–hand by Dean Taylor in 1927, when he employed a woman as a half–time librarian and a half–time stenographer to extend the library's hours, solved only part of the problem. A survey sent to a number of engineering schools in 1928 by John A. Focht, chairman of the faculty library committee, revealed that the College's collection of about forty–two hundred volumes ranked near the bottom of the list. The engineers moved into their new building in 1933, where more room and the employment of a full–time librarian in 1935 prompted the transfer of volumes stored at the Main Library. The selection of important works remained limited, however, and circulation began to decline in the years before Dean Woolrich arrived.[20]

Under Dean Woolrich the library acquisitions program accelerated. The staff added new periodical subscriptions and completed old collections of back issues. The engineering faculty assumed a more active role in developing the holdings, resulting in a greatly improved central reference collection, and the purchase of more current works in all fields. The faculty began requiring that a copy of all theses and dissertations be deposited with the library before graduation, creating a valuable source of research information. The library assumed control of all audiovisual materials in the College in 1942, establishing a collection that would greatly increase in size and utility within a few years. Circulation of volumes from the Engineering Library and the Architecture Library doubled from 1935–1936 to 1936–1937, and continued increasing rapidly as enrollment grew.[21]

Professor William A. Cunningham initiated the establishment of a reference library in the new chemical engineering building, as the Department was now located some distance from the Chemistry Library. Following Cunningham's lead, Petroleum Engineering also equipped a reading room in its new quarters. When Dean Woolrich came to the University in 1936, the Engineering Library contained less than eight thousand volumes; when he retired in 1958 the collection totaled nearly thirty–two thousand works, with nearly a thousand more shelved in the branch reference reading rooms. Architectural Engineering students also had access to over six thousand books and more than eight thousand plates and folios in the Architecture Library. These figures are easily dwarfed by the present holdings, but considering the budgetary restrictions and academic distractions during much of Dean Woolrich's tenure, the increased scope of the libraries appears as a great achievement of the engineering faculty and staff, and was a boon to the development of course work on all levels.[22]

Dean Woolrich's concern for student development extended beyond curriculum innovation. The Engineering Students' Association was founded in 1937 to give them a voice in academic affairs and bring greater progress toward professionalization through active organization. Shortly after coming to The University, Woolrich also began an advisory system, appointing faculty committees on registration and placement. This became the permanent charge of Edward C. H. Bantel, who had continued to serve as assistant dean after Taylor's departure. Bantel effected many useful changes in the registration and placement procedure before his retirement in 1943. Charles E. Rowe, his successor, was less colorful but just as meticulous in caring for student needs, as was Focht, Dean Woolrich's third assistant dean who took over in 1950. Advisory systems were initiated also in the separate departments of the College; the block program of electives begun in 1953 by John J. McKetta, Jr. chairman of Chemical Engineering, was adopted worldwide as a model for the proper coordination of course work with future career goals.[23]

Under Rowe, placement became the separate responsibility of Ruby Welch for several years until a permanent office was established in 1947 under W. R. Hudson, who was appointed Special Assistant to the Dean in

Charge of Placement. As one of the first academic placement offices established specifically for engineers in the South, Hudson's organization had a definite responsibility for leadership in developing similar programs. Hudson initiated the formation of the Southwest Placement Association (SPA) in 1948 and served as its first president. Billy H. Amstead inherited both the placement office and the presidency of the SPA from Hudson. Amstead continued the tradition of development: the special needs of the growing number of foreign students in the College of Engineering necessitated a reorganization of effort. The placement facilities were made available to the Departments of Mathematics, Chemistry, Geology, and Physics, and served as a model for engineering schools around the world.[24]

Dean Woolrich assumed control of the College of Engineering at a crucial time for research development. Federal funds for advanced study in engineering had been made available as early as 1910, but more often than not were earmarked solely for the use of the land–grant colleges, whom Congress had initiated with the Morrill Act of 1862. These schools had formed the Land Grant Association (LGA) and successfully lobbied for additional support in the first decades of this century, widening the gap between themselves and the separate state institutions. When the TVA also restricted its largesse to land–grant schools, the dispute escalated. Seventeen presidents of state universities allied in 1938 to create two lobbying associations, one each for engineering and business administration. Dean Woolrich led the former organization as national president. They made little headway against the more powerful LGA lobby until the following year, when a number of endowed private universities threw their influence behind the state institutions. The Executive Council of the LGA surrendered and called a joint conference; the result was the Engineering College Research Association, an alliance of all engineering schools to pool resources and share information, which later led to the creation of the National Science Foundation for Scientific and Engineering Research (NSF). This organization would provide the impetus for a revitalization of American engineering and science in the postwar period.[25]

The faculty of the College of Engineering at The University of Texas, anticipating such a reorganization of research effort, laid plans in 1937 for an office within the school to utilize federal funds when they should become available. The Bureau of Engineering Research (BER) was removed from the direct control of the Division of the Conservation and Development of the Natural Resources of Texas within the Bureau of Economic Geology and Technology, where it had operated since 1915, and was integrated into the engineering program. Stanley P. Finch continued as director until 1941, when he resigned in favor of Dean Woolrich. Raymond F. Dawson served as the associate director of the BER until his resignation in 1959, when Dean William W. Hagerty assigned William A. Cunningham to the post.[26]

Money did not flow immediately into the BER, but the faculty and staff accomplished much research of a limited technical nature before World War II. Dean Woolrich continued the work he had begun with the TVA in finding new uses for cottonseed and began research in refrigeration. Luis H. Bartlett joined the BER to conduct research in refrigeration and quick freezing of food. Improved methods of air conditioning applicable to the Southwest for cooling homes and factories were explored. Byron E. Short completed preliminary studies in heat transfer in an effort to produce an economical heat exchanger for industrial use. The BER continued to provide facilities for testing materials to road construction companies in Texas and Dawson conducted the first soil mechanics laboratory in the Southwest in 1930, providing important information on building and road foundations.[27]

The chemical engineers conducted separate research in the Bureau of Industrial Chemistry (BIC), directed by Schoch. Their efforts retained Schoch's original goal of aiding the people of Texas to better utilize the natural resources of their state. Research focused on uses for cotton, polyhalite, lignite, natural gas, clays, ceramic materials, and potash. Schoch's most ambitious project was an attempt to devise a process to economically convert methane into acetylene. The BIC abandoned other studies, such as those focusing on cotton, once the war began, but Schoch renewed his efforts for the production of acetylene because it could be used for synthetic rubber. He failed to derive a process that was financially viable, despite additional federal funding, but the effort resulted in many useful patents and a great store of new information. The BIC was integrated into the BER in 1953 after the retirement of Schoch, its director since its creation as a separate center for research in 1915.[28]

With each of the research bureaus at The University of Texas going its own way, some method had to be devised to coordinate their efforts. The Board of Regents on May 21, 1938, announced the formation of the Texas Industrial and Commercial Resources Council of The University of Texas. It consisted of the Bureaus of Engineering Research, Industrial Chemistry, Business Research, and Economic Geology. Each organization would continue to operate independently, but the Council would act as a "clearinghouse" to disseminate information and to bring industrial support to the programs. Through this program, The University would work with industry to bring Texas out of the Depression, and the engineers would help lead the way to development and progress. The faculty and students of the College of Engineering found themselves with new responsibilites, and Woolrich discovered another tool to instill an even greater sense of professional involvement. The Council expired when it became apparent that its goal had been accomplished in the economic boom accompanying the United States' entry into the war.[29]

Dean Woolrich and the engineering faculty began one final project in the years before World War II that would contribute greatly to the professionalization of the students and staff and establish closer links between the College and industry. Publication of a journal had been planned in 1930, and the *University of Texas Engineer* debuted the next year to wide acclaim, but funds failed as the Depression intensified. The idea resurfaced in 1938, just when concern was greatest for coordination between engineering research and industry support. The *Journal of Architecture, Engineering, and Industry* commenced in September 1938. Short was its first editor, followed by Werner W. Dornberger, Millard V. Barton, and Billy H. Amstead, who presided over its demise in 1953. The title was changed to the *Journal of Engineering and Industrial Research* following the separation of the School of Architecture from the College of Engineering in 1951, but during its short life the publication maintained a high level of student and faculty involvement and brought favorable recognition from its intended audience, the professional and industrial leaders of Texas. In 1953, *Engineering–Science News*, a newsletter, replaced the *Journal of Engineering and Industrial Research*, continuing to give information on College research activities and other events for five more years before its own demise.[30]

The academic reorganization of the College of Engineering under Dean Woolrich before World War II remained limited, due to the poor financial condition of The University, but improvement could be measured in some very clear statistics. Enrollment increased through the five–year period from 1936 to 1941, peaking at 1,806 in the fall of 1939. The proportion of graduate students during the same period steadily grew, resulting in a respectable number of postbaccalaureate degrees in engineering. The figures would be eclipsed by the postwar flood of students sponsored by the G.I. Bill, but were quite good for the period: as the war began, the College ranked twelfth nationally in enrollment. Improvement meant not only an increase in quantity, but also in quality: The University had 62 alumni listed in *Who's Who in Engineering* in 1937, but by 1948 the roster had grown to 113 graduates, many of whom enrolled in the College after Woolrich became dean.[31]

President Rainey led The University of Texas into the worldwide effort to win World War II. He believed it was a war to be won by men and women who knew their science and engineering. Rather than training or indoctrinating students for their role in the conflict, Rainey fought to ensure that each individual received a true education in his chosen field. Dean Woolrich echoed those sentiments: before the United States entered the war he wrote, "modern wars are battles of machine production;" once the country was engaged, he labored to keep the College separate from the trade school program of the Department of Education. Woolrich played a key role in the wartime training programs, serving on the national Committee on Education and Training for Defense Mapping and as director of Region 17 of the National Defense Program, which was designed to produce technically educated men and women at an accelerated rate for both the military and industry.[32]

Despite Woolrich's opposition, the College of Engineering offered vocational instruction for the Department of Education's national training program. The mechanical engineering laboratories were completely refurbished, then both faculty and industry personnel taught courses at night to apprentice welders and machine-shop operators. The electronics division within the Department of Electrical Engineering trained several hundred men and women bused to The University from San Antonio on an eight–hour shift schedule. None of the enrollees earned college credit, but all gained valuable experience in technological production techniques and trade applications. These graduates played a crucial role in the creation of new wartime industry and the retooling of old plants in Texas after 1941.[33]

The College participated more actively in the Engineer's Defense Training program. Also drawing on the talents of both faculty and businessmen, EDT classes emphasized the practical side of technical training. Students again received no college credit, but swarmed into The University to take courses in aeronautical, civil, electrical, and mechanical engineering, as well as naval architecture, drafting, and related subjects. The classes met from October 1940 to September 1941, then were extended under a new title: Engineering, Science, and Management Defense Training. By September 1942, twenty–five hundred had obtained certificates of completion from The University of Texas. The pace accelerated in July 1942, when the name was changed to Engineering, Science, and Management War Training. New faculty were employed to teach extension courses at industrial sites in over thirty Texas cities and towns. They taught chemical engineering basics to workers in munitions and chemical factories, sanitary and civil engineering to airfield construction employees, and petroleum engineering to aviation gasoline and petrochemical manufacturers. Fourteen thousand students received certificates upon completion of their courses before the program ended on June 30, 1945. The University of Texas ranked sixth in the United States in the production of skilled technicians during World War II.[34]

Because well-educated engineers were needed quickly after 1941, the normal curricula in each department were compressed until a student could obtain a bachelor of science degree in thirty–two months. Classes met twelve months of the year, placing a great strain on the faculty who were already teaching courses in almost every corner of the state. Civilian enrollment dropped, but the classrooms were filled with enlistees from the U. S. Navy V–12 program; in the fall of 1943 the combined enrollment of civilians and Navy recruits in engineering reached 2,256, a new record. The military enrollees were candidates for a baccalaureate degree; they lived under military discipline and training, but regularly attended engineering classes on a tri–semester schedule designed to be the equivalent of a four–year curriculum.[35]

Military demand prompted the revitalization of the Department of Aeronautical Engineering. A graduate program begun in 1939 as an adjunct of the Department of Mechanical Engineering had met with a favorable response from students and industry. Dean Woolrich encouraged its growth, in part be-cause of his own experience conducting a flight and ground school at the University of Tennessee. In 1940 a Civilian Pilot Training course, under the auspices of the Civilian Aeronautical Administration, began with Venton L. Doughtie as di-rector. The men who completed the flight and ground training became the back-bone of the army and navy air corps; by May 15, 1942, 192 of the 225 graduates had enlisted. Seven of those who completed the course were women. The course work later became the core of the U.S. Navy V–12 Flight Training Group, which produced more than a thousand additional pilots and navigators. The College recruited Milton J. Thompson from the University of Michigan to direct the ex-pansion of the curriculum in aeronautical engineering; in 1942 Thompson pre-sided over the creation of a new department. The University of Texas became one of only seven schools selected by the Curtiss–Wright Corporation to conduct its Engineering Cadette Program, in which 100 women received an intensive forty–week course in mathematics, aircraft drafting, mechanics, and principles of flight. Many took key positions in wartime industry and remained for long careers after the war ended.[36]

The Curtiss–Wright Engineering Cadette Program represented one of the first organized efforts by the College to recruit women. The bill that created The University had been specifically amended to allow females to attend, but they had traditionally preferred disciplines other than science and engineer-ing. The first woman to earn a degree in the College had been Nellie Jefferson, who earned a bachelor of science in architecture in 1915, then worked for two years as an instructor in engineering while she worked on a graduate degree. Ruth W. Lawhon earned the first engineering degree in 1929, when she took a baccalaureate in architectural engineering from the College. Women engineers from The University during this period, despite their small number, won plaudits for their achievements. Leah Moncure, who earned a bachelor of science in civil engineering in 1937, became the first woman to register as a professional engineer in Texas and the first to be elected a life member of the National Society for Professional Engineers. In spite of the example provided by these and other women, including the Cadettes, female engineering enrollment remained only a small fraction of the total; in 1957, Woolrich's last year as dean, only twenty–three attended courses in the College.[37]

Only basic research necessary to the military continued between 1941 and 1945. Many of the engineering faculty were drafted into the armed services; those who remained taught enormous course loads on campus and across the state. Graduate student enrollment plummeted, further restricting the staff formerly available for research. Schoch in the BIC did continue his work on producing acetylene for synthetic rubber, and studies in the BER on food preservation through freezing or dehydration resulted in a number of patents granted to Woolrich, Bartlett, and Howard E. Brown. In general, however, real progress came with peace.[38]

Several factors combined for the rapid development of the College of Engineering after the war's end, but the most spectacular was the increase in the number of students. Enrollment skyrocketed, paralleling the national boom in large part due to the financial aid extended to veterans. Engineering enrollment in the fall of 1936 totaled 1,443; after the war's end, the figure climbed to 4,312 in the fall of 1946, about 3,000 of whom were veterans. There had been some concern expressed about the quality of these students before they arrived; discussion focused on whether they would be unbalanced by their wartime experience, or would be attending school just for the money and not be serious about their education. The new arrivals surprised the doomsayers, as they were generally more mature and attentive than classes before the war. The greatest change came in graduate education, as many returned for refresher courses or to advance their knowledge to a point commensurate with their military rank. The outbreak of the Korean War brought another sharp drop in both undergraduate and graduate enrollment, but the College registered a net gain in almost every department through the last decade of Woolrich's tenure as dean.[39]

Increasing enrollment alone did not revitalize development in the College of Engineering; it simply provided a tremendous amount of human potential for professional education. The world needed a different kind of engineer than that commonly seen before the war, "one who had more profound understanding, more extensive scientific knowledge, and more highly cultivated analytical and creative powers." Industry and academia demanded engineers with extensive graduate education, especially those with the doctoral degree. Engineering as a profession and as a discipline underwent a period of unprecedented and rapid evolution after World War II as the introduction of scientific advances fueled by economic prosperity led to intense technological competition at home in the United States and abroad. The public, through wartime programs, had also become more appreciative of the services of the professional engineer, and added their voice to the clamor for more advanced instruction and research. Texas particularly needed more technologically proficient graduates. In 1940, the state reached the breakpoint when the federal census revealed over half of the state's population was urban. New natural gas, airplane, and chemical plants sprouted during the period just before and during the war, along with more complex radio broadcasting networks and the first television station at Fort Worth in 1948. Within another decade, Texas had become a national leader in electronics manufactures.[40]

The period of transition for the College of Engineering at The University actually began in 1938 with the accelerated hiring program prompted by the ECPD report. "Temporary" faculty came during World War II to help with extended course work, then remained as an integral part of further curriculum development. After the war additional instructors aided the effort to educate the flood of student veterans; the best of them also found their niche in the growing

Leah Moncure, who graduated from the University of Texas at Austin in 1937, became the first woman to register as a professional engineer in Texas. [College of Engineering, The University of Texas at Austin]

College. Nearly every one of these new faces had a doctoral degree when they arrived, or earned it soon afterward. They came from points all over the United States, negating the charge of "academic inbreeding" leveled by the ECPD in 1937.

New faculty expanded each department into untapped areas of research and instruction. The triad of Bryant, Correll, and Ramsay, who led Electrical Engineering under Dean Taylor, gave way to Robert W. Warner, who served as chairman from 1937 to 1945, and Burns N. Gafford, who succeeded him and remained until 1964. They were joined by Ralph A. Galbraith and Edwin W. Hamlin, and the Department moved beyond power transmission to electronics and communication by radio and television. Archie W. Straiton added new graduate research programs in microwave propagation. The first woman faculty member was Edith Clarke, who came to the College as an associate professor of electrical engineering in 1947 after a long career with General Electric. John J. McKetta, Jr., came in 1946 and later directed the Department of Chemical Engineering in one of its most vital periods of development, alternating with Cunningham and Kenneth A. Kobe as chairman until becoming Dean of Engineering in 1963. Research by Kobe and McKetta soon thrust their program into the forefront of chemical technology in the United States. Phil M. Ferguson of Civil Engineering won great recognition for his work in materials, especially concrete, and Ernest W. Steel and Earnest F. Gloyna pushed sanitary engineering into a new and broader field, environmental health engineering. Ferguson succeeded Stanley P. Finch as chairman in 1943 and remained until 1957, when Steel served for a year. In Petroleum Engineering, George H. Fancher and Harry H. Power directed the transition of course work from descriptive technological courses to those employing a more quantitative approach. Dana Young's contribution in engineering mechanics led to his appointment as a dean at Yale University. Senior faculty provided the necessary leadership in the drive for progress; for example, Short initiated new work in heat transfer and served as Acting Dean when Woolrich spent a year as science attaché to the United States Embassy in London.[41]

Funding for new research flowed into the College of Engineering from both industry and government, but primarily the latter. In 1945 the Defense Research Laboratory (DRL) organized on campus under Thompson of Aeronautical Engineering and C. Paul Boner of Physics to continue advanced research in military technology. Many of the engineering faculty worked there, and slowly the program broadened into fields with more general applications in civilian life. Initially, research focused on systems for the guidance and control of missiles, especially radar, and the mechanics of underwater sound travel. Aeronautical and Mechanical Engineering used the facilities for research in thermodynamics and flight mechanics, valuable to both military and commercial aircraft.[42]

The Electrical Engineering Research Laboratory (EERL) also began in 1945. Hamlin and Straiton directed advanced study in microwave transmission of radio signals and applications of radar. They were the first to use some of the simple computers available soon after the war ended, developing more sophisticated systems for later use. Hamlin particularly focused on the progress of the field of microelectronics. The EERL from the beginning worked more closely with graduate students than the DRL, primarily because most of its work was not as highly classified. Its research in the atmospheric propagation of radio broadcasts led to more interest in meteorology, and eventually to the creation of a separate department in the College of Engineering. The EERL also aided the Department of Aeronautical Engineering with the creation of even more sophisticated electronic guidance systems. Efforts by the EERL and the DRL often overlapped, divided only by the level of classification. Both organizations remained the focus of research activity for many years.[43]

The BER and the BIC also benefited from the influx of faculty and funds. The bureaus expanded previous fields of research, testing materials such as tile and concrete for construction as well as refining techniques of refrigeration, freezing, and air conditioning. Additional projects, however, included specific heat studies, petroleum research, the disposal of oil–well salt waters, and applications of electron microscopy to metallurgy. The BIC developed studies in ceramics, leading to the creation of the short–lived Department of Ceramics, as well as research in rubber, refrigerants, fluid mechanics, and thermodynamics to supplement the work initiated elsewhere. As president of The University of Texas, Theophilus S. Painter initiated new rules for advancement and tenure in all departments. Commonly called "publish or perish," the new philosophy precipitated after World War II an increase in the number of doctoral degrees held by University faculty, including the engineers. The College became part of a national trend which saw the number of doctoral degrees in engineering awarded annually increase from 82 in 1937 to 647 in 1958, the year Woolrich retired. The result was an increase in the quality of education for engineering students in Austin at all levels, and an unprecedented emphasis on research.[44]

The most successful engineering research complex developed at The University of Texas during Woolrich's administration has been the Off Campus Research Center, renamed the Balcones Research Center (BRC) in 1953 for the geological fault that bisects the original tract. J. Neils Thompson of Civil Engineering was instrumental in acquiring the buildings, which had been a magnesium plant during the war. He became its first director, assisting in the establishment of twenty–seven laboratories from numerous diverse fields at The University of Texas. Many vital facilities, such as wind tunnels for Aeronautical Engineering, were constructed at the BRC quite early in its history. J. Neils Thompson and C. Read Granberry, through Congressman Lyndon B. Johnson, successfully negotiated a contract for the purchase of the site from the federal government in 1949. By the terms of the agreement, the payments for the plant were to be made in educational benefits over a twenty–year period, an obligation The University met easily.[45]

Much initial engineering research centered on the petroleum industry; of seventeen units at BRC in 1951, five years after it opened, six conducted studies for the oil production business. This work led in part to the creation of the Texas Petroleum Research Committee (TPRC). The TPRC was established through a joint resolution of chairman Ernest O. Thompson of the Texas Railroad Commission and the regents of The University of Texas and Texas A&M. Fancher of the College of Engineering in Austin became the first director in 1950 and appointed an assistant director at each institution to initiate research by graduate students, who composed a majority of the staff. The emphasis was on enhanced secondary recovery from Texas fields. In 1954, the TPRC published the first comprehensive reconnaisance survey of the oil resources in the state. Of course, engineering research at The University did not center entirely on petroleum; by 1958 there were nearly twenty diverse organized research laboratories identified with the College, a majority of them housed in the BRC complex which totaled thirty–four buildings.[46]

Advanced study by the faculty prompted further innovation in undergraduate and graduate course work. Many new programs began, and older programs reorganized once more to keep abreast of developments. The five years between the return of the veterans from World War II and the decline in enrollment following the outbreak of the Korean War was a period of academic chaos, as members of the faculty lobbied for recognition of their programs as separate departments. Most of the ideas initiated then have remained integral parts of the College curriculum.

The optional course of electives in sanitary and public health engineering, offered by the Department of Civil Engineering, was revived in 1945. The importance of this field had been recognized since the creation of a separate program in engineering at The University of Texas in 1895, but enrollment had been erratic, despite the fine work done by Quinton B. Graves and Steel in the graduate program initiated in 1937. The combined graduate and undergraduate option limped along until the employment of Gloyna in 1947. He assumed responsibility for instruction in wastewater treatment from Chemical Engineering, where it had fallen into disfavor, and combined it with plant operations courses from Civil Engineering for a new discipline: sanitary engineering became environmental health engineering in 1962. Recognition of its new status came earlier, when in 1957 it was accepted as an accredited option for the doctoral degree.[47]

The BIC employed Forrest K. Pence in July 1940 for his experience in the ceramic industry. He became the director of the Research Laboratory in Ceramics, a new division of the BIC, and chairman of the nascent Department of Ceramic Engineering, one of eleven undergraduate programs in the United States, in 1945. His work went beyond clay to include the technology of all earthy or nonmetallic minerals, including glass, terra cotta, cements, insulation materials, asbestos, and other minerals. The ECPD awarded accreditation in 1948, and in 1949 the Department offered a master of science degree. Pence returned to full–time research in 1950; E. Joseph Weiss, then Robert L. Stone became chairman of Ceramic Engineering. The Research Laboratory in Ceramics was incorporated into the BER when Pence retired in 1954, and the Department was discontinued because of falling enrollment in 1959; only eighteen students had declared ceramic engineering as their major the year before. Weiss transferred to the Department of Chemical Engineering, where he continued his work, developing a graduate degree program in materials science. A vocal minority of the faculty in 1945 had argued that a curriculum in ceramic engineering could not be supported and predicted that the more accepted Department of Chemical Engineering would overshadow it in placing its graduates. They had been proven right; only the veterans, with whom the ceramic engineering program had proven quite popular, had attended in any significant number.[48]

Eugene P. Schoch, as the director of the Bureau of Industrial Chemistry, earned lasting recognition as a leading pioneer in the development
of the chemical engineering profession in the South. [Collection of
William A. Cunningham]

Another short–lived program in meteorology began as an adjunct to the EERL in 1946 under the active sponsorship of Kenneth H. Jehn. The committee which recommended its extension to Dean Woolrich intended it to be a "program of limited scope," and followed the example of MIT and other leading institutions by placing it in the Department of Aeronautical Engineering, forestalling attempts to make it a separate department. However, in September 1950 the College offered a bachelor of science in meteorology in spite of continued opposition from some of the faculty. The establishment of the Texas Commission on Higher Education and the subsequent "freezing" of all programs effective October 1950 halted renewed efforts to begin a graduate curriculum. The undergraduate program was never accredited by the ECPD, and the curriculum was absorbed later into the engineering science program, then into the Department of Civil Engineering. During its brief existence, however, the meteorology program earned national recognition for its innovative research and in 1953 co–hosted the 125th meeting of the American Meteorological Society, attended by over two hundred delegates from the United States and overseas.[49]

The Department of Engineering Mechanics was activated February 1, 1947, with Dana Young, formerly a professor of theoretical and applied mechanics in Civil Engineering, as chairman. The program, which combined elements of engineering, physics, and mathematics to solve engineering problems through a more direct application of scientific principles, had been discussed as early as 1944, but it was not until 1947 that the College cleared the last administrative hurdle. The new department offered only graduate courses leading to the master's or doctoral degrees. Most of the faculty, like Young, came from Civil Engineering, including Banks L. McLaurin, who graduated from The University of Texas in 1911 and had taught in the College since 1925. With strong support from the established disciplines, the new department flourished, granting its first doctoral degree in 1951, only four years after its creation. Dean William W. Hagerty, who succeeded Woolrich, was a professor of engineering mechanics, and continued to foster its development during his tenure at The University of Texas.[50]

The more established departments shifted gears under the impact of accelerated engineering research and development. Civil Engineering deemphasized traditional surveying requirements and offered more electives in technical fields, stressing graduate work as necessary for student specialization. The Department awarded its first doctoral degree in 1954 to Earl I. Brown, who later became the dean of civil engineering at Duke University in North Carolina. Doctoral degrees were offered for the first time by two other established departments, Aeronautical and Petroleum Engineering, in 1955, and Short reported in 1957 that graduate course work in nuclear engineering as a minor field within the Mechanical Engineering curriculum had been devised. The College also initiated a master of science in industrial engineering in 1951, which focused on plant design and operation. Drawing, always a service branch, shifted its emphasis from skill in reproduction to the study of language and methods used by engineers and architects to design and record their ideas and solve problems graphically. Enrollment overflowed its usual quarters after World War II, forcing a temporary return to wooden barracks for classrooms, but under James D.

McFarland, who succeeded Walter H. McNeill as chairman in 1951, enrollment stabilized.[51]

The Department of Architecture outgrew the bounds of the College of Engineering shortly after the war ended and enrollment boomed. By 1948 the program was the third largest in the United States; only the Universities of California and Illinois outstripped it in number of students. Recognition of this growth resulted in the creation of a semiautonomous division in 1948, directed by Hugh L. McMath. The program continued to expand dramatically; the number of faculty doubled from 1945 to 1950, supporting a broad curriculum that included an increasing amount of course work in the humanities and business administration. A new baccalaureate plan adopted during World War II trained students in regional and city planning, a dynamic new field attracting many enrollees. The School of Architecture organized in 1951, with Harwell T. Harris as chairman. Werner W. Dornberger chaired the Department of Architectural Engineering, which remained within the College of Engineering, laboring along with Ferguson to keep an independent identity for the discipline through another two decades. Their courses retained a close adherence to the traditional engineering focus on materials and structural design, unlike architecture, which borrowed a greater emphasis on aesthetics and form from the fine arts.[52]

The splintering of traditional engineering curricula had reached a critical stage by 1950. The ECPD recognized over twenty individual disciplines, with at least that many more petitioning for accreditation at the baccalaureate level. The organization funded a thorough study by the ASEE from 1951 to 1953. The resulting report became quite controversial as it recommended the suspension of research and engineering sciences at many of the smaller schools in favor of a greater concentration on production and public service engineering. A revised opinion in 1954 backed down from the earlier stand, but the net effect was the reversal of the trend toward increasing specialization. The faculty of the College of Engineering at The University of Texas concurred with that judgment and with the position that all who taught engineering at the rank of associate professor or above should be registered professional engineers. They considered the idea of a "professional degree" requiring thirty more hours of course work beyond the baccalaureate, but dropped it in favor of remaining in line with national trends toward professional consolidation of curricula. The engineering faculty as a body had become very conscious of their position within the movement for progress in technological education in the United States.[53]

Dean Woolrich failed to get a large measure of the national recognition he craved for the College of Engineering because he did not receive the funding for some of his most ambitious plans. He had served as secretary to two engineering college foundations before coming to The University of Texas, and had observed the creation and operation of eight foundations, including one for the School of Architecture, while in Austin. He clearly realized the value of such an organization, and in 1954 began consulting with Hulon Black, director of the University Development Board, about a permanent fund for the College of Engineering. The Board of Regents announced the creation of the Engineering Foundation on March 12, 1955. It would be responsible for soliciting funds and supervising their disbursement through salaries, grants, and fellowships, coordinating curriculum evaluation, and keeping abreast of current educational trends as an advisory association for the dean. In doing so, the Foundation would encourage new research and foster academic development in the College.[54]

Woolrich remained an advisor to the Engineering Foundation for a year after his retirement as dean, supervising the progress of one of his strongest legacies to the College. The Foundation benefitted from the dedication of faculty such as Cunningham, Straiton, and McKetta, who worked closely with active alumni led by Joe J. King, George L. MacGregor, William J. Murray, Jr., Clarence L. Linder, William B. Franklin, and Ernest Cockrell, Jr., to establish a permanent financial endowment and provide direction in curriculum development. They adopted an initial goal of raising $1.5 million over a five–year period, but their actual achievement eclipsed that. The Foundation did not hesitate to act through its mandate to "undertake those projects that are not normally permissible under the rules and regulations laid down by the Legislature and the Texas Constitution for the greater development of the College of Engineering." Engineering education at The University of Texas has benefited greatly from that early resolution.[55]

COLLEGE OF ENGINEERING FOUNDATION ADVISORY COUNCIL CHAIRMEN, 1957–1986

| 1957–59 | George L. MacGregor | Texas Utilities Company |
|---------|---------------------|-------------------------|
| 1959–60 | Joe J. King | Tenneco, Inc. |
| 1960–61 | William J. Murray, Jr. | Independent Consultant |
| 1961–62 | William B. Franklin | Humble Oil and Refining Company |
| 1962–63 | †R. W. Olson | Texas Instruments, Inc. |
| 1963–65 | John Hume | Texas Utilities Company |
| 1965–67 | †Lawrence B. Jones | Mosher Steel Company |
| 1967–69 | John L. Tullis | AMF, Inc. |
| 1969–70 | Charles F. Jones | Humble Oil and Refining Company |
| 1970–73 | Bob R. Dorsey | Gulf Oil Corporation |
| 1973–74 | John E. Kasch | Amoco International Oil Company |
| 1974–75 | †Melvin H. Gertz | Purvin and Gertz |
| 1975–76 | John W. Sheehan | Shell Oil Company |
| 1976–78 | Robert L. Parker, Sr. | Parker Drilling Company |
| 1978–79 | Ernest H. Cockrell | Cockrell Oil Corporation |
| 1979–80 | Paul D. Meek | Fina Oil and Chemical Company |
| 1980–81 | R. Earle Wright | Texaco, Inc. |
| 1981–82 | Perry G. Brittain | Texas Utilities Company |
| 1982–83 | John T. Files | Merichem Company |
| 1983–84 | Charles M. Simmons | Western Company of North America |
| 1984–85 | Louis A. Beecherl | Texas Oil and Gas Corporation |
| 1985–86 | Bobby R. Inman | Microelectronics and Computer Technology Corporation |

†Deceased

The progress of the College of Engineering received international recognition: when Chulalongkorn University in Bangkok, Thailand, resolved to upgrade its engineering program it called on The University of Texas for assistance. The project was initiated by Harold Stassen of the U. S. International Cooperation Administration in a broad effort to extend aid to underdeveloped countries through agriculture, engineering, education, political science, and industrial modernization. Engineering faculty from The University of Texas worked in Thailand, laboring to improve both the teaching of technical disciplines and living conditions in the surrounding countryside. Ernest W. Steel, of Civil Engineering, and Harry L. Kent, Jr., of Mechanical Engineering, built the first sanitation laboratory in Asia at Chulalongkorn in 1955, and others from Austin soon followed, including James J. Pollard of Architectural Engineering, Wayne E. Long of Mechanical Engineering, Raymond F. Dawson of Civil Engineering, and even Dean Woolrich in 1956. Of nineteen faculty from Chulalongkorn who came to the United States for advanced studies during the same period, eight attended The University of Texas, more than any other college of engineering in the country.[56]

Dean Woolrich succeeded in creating a more professional College of Engineering. The teaching facilities and research laboratories had all progressed greatly during his administration. Enrollment increased almost threefold to a peak of 4,312 in 1947 before subsiding to a more manageable level by his retirement in 1958, but still remained more than twice that of twenty–two years before. Dean Woolrich awarded three times more diplomas in fewer years than Taylor; indeed, enrollment and degrees granted in the College exceeded that for every other engineering institution in Texas. The annual budget, a focus of many hard–fought campaigns, increased to almost $1.7 million in fiscal year 1958, eighteen times that for 1936, indicating the extent of the development of research and technical education in the postwar period. Many new faculty embraced the goals of certification and accreditation, pushed the College into the mainstream of engineering education in the United States, and won recognition for their leadership. Dean Woolrich prepared the groundwork, through the Engineering Foundation, for overcoming the final economic obstacles in the future. The College under his successors would not have to surrender its objectives so easily due to economic hardship and could progress more rapidly because of the respect won by Dean Woolrich and the faculty as professional engineers.[57]

# AN EXPERIMENT WITH ENGINEERING SCIENCE:

*Dean William W. Hagerty and the College of Engineering, 1958–1963*

The two decades after World War II were a period of accelerating evolution in scientific discovery and engineering development in the United States stimulated by a greater emphasis on research by government and industry. As the body of scientific knowledge grew, the need for engineering applications multiplied in tandem. The economic boom sustained by the progressive innovations of the engineers generated an irresistable momentum as all sectors began demanding larger numbers of better–educated engineers. Industrial leaders and engineering educators realized the importance of graduate–level engineering education. In Texas, new technological industry altered the existing economic base of petroleum and agriculture; by 1959, the state ranked eighth in electronics manufactures.[1]

Recognition of accelerating technological development led to a broad-scale and universally adopted modification of undergraduate programs and the expansion of graduate engineering education. Institutions of higher education throughout the United States raised teaching salaries, recruited new faculty, and introduced courses incorporating the concept of "engineering science" as an important adjunct to the traditional engineering curricula. Many engineering practitioners and educators agreed that a four–year undergraduate education alone was no longer sufficient for many advanced analysis and professional design requirements. Graduate work stimulated the original research and critical approach necessary for innovation, product development, and ultimate economic leadership. Increased financial support from the National Science Foundation (NSF), National Institute of Health, and Joint Services Electronics Program of the Department of Defense, along with pressure from accrediting agencies, primarily the Engineering Council for Professional Development (ECPD), further accelerated development.[2]

Industry and engineering colleges in Texas actively participated in developing technology on all levels, contributing their own research and engineers to the national trend. One of the more spectacular milestones in the state's development was the selection of Houston as the focus for the activities of the National Aeronautics and Space Administration (NASA) in the Southwest. The Manned Spacecraft Center began operations in July 1962, employing numerous graduates of The University of Texas. The federal decennial census in 1970 reported that Houston had become the first city in Texas with over one million inhabitants, reflecting the impact of NASA and other technological industries on it and other urban centers across the state. Such development had a great influence on the College of Engineering at The University, leading to progress in curriculum development and research.[3]

These changing criteria influenced the selection of the next dean of the College of Engineering. The regents assigned the task of molding a new academic direction to William W. Hagerty, who succeeded Woolrich on September 15, 1959. Dean Hagerty was from Holyoke, Wisconsin, a midwesterner from a small town like his predecessor, but there the resemblance ended. His professional development reflected the recent change in engineering education effected in the United States. He earned his undergraduate degree at the University of Minnesota in 1939, then began his career as an instructor of mechanical engineering at Villanova in 1940 and then the University of Cincinnati in 1941. Hagerty became an instructor at the University of Michigan in 1942, rising to the rank of full professor in nine years while completing his doctoral degree in engineering mechanics, awarded after completion of a dissertation in fluid mechanics in 1947.[4]

Hagerty's achievements attracted notice, and he became dean of the School of Engineering at the University of Delaware in 1955, where he was responsible for "major advances" in personnel, teaching, research, and physical plant development. He felt constrained by the small scope and budget of the engineering program at Delaware, however, and welcomed the opportunity to direct the College of Engineering at The University of Texas, where the presence of former colleagues and students such as faculty members Walter L. Moore of Civil Engineering and John J. McKetta, Jr., of Chemical Engineering promised new and possibly greater opportunities.[5]

Dean Hagerty emphasized engineering education for a dynamic, changing profession. Developments in industrial application and research had become so rapid that engineers more than ever were encouraged to consider continuing education as a vital part of their professional career. Unlike Woolrich, Hagerty was blunt, competitive, and intolerant of incompetence. At the same time, he emphasized that an "atmosphere of enthusiasm conducive to good teaching and research" was important to progress, and encouraged teamwork. He always thought big; as dean, his efforts focused on promoting research, improving teaching, and gaining national recognition for the College, primarily in the field of graduate education but also on the undergraduate level.[6]

Dean Hagerty came to the College of Engineering with the specific charge, official or not, to "clear out a lot of deadwood" and to change the course of engineering. With his ambitious style, he gave the flywheel a twist, and the College rolled forward. He determined the transition at The University

Billy H. Amstead, Assistant Dean of Engineering from 1959 to 1970, William W. Hagerty, Dean of Engineering from 1958 to 1963, and John J. McKetta, Jr., Dean of Engineering from 1963 to 1969, pose at the unveiling of Hagerty's portrait, which now hangs along with those of the other former deans on the tenth floor of Ernest Cockrell, Jr., Hall. [College of Engineering, The University of Texas at Austin]

of Texas from a more traditional engineering program to a curriculum that included the concepts of engineering science then in vogue, establishing new ties with the natural sciences. As part of the process, the recruitment of more faculty with doctoral-level education and the construction of more complex facilities changed the emphasis within the College from putting undergraduates through a definite program to preparing them for a changing future, especially by a greater concentration on graduate education and research. Dean Hagerty enjoyed strong support from the University administration and increased funding from numerous outside sources, coordinated by the Engineering Foundation, to expedite development.[7]

President Logan R. Wilson appointed Hagerty after making a personal visit to the University of Delaware to observe the changes he had effected there. Wilson had several items on his desk that influenced his recruitment of a young, aggressive dean of engineering. Most important was a final report from the ECPD, which had inspected the College of Engineering in April 1958. The ECPD had accredited the engineering curricula for only two years and told Wilson that significant improvement in engineering faculty, facilities, and course work would have to take place before full accreditation could be restored. The advisory council to the dean of engineering, organized just a few years before Dean Woolrich retired, reported directly to the chancellor of The University, and it substantially agreed with the ECPD. A faculty member from each department in the College sat on the council, so its advice that a new dean should be someone who would "shake things up" carried great weight.[8]

President Wilson did not act only on the advice of others; he had strong ideas of his own regarding the proper conduct of higher education. Speaking at the Conference on Issues Confronting the State University, held at The University in 1958, he said, "More and more, our state universities will be working on frontiers of knowledge where future needs must be anticipated." At the same time, any expansion of public education must combine "economy of effort with effectiveness of result." Better ways of teaching should be devised to facilitate a streamlining of course offerings on the undergraduate level and the development of more progressive curricula in the graduate and professional schools. Rapid growth in knowledge did not have to result in more courses and departments: "Less cumbersome and more economical ways of organizing subject matter in terms of fundamental concepts will be found." In Hagerty, with his definite ideas on the importance of an engineering science program, Wilson believed he had found his man: "We consider The University of Texas fortunate in securing as dean one of America's leading young educators in science. Dean Hagerty's training and experience are ideally suited to the further development of a great College of Engineering."[9]

Chancellor Harry H. Ransom also actively supported the College of Engineering. Recognizing that The University at its seventy–fifth anniversary in 1958 was not of the "first class," he initiated a number of reforms, spending unprecedented amounts of money for new faculty, books, and facilities. Research and teaching efforts took on renewed vitality across the campus. Good programs such as those of the College of Engineering were given even stronger support. Faculty salaries and student numbers doubled from 1957 to 1969, while the number of nationally ranked graduate faculties at The University increased from two to twenty–three during the same period, out of a total of thirty–four listed in the survey. The University of Texas also became "the leading producer of doctorates among all institutions in the South and Southwest," a total of 411 during the academic year ending in 1969.[10]

Ransom appeared to be particularly pleased at the progress of the College of Engineering under Dean Hagerty and frequently visited to present new ideas and encourage further development. In July 1959, he commended the College for its practical use of the University Excellence Fund, established to sponsor the change he envisioned. The engineers' program, Ransom beamed, was the best in The University. During 1960, when these funds were disbursed directly through the Office of the Chancellor, support for engineering grew to $50,000. In February 1962, Ransom again commended the engineering faculty on their progress. Engineering fellowships and research assistantships in two years had grown from $172,000 to $213,000, and faculty development funds doubled from $58,000 to $116,000. Government contracts swelled from $1.4 million to $2.1 million in the same period. Support from the Engineering Foundation, just five years old, had tripled between 1960 and 1962. More than $2 million from outside sources had been donated for fellowships. Ransom, reviewing this progress, told the engineering faculty, "Nobody can convince me that the people who are spending that money are throwing it away on a losing horse and nothing can convince me that the prospect of that horse's progress around the track in the next years is not going to be reasonably speedy and reasonably sure." [11]

Hagerty, at 41 the youngest dean ever appointed in the College of Engineering, delineated a set of vigorous academic goals in the *Alcalde*, The University's alumni magazine. He wrote, "Since engineering college graduates reach their maximum effectiveness ten to thirty years after graduation, long range predictions as to future needs are required whenever new curricula are formulated. In engineering parlance we must operate with about twenty years' advance lead." Reform in the past had led to an endless subdivision of programs and an increase in requirements, until only a minority of students could finish in four years; most needed five. In order to provide for the "ten–year future," substantial revision of both graduate and undergraduate curricula was necessary. Most important, Hagerty believed that "the first degree should be obtainable by qualified students in a four year program." At The University he would reduce the professional content of the course work while emphasizing and increasing the math and science. "Considering only those who graduate, our programs should be designed for approximately the middle two quarters." For those in the top quarter, some flexibility to take more advanced courses or graduate work was to be allowed. [12]

Dean Hagerty was concerned that a professional "philosophy" for the College of Engineering be established. For the first time, a clear definition for the engineering program appeared in the catalog:

> The engineer is a professional person who, through a knowledge of the mathematical and physical sciences acquired by study and practice, applies judgement to develop ways of utilizing economically the materials and forces of nature for the well-being of mankind by:
> 1. Predicting the behavior of technical devices or processes under specific operating conditions.
> 2. Developing and utilizing structures, machines, apparatus, manufacturing processes or works.
> 3. Constructing, designing, and operating scientifically systematized devices or processes.
> 4. Developing natural resources in accordance with sound principles of conservation. [13]

This creed, which embodied the changes effected in all fields of engineering since World War II, reflected a studied focus on engineering expertise through scientific knowledge. By doing so, this manifesto signaled the move from the "boots and britches" school of engineering, of which Dean Taylor was so much a part, to modern engineering, dominated by emerging technology and characterized by rapid change.

Dean Hagerty proposed a program of reform almost immediately after his arrival. On September 11, 1958, before taking office, he informally addressed the department chairmen on the problems he believed would require immediate attention. The quality of freshman enrolling in the College was perceived to be low; his proposal was to raise entrance requirements. The new dean said that he understood much of the laboratory equipment necessary for teaching was "inadequate, obsolete, or non–existent," and put forth a five–year plan for replacement. In order to facilitate reform, the College administration, especially at the department level, would be trimmed of duplication. Faculty committees would be reduced, and the chairmen would be given more authority. All curricula would be strictly reviewed, particularly the first two years of each degree plan. Dean Hagerty summarized his goals at a later meeting with the entire faculty: "My idea of the Dean's responsibility is to promote, maintain, and further develop a climate of strong teaching, research, interest in students, and interest in engineering problems."[14]

Dean Hagerty postulated his explanation for the provisional two–year accreditation by the ECPD and put forth an official plan on October 29, 1958. He organized the weaknesses pointed out by the ECPD into four categories: lack of student quality, relatively weak admission requirements, apparent absence of the necessary scientific base for many curricula, and a poor "attitude and atmosphere" within the College among both faculty and students. He proposed definite change in each area. The College would raise admission requirements, much as the Universities of California and Michigan had already done and as President Wilson was doing in other departments on campus. Advanced standing examinations would be given to each freshman, and entrance in the summer would be encouraged to remedy deficiencies in science and mathematics. Minimum standards of scholastic performance while enrolled in the College would be established along University guidelines, while rules for scholastic probation and expulsion would be strictly enforced. Every course taken would count toward the final grade–point average, computed on the University scale. The chairmen endorsed the proposals, and they were quickly approved by the general faculty and President Wilson.[15]

To expedite development, Dean Hagerty changed the administrative structure of the College of Engineering, giving more authority to the department chairmen. Although the chairmen under Deans Taylor and Woolrich had functioned as executive officers for the dean, they often had to share their authority with others within their department, notably the members of the Dean's Advisory Council, budget councils, and Graduate Dean's Council. Dean Hagerty enacted a series of reforms to allow chairmen a greater voice in the administration of the College. He discontinued the practice of rotating chairmanships within departments every few years. The chairmen met every two weeks with Dean Hagerty to discuss policy, and their decisions were passed on for endorsement to the engineering faculty, which ceased to meet regularly.[16]

These two actions, which allowed the chairmen a greater measure of control, proved to be unworkable, but desire for streamlining the College administration in the interest of efficiency endured. The number of standing committees in the College was reduced by half, and a limit of four members was placed on the remaining assemblies. Dean Hagerty wanted supervision of development to be in the hands of a few faculty who could act quickly if necessary. He would often discard an idea that did not gain unanimous, or nearly unanimous, support from the chairmen and the engineering faculty concerned in the matter.

In truth, they endorsed most of his proposals, and through their unity wielded much influence in the general faculty meetings of The University. Although Dean Hagerty reduced the number of committees within the College, he fought to have the engineers properly represented in every campus organization.[17]

Dean Hagerty also reorganized the operation of the Dean's office. Assistant Dean John A. Focht reached retirement age in 1959 and was succeeded by Billy H. Amstead, director of the Engineering Placement Office and an associate professor of mechanical engineering. Focht had served as an exceptional student counselor for nine years, and University regulations permitted continuing his employment in a nonadministrative position until he reached the age of seventy. Dean Hagerty, with the support of President Wilson, appointed Focht as an academic counselor until his final retirement in 1964. Joe L. Bruns, also from the Department of Mechanical Engineering, succeeded Amstead as placement director, but changing his title to Assistant to the Dean of Engineering put him under the direct supervision of both Hagerty and Amstead. These steps expedited cooperation with the Engineering Foundation through the dean's office and standardized the counseling system. In 1960, Raymond F. Dawson, associate director of the Bureau of Engineering Research (BER) since 1941, asked to be relieved, saying "a younger, more aggressive person" would accelerate the BER program. Hagerty appointed William A. Cunningham of Chemical Engineering to the position. Cunningham had recently finished a term as national director of the American Institute of Chemical Engineers, from 1956 to 1959, when he assumed direction of the BER in summer 1961. Dawson continued to be active in research as a member of the Department of Civil Engineering, conducting studies for the NASA complex in Houston.[18]

Possibly the most beneficial bureaucratic innovation under Dean Hagerty was the organization of departmental visiting committees. Petroleum Engineering had created the first such advisory board in The University when it appointed fifteen prominent industrial leaders to serve on a "blue–ribbon" panel in 1954. Among the members were Ernest Cockrell, Jr. and William J. Murray, Jr., both of whom greatly aided the College through the Engineering Foundation. Dean Hagerty and other faculty, observing the enormous benefit in direction and revenue that Petroleum Engineering received, pushed for the establishment of a similar organization in every department. In 1959 visiting committees were formalized by the chairmen, but their effective implementation would have to wait several more years. A good number of visiting committee members also served on the Advisory Council of the Engineering Foundation, where they effectively lobbied for implementation of their suggestions.[19]

The key factor in much of the progress in the College during Dean Hagerty's tenure was the financial support and direction imparted by the Advisory Council of the Engineering Foundation. At the time of its first meeting in 1957, many industries paid salaries from 50 percent to 100 percent above University scale, enticing good faculty away. Other engineering colleges also lured many teachers from The University of Texas with greater salaries and supplements for research. Dean Hagerty used Foundation funds to provide faculty with trips to professional conventions and salary supplements. Each permanent member of the College was allowed one trip to a technical society meeting each year to facilitate professional development and to accelerate recruitment by their proselytizing. Dean Hagerty rewarded superior teachers and researchers alike with grants provided by the Foundation. He also expanded the visiting lecturer program, bringing speakers from around the world to talk with faculty and students.[20]

Dean Hagerty used much of the money flowing into the College from the Engineering Foundation to aggressively recruit new faculty. It should be noted that before 1945 few engineering teachers in the United States held a doctoral degree, and by 1959 only 15.8 percent of engineers entering academia held a doctorate. The College under Dean Hagerty employed 40 new faculty with doctoral degrees, bringing the proportion on the engineering faculty at The University to 70 percent. Because of his emphasis on the scientific background of engineering, Dean Hagerty brought in new faculty with a greater knowledge of scientific theory as models for enhanced engineering science involvement. Some of them were not engineers, and in a few cases the appointments met with resistance from the resident faculty. Consequently, some of the nonengineering faculty did not stay, but the emphasis on the importance of scientific theory in engineering lingered.[21]

Perhaps the most important impact of the Engineering Foundation was the input from the industry representatives on the Advisory Council. Through their breadth of vision and their suggestions for curricula improvement in the College, they supplemented the effort of the faculty for development. The Foundation organized an evaluation committee, which reviewed the engineering program along with the ECPD in 1958 and reached similar conclusions on the changes needed. The Advisory Council of the Engineering Foundation incorporated the recommendations of both the ECPD and the Committee of 75 in its initial mandate to Dean Hagerty. The Committee had been created by The University on the occasion of its seventy–fifth anniversary to evaluate its academic status. The result was an unexpected attack. Commenting on research, the Committee reported, "It clearly represents one of the greatest single weaknesses of the University." It declared the program was deficient with respect to scope, quantity, and quality, and concluded, "There is little evidence that it has often resulted in discovery of new facts or in increasing or deepening knowledge and ideas." As to the College of Engineering, it stated: "In the opinion of both the faculty and the evaluation committee of the Engineering Foundation, the College of Engineering has not yet attained the rank among the top engineering schools that its strategic location in this area of great population and industrial growth would suggest." President Wilson added, "It is our obligation to translate these aims into action." The Advisory Council of the Engineering Foundation placed the responsibility on Dean Hagerty.[22]

Each department in turn benefited from the mandate for progress, but of immediate concern was Aeronautical Engineering, which had been specifically targeted by the ECPD as being in need of a "strong permanent staff." Hagerty appointed Milton J. Thompson, the founder of the department and its mentor for almost twenty years, as its new chairman. Thompson, recognizing the changes effected by the development of jet engines and space technology, changed the name to Aerospace Engineering and intensified the close relationship between his program and the Department of Engineering Mechanics. He served from 1958 to 1959 as chairman of Engineering Mechanics and spent three

Edward C. H. Bantel, on the right, was the second member of the engineering faculty at The University of Texas at Austin and served as Assistant Dean of Engineering from 1913 to 1942. Pictured with him, on the left, is John A. Focht, Assistant Dean of Engineering from 1950 to 1959 and still active in College affairs. In the center is Ben Freeborough, an employee of the Texas Highway Department. [Collection of John A. Focht]

years on the budget council of that department. The first course on space flight mechanics taught in the College was a joint effort of Aerospace Engineering and Engineering Mechanics. Byron D. Tapley, who earned his doctorate at The University of Texas and was appointed assistant professor in 1960, taught the class, which incorporated the research knowledge he gained while supported by grants to the Structural Mechanics Research Laboratory and the Defense Research Laboratory in Austin.[23]

John J. McKetta, Jr. chaired Chemical Engineering from 1958 to 1963. Under his leadership, curricula expanded to include new methods in process design and analysis, especially for use in the petrochemical industry. Graduate course work and research relied greatly on the development of computer–enhanced techniques for data compilation and interpretation. Howard F. Rase continued inquiry in fields related to catalysis, and Matthew Van Winkle pioneered new processes for distillation. The courses in ceramic engineering were incorporated into a program in materials science with funds from the NSF and other government agencies concerned with aerospace and other innovative applications. A departmental visiting committee provided guidance and contact with industry, vital to the Department's continued goal of enhancing industrial development in Texas using the state's natural resources.[24]

The Department of Civil Engineering, like Electrical Engineering and Chemical Engineering, had a history of stable direction from a few good faculty. Dean Hagerty largely left administration of such departments to these members. In Civil Engineering, this leadership came primarily from Chairman Walter L. Moore and senior professor Phil M. Ferguson, who had won an international reputation for his work in materials, especially concrete. One significant addition was John E. Breen, who joined the College in 1959, then earned his doctorate in 1962. Breen was associate director of the Civil Engineering Structures Laboratory from 1962 to 1967, when he succeeded Ferguson as director. Breen earned acclaim for his own research in prestressed concrete structures. Within fifteen years of earning his doctoral degree from The University, Breen had been appointed the John J. McKetta, Jr., Professor of Engineering at the College and had become the first doctorate from The University elected to the National Academy of Engineering (NAE), the most prestigious honorary engineering association in the United States. Breen, together with other Civil Engineering faculty later elected to the NAE such as Ferguson, Lymon C. Reese, and Earnest F. Gloyna, developed new curricula and research that answered the demands of Texas. During this period, too, they worked closely with the Department of Architectural Engineering, chaired by James J. Pollard from 1957 to 1961, then by Franklin B. Johnson until 1964. With a shared interest in structures, the two departments cooperated in courses and research on materials and design on both the undergraduate and graduate level.[25]

Electrical Engineering under Burns N. Gafford continued to open new vistas in research and curriculum, pushed by the addition of important new people. Clarence L. Coates was very energetic in expanding the Department's work with microelectronics and the construction and application of computers. Hagerty brought in Arwin A. Dougal from the University of Illinois to initiate studies on the utility of plasma and lasers. Dougal received enough funding to establish the Plasma Dynamics Laboratory at The University, which became noted, among other distinctions, for furthering the development of holography. He later served in the office of the Secretary of Defense for a year, in recognition of his work, but returned to The University to continue his research and teach. Texas increasingly relied on the electronics industry for a sound economy, and the Department of Electrical Engineering responded with further expansion into new fields of technology, including new methods of power generation as well as devices for communication and data analysis.[26]

Dean Hagerty, as a professor of engineering mechanics, took a special interest in that department's progress. He personally supervised the budget council, and brought several new faculty into the program. Along with Tapley, Lyle G. Clark brought new life into the curriculum, attracting funds from NASA and other generously endowed national programs. Research expanded into new fields, bringing further progress in the classes offered. Clark had been a student of Hagerty's at the University of Michigan, where both earned doctorates in engineering mechanics, and worked under him again at Delaware as chairman of the Department of Mechanical Engineering, then acting dean after Hagerty's departure for Texas. Although Clark's initial appointment in 1960 was as a professor of mechanical engineering, both he and Tapley were later chairmen of Engineering Mechanics, the latter presiding over its merger in 1969 with the Department of Aerospace Engineering.[27]

Under the direction of Venton L. Doughtie, Harry L. Kent, Jr. and Carl Gatlin, the Department of Mechanical Engineering continued to develop course work in the more traditional fields of mechanical systems and heat transfer, but also expanded into nuclear power. Byron E. Short, chairman of the faculty committee appointed to develop a curriculum, petitioned the Atomic Energy Commission for several years with little success while Woolrich was Dean. He did succeed in establishing a fifteen–hour plan of study for a minor in the doctoral program, but failed to stir any interest among the University administration for further development. The Visiting Committee chaired by George L. MacGregor proved to be the key. MacGregor and other Texas utility owners realized the limitations of fossil fuel and wanted to foster research in power generation by nuclear fusion, bypassing the more volatile fission process. They initiated a thirty–year project under Hagerty's administration, with the support of both Logan and Ransom.[28]

With broader support the program in nuclear engineering began to take shape, coordinating the efforts of several departments. In Electrical Engineering, Dougal developed innovative studies in fusion mechanics. His research was funded in part by the Texas Atomic Energy Research Foundation and the Atomic Energy Commission (AEC), which had finally been persuaded to contribute. The Chemistry and Chemical Engineering Library became an official depository of valuable classified and unclassified material from the AEC and chemical engineering faculty under the chairmanship of McKetta supplemented their research in petrochemicals with new inquiry into irradiation of materials. The AEC purchased a TRIGA Mark I fission reactor for the College, which they installed in Taylor Hall in 1963. It was primarily a teaching unit, but was large enough to facilitate research in materials. Jack A. Scanlan was appointed director of the Nuclear Reactor Laboratory, which was organized around the reactor. The unit, which contained Uranium 235, appeared small, but was capable of sustaining ten kilowatts in a steady state and could be pulsed to twenty–five million kilowatts for a few seconds, more power than that required by the City of Austin in a single day.[29]

The TRIGA Mark I reactor went critical in August 1963 and was used almost exclusively in developing nuclear coursework and graduate student experiments. It was one of only two in the country capable of such broad transient operation, and was unique in the Southwest. The University accepted the first doctoral candidate in nuclear engineering in July 1962 and granted the first degree in 1964. Undergraduate interest had been slight until construction of the Nuclear Research Laboratory commenced in 1962, then enrollment "skyrocketed." The course work remained interdisciplinary, conducted in the Departments of Mechanical, Chemical, Civil, and Electrical Engineering under Scanlan, Eugene H. Wissler, Gloyna, and Dougal respectively. The research focus in nuclear engineering later changed, as the effort to develop a fusion reactor became the primary goal, but the program in the Department of Mechanical Engineering retained a broad spectrum of study and research focusing on the TRIGA.[30]

Gatlin came to the Department of Petroleum Engineering from the University of Tulsa in 1959. He advanced quickly, becoming a full professor and chairman of the Department of Petroleum Engineering in 1961, then of Mechanical Engineering in 1963. He followed Hagerty to Drexel in 1964, accepting an appointment as Vice–President for Research. Gatlin's successor as chairman of Petroleum Engineering in 1963, Ben H. Caudle, continued the work begun by Gatlin, using scientific research to increase the amount of oil recovered from a well and refine it for maximum utility. Caudle came as a research engineer to The University of Texas in 1961, after working for Atlantic Refining Company in Dallas. The progress of the Department of Petroleum Engineering depends to a great extent on the fortunes of the petroleum industry, but the faculty at The University of Texas earned national recognition as leaders in research and instruction because of their commitment to excellence in research and teaching. This devotion to the future of petroleum and petroleum–related enterprise in Texas helped them survive a period of depressed enrollments when many departments of petroleum engineering in the United States were closed. [31]

Curriculum reform in the College of Engineering under Hagerty focused on reducing degree requirements while increasing the amount of science incorporated into the course work. At the same time, following the plan outlined by President Wilson, programs that attracted few students or unnecessarily duplicated work done elsewhere were eliminated, along with mandatory classes on outdated professional techniques. Reorganization of the grading system and the raising of standards challenged students to work, and they responded with an effort that resulted in a visible increase in the morale and quality of the engineering graduates from The University. The initiation of a standardized curriculum for the first two years of study in the College of Engineering facilitated an interdisciplinary approach and encouraged transfers from other schools. William A. Cunningham chaired the committee that presented the proposal for a "core curriculum," and the chairmen unanimously adopted it.[32]

Requirements in engineering drawing were reduced, while surveying was practically eliminated from the curriculum and the surveying camp begun by Leland C. Barclay at the Balcones Research Center was discontinued.

The curricula in meteorology and ceramic engineering were eliminated in 1959, and the master of science in communication engineering was cancelled in 1963. The remaining undergraduate degree outlines and options were arranged in blocks much like those adopted for use by MIT and Stanford. Ceramic engineering became a materials science block option in chemical engineering, and meteorology was absorbed into the engineering science degree program. The creation of block outlines stopped the dilution of resources into lesser programs such as ceramic engineering and meteorology, and allowed greater ease of choice in degree programs by eliminating the rigid boundaries between disciplines. Each block option became, in effect, a minor that could be expanded into a major. The dean's advisory council was committed to moving ahead, often rallying the rest of the faculty in support of such measures. Changes in title indicated progress as Aeronautical Engineering became Aerospace, while sanitary and public health engineering developed into environmental health engineering, reflecting the increasing concern with air and water quality.[33]

The College of Engineering used Engineering Foundation funds to bring computers into the classroom as well as the laboratory. The first simple computers had been installed at the Balcones Research Center shortly after World War II, and a Computation Center had been established on campus in 1958 when an IBM 650 was installed in the Experimental Science Building. The faculties of Electrical and Chemical Engineering pioneered methods for data compilation and analysis in their research, and by the early 1950s all engineering faculty used the new machines, but there remained few facilities for the students. Dean Woolrich's plans for an Engineering Computation Center in Taylor Hall had not been implemented before his retirement in 1958. The University of Texas Computation Center was completed in 1961, but initially was reserved for faculty use only.[34]

Dean Hagerty changed the content of the freshman orientation course in engineering to include instruction in computers. He appointed Jack Lenhart, of the Department of Drawing, to conduct the class and instructed him to allow no student to pass the course without successfully running a program through the computer, which was donated by the Royal McBee Corporation. The students quickly exhausted the LGP 30 analog machine, so Hagerty persuaded IBM to donate a 1620 for freshman instruction. He expected to implant in the young students a recognition of the computer's potential, and through them to prod some of the more reluctant faculty into supporting further development in the field. Leonardt F. Kreisle of Mechanical Engineering succeeded Lenhart in 1962 as director of the freshman computer effort. Under Cunningham, the BER established the Engineering Data Processing Center, which held three computers, including a PACE 221R analog machine used to analyze the behavior of guided missiles and other automatic control systems. This operation remained the only computation center available for student use at The University for several years. The facility has been upgraded continuously and, now under the direction of the Computation Center, has remained in Taylor Hall.[35]

Dean Hagerty considered his best accomplishment in reforming the undergraduate curriculum in the College to be the organization of the engineering science program. The development of engineering science as a discipline had originated during the technological footrace after 1945, spurred by the funds being made available for research by the NSF and other organizations for scientific study. Engineers felt left out and began tailoring many of their projects to conform to an ill-defined concept called "engineering science." This discipline gained a clearer form in the American Society for Engineering Education report on engineering education in 1954, which stated that any school of the first class should have a flexible program incorporating the latest scientific advances with practical application. The model developed at the University of Michigan stressed brevity as well as a sound background in general scientific theory in its curriculum designed to provide for the superior engineering student.[36]

The College of Engineering at The University of Texas watched the development of engineering science with interest. Engineering at The University had evolved with a firm background in the applied sciences and mathematics, unlike other schools whose course work was rooted in the mechanical arts. They also equated the idea with an honors program for exceptional students, which they had actively considered establishing. Dean Woolrich had appointed a faculty committee in 1957, chaired by William J. Carter of Mechanical Engineering, to report on the desirability of creating an undergraduate program in engineering science, but their opinions brought only more work. They did favor such a program for "better students" more than an honors curriculum and thought the College could support it, but could reach no more definite conclusions.[37]

Hagerty put spark in the engineering faculty's consideration of an engineering science program. He found Carter supportive of the idea, and retained him as chairman of the faculty committee. Carter presented the departmental chairmen with a tentative proposal for in-house consideration on December 17, 1958, and on March 5, 1959, they approved the proposal as submitted to the engineering faculty at large. Engineering science would be a degree–granting program, designed to serve the needs of students whose aptitude lay in mathematics and science and who intended to use those disciplines as tools to solve engineering problems. It was anticipated that many of them would attend graduate school. The new program would not duplicate "in purpose . . . and product any of the standard professional curricula now being offered." Only four years in duration, and requiring just 128 hours, it was shorter than the ordinary curriculum, but included twenty–seven hours of electives to breed "cross–fertilization." It made provision for training in fields where no degree was then available,such as nuclear engineering, space technology, and geophysical engineering. The faculty did not plan to restrict enrollment, but expected to attract outstanding students.[38]

The engineering science program began in the fall of 1959 with thirty–five students. They were presented with a variety of optional curricula: atmospheric science, which was an updated version of meteorology and was approved by the American Meteorological Society; energy conversion, including classes on the production and transmission of power and reactor physics; two choices in engineering mechanics, solid mechanics or space technology; geodesy; materials; nuclear energy; physical electronics; water resources and environmental science, which included courses in public administration; and engineering physics, which was a controversial option and was soon dropped. Ten of the first class earned a baccalaureate degree, and eight went to graduate school.

Seventy–two entered in the spring of 1963, Hagerty's last semester as dean. Overall, the early results were favorable, raising high expectations for the future.[39]

Dean Hagerty considered engineering science a success. Although under his direction it remained a degree–granting program, he did not lose good engineering students to the Departments of Physics, Mathematics, and Chemistry. Engineering science allowed greater flexibility in the accreditation limits; for example, if a desired program was not offered by the Department of Chemical Engineering, the student could move into one of the engineering science fields or even create a new major. Dean Hagerty retained the concept of a high–level program with restricted enrollment and broad curriculum; not exactly an honors program, but one intended to attract the best students from each department. Unfortunately, engineering science as a discipline received a cool reception from industry; its needs were fulfilled by the more established curricula, and the stress on scientific theory seemed to subtract from the practical aspects of engineering. Many schools reduced their support for engineering science after the first flush of success, including The University of Texas. Engineering science never became a separate department, but as a degree program it continued to provide for those students with abilities in the sciences and mathematics whose plans did not fit the standard outlines of the traditional departments.[40]

The Engineering Foundation received its first report of progress from Dean Hagerty only six months after he assumed office. The raising of entrance requirements had been the Foundation's idea, and it was satisfied to see it implemented so quickly. The Foundation also did not protest when Dean Hagerty informed them that some of the less professional courses were being dropped or condensed to make room for more science and more flexibility in liberal arts electives. Following its recommendation, four research programs had begun under The University Excellence Program, with more undergoing development with government and industrial sponsorship. Because of the emphasis on teaching quality, additional faculty were brought in to replace older professors, while remaining members were encouraged to upgrade themselves and more visiting speakers came to campus. The College was recruiting superior college seniors in twenty–five Southern and Southwestern schools for its graduate program. Obsolete equipment had been discarded, while construction of a new Engineering Laboratory Building, the first since 1942, had begun.[41]

Hagerty's reform efforts extended to the Engineering Foundation also. After a year as dean, he proposed a fund–raising program to "enliven" the Foundation because contributions had begun to fall below the level necessary to implement the innovations of the faculty in the College. The result of discussion among the department chairmen was the College of Engineering Associates Program, in which firms gave funds to the College in return for limited consulting services and extension courses. Many colleges already had such programs, including the California Institute of Technology, MIT, and Rice University. Humble Oil and Refining, on May 8, 1961, became the first Industrial Associate of the Engineering Foundation at The University of Texas. A steady stream of companies followed, guaranteeing an operating budget for the Foundation. More revenue was generated a few months later when every class secretary from the first graduates to 1958 was "activated" through the dean's office to raise additional funds for the Foundation.[42]

The reciprocal relationship between the College of Engineering under Dean Hagerty and the Engineering Foundation resulted in rapid academic and research development. In its first four years the Foundation had been a "catalyst" in increasing entrance requirements and academic standards while reducing the actual number of hours needed for a degree. Freshmen now received instruction in computer programming, giving them a headstart for completing their curricula, and it was possible for a student to earn a doctorate and enter the marketplace after only three years of graduate work. New scholarship programs had been introduced to encourage better students to enroll, and the number of graduate students had increased by nearly half in a period of generally declining engineering enrollment. Thirty–six new faculty had been recruited, in large part because of the benefits available through Foundation support.[43]

Outside agencies supplemented the Engineering Foundation funds. The operating budget of the College of Engineering for teaching and research expanded during Dean Hagerty's tenure from almost $1.7 million in 1958 to over $3.1 million just five years later. A grant from the Ford Foundation gave the College its first great opportunity for significant development. During this period, the Ford Foundation still actively fostered science and engineering; only later would it direct its efforts exclusively into liberal arts and the social sciences. The faculty actively courted the Ford Foundation; on November 11, 1959, Dr. Carl W. Borgmann, a director of the Ford Foundation, visited the campus and met with the engineering faculty and The University administration. The Ford Foundation had previously awarded the University of Michigan a three–year grant of $900,000 to accelerate the introduction of computers in classrooms for engineering studies. Dr. Donald L. Katz, dean of engineering at Michigan, met with the chairmen to repeat his invitation for Texas faculty to participate in the new program, up to $90,000, and to describe the benefits of the Ford Foundation award. Some of the engineering faculty later accepted the Michigan offer, bringing the first benefits of the Ford Foundation to the Austin campus. The chairmen were sold, and Chancellor Ransom added his support to the courtship of the Ford Foundation.[44]

The Ford Foundation in December 1960 announced it would grant the College of Engineering a total of $975,000 over three years to expedite education at the doctoral level. This award was the largest of four given by the Foundation that year to strengthen and expand engineering education in Southern universities. Other allotments were given to the Georgia Institute of Technology, the University of Florida, and North Carolina State University; they and The University of Texas awarded nearly all the engineering doctorates each year in the South. The Ford Foundation selected Texas for the most generous endowment because of the engineering faculty recruitment program during Hagerty's first two years in office as well as the practical use of money from the University Excellence Fund and the Engineering Foundation for faculty development and graduate education. Ransom was elated, "The Ford Foundation's generous recognition of the Texas engineering program under Dean Hagerty's leadership is a fine prophecy of great things to come in the science development program at The

University." During the first year of the grant, requests for admission to the graduate program in engineering almost doubled, indicating the impact of this windfall on the College.[45]

Under the terms of the grant, the College of Engineering had to raise $450,000 of its own in three years. An outright award of $525,000, to be disbursed immediately, included $150,000 for the development of present faculty, $100,000 in graduate fellowship funds, $200,000 for loans to doctoral students that could be amortized through teaching service, and $75,000 for discretionary expenditures. The remaining funds would be given over a three year period if the College matched the amount. The chairmen established a Fund Plan, then, with support from the University administration and alumni such as Cockrell and Murray of the Engineering Foundation, raised well over $1 million. The College used the money to improve the faculty, to provide a fellowship fund for outstanding doctoral candidates, and to fund emergency loans for all graduate students. Faculty who expected to remain with the College for another fifteen or twenty years were funded through graduate work at other institutions. The College also initiated efforts to aid other engineering colleges in Texas by providing up–to–date graduate education for their faculty at The University in Austin.[46]

The Ford Foundation's largesse was of enormous benefit for the College, some of it in a backhanded manner. The directors of the Foundation, in trying to set criteria for their awards, asked engineering schools around the country for an estimate of the average time required for a truly exceptional graduate student to earn a doctoral degree. The consensus was three years, and the Ford Foundation and other organizations set that period as the limit of their support for any graduate student. This in turn led to numerous attempts by the schools, including The University of Texas, to standardize a three–year doctoral program in engineering for all students in order to ensure outside funding, despite the fact that not all students were able to finish so quickly. The trend toward a three–year degree became the focus of academic debate for a time, because some alleged that a "fixed–time" requirement would lead to grade inflation and a misdirected emphasis on training, not on true education. It is an indication of the integrity of the College of Engineering that they quickly realized their mistake and eliminated the three–year doctorate from the curriculum, throwing their resources once more into a graduate program capable of producing engineers prepared for an ever–changing world.[47]

The National Science Foundation, although initially slow to respond to the College of Engineering's requests for support, in the balance has been of immeasurable benefit. The NSF, founded during Roosevelt's presidency, was just emerging in Washington through the impetus accorded science in education by the National Defense programs. Its focus was almost entirely on physical and natural science, making it difficult for engineers to obtain NSF funds for research. The faculty of the College loudly protested an apparent stonewalling by the national organization, enlisting the aid of C. Paul Boner, of the Government Sponsored Research Office at The University of Texas, to help them. Boner boasted that 100 percent of his requests were being approved by the NSF, despite the national average of only 25 percent approval, and willingly helped the engineers with their plight.[48]

Their cause was further aided by the establishment in 1961 of an engineering division within the NSF to replace the Engineering Sciences Program Office, broadening the research scope of the organization. During the next fiscal year $7.5 million was disbursed by the NSF in the field of engineering, with the promise of more to come. The College of Engineering's share increased from less than $100,000 in fiscal year 1958, given entirely to John J. McKetta, Jr., and David M. Himmelblau in Chemical Engineering and Enrico J. Volterra in Engineering Mechanics, to over $300,000 in fiscal year 1961. The NSF also contributed $500,000 to the construction of the Engineering Science Building, which was completed in October 1964.[49]

The National Defense initiative also brought funds into the College from the Advanced Research Projects Agency (ARPA) and the Defense Advanced Research Projects Agency (DARPA). Both agencies depended on the Department of Defense for funds and supported studies in materials and materials science. The difference lay only in the source of the money invested, from either budgets earmarked for civilian research development or those reserved for purely military studies. The two organizations focused their support primarily on East Coast schools, but Dean Hagerty persuaded them to invest in The University of Texas, initiating a relationship that would prove quite fruitful to his successors. ARPA funded the equipping of a Materials Science Center in the new Engineering Laboratories Building in 1960, along with the NSF, and later contributed to the construction of the Engineering Science Building.[50]

Other outside agencies contributed generously to the development of the College of Engineering under Dean Hagerty. NASA awarded several substantial grants, including $100,000 in 1962 to expand graduate studies in the space sciences. The AEC supported the program in nuclear engineering, buying equipment and supplying both money and technical advice for curriculum development. The AEC also supported inquiries by Gloyna and Joseph F. Malina, Jr., in the Environmental Health Engineering Laboratory into safer methods for transport and disposal of nuclear and other hazardous waste, studies that were further developed with funding from the National Institute of Health and other federal agencies. The American Institute of Steel Construction awarded The University $150,000 for a three-year study on fatigue testing of materials. Increased outside support from organizations such as these for graduate education facilitated an important expansion of both the faculty and physical plant. The result was a steady growth in the number of engineering doctorates awarded each academic year: thirteen in 1961, twenty-seven in 1962, thirty-eight in 1963, then seventy in 1964, a University record.[51]

Upon assuming office, Dean Hagerty proposed to the chairmen a ten-year plan for building construction by the College, using the generous funds he anticipated would come through the faculty's efforts to draw donations. First was the Engineering Library; another room was turned over to the librarians in Taylor Hall and work was completed in 1961. Volumes stored in the attic were placed on more accessible shelves, and a pilot open-stack program was initiated. Holdings increased from 37,500 books and bound periodicals to over 40,000 in just two years, once space became available for new acquisitions. The attic of the Petroleum Engineering Building was finished, allowing more space for new faculty offices, classrooms, and laboratories.[52]

These projects, however, were quite small when compared with the two building proposals initiated under Dean Woolrich and included in Dean Hagerty's ten–year plan. Venton L. Doughtie, professor of mechanical engineering and chairman of the building committee for the College, reported in November 1956 that the Regents had approved $1.25 million for a new engineering building to be called Engineering Laboratory and Shop Building Number One. Another request for Engineering Building Number Two had already been submitted, but the proposed second building was rejected by the regents. In 1960, research groups from the Departments of Engineering Mechanics and Aerospace, Civil, Chemical, Mechanical, and Electrical Engineering, as well as Drawing, moved into the new Engineering Laboratories Building. There was some delay in settling in because of a lack of proper equipment and design, but with additional financial aid from ARPA and other agencies the W. R. Woolrich Laboratory Building, as it was renamed in 1977 in honor of the former dean, became a useful adjunct to crowded Taylor Hall.[53]

Chancellor Ransom wrote Dean Hagerty in July 1959 that the NSF had initiated a program to support the renovation or construction of graduate–level research labs in the natural and engineering sciences at institutes of higher learning. Each grant required 50 percent matching funds from participating schools, and the chancellor wanted suggestions from the chairmen of the College for a proposal to be submitted. The College laid plans for an Engineering Science Building, and Hagerty appointed J. Neils Thompson, director of Balcones Research Center, chairman of a new building committee. They set September 1964 as the target date for occupancy and estimated the total cost at over $3.3 million. The NSF contributed a half million dollars to the project before the regents approved a broad science development program for The University of Texas in January 1960, underwriting the cost, which eventually grew to over $6.8 million.[54]

When completed, the Engineering Science Building consisted of a narrow tower containing a Van de Graaf accelerator, operated by the Department of Physics, and a large conventional structure of six floors and a basement. Enclosing a total of 206,185 square feet, the new building provided much needed research space for five engineering departments: Civil, Chemical, Mechanical, and Electrical Engineering, as well as Engineering Mechanics. The engineering classrooms and laboratories occupied the majority of the building, except for a few offices for Physics on the first floor and some communal shops in the basement.[55]

Engineering research prospered under Dean Hagerty. He always insisted The University came first in research, and constantly attacked work and consulting done by faculty that detracted from that goal. Initially, outside projects offered more funds than those sponsored by the College, but increasing support from numerous outside agencies through the Engineering Foundation helped to restore some balance. At the same time, Dean Hagerty made it clear he wanted the faculty to be working on "engineering problems of the future," not "pick and shovel work." The emphasis on projects of regional or national importance further increased the prestige of The University and brought Texas research to the forefront.[56]

The Balcones Research Center, directed by J. Neils Thompson, was the scene of intensified activity during this period. The Engines Research Laboratory, established in 1949, became the Mechanical Engineering Propulsion Laboratory, initiating research on high–speed air turbulence under the supervision of Kenneth Rathbun, then J. Parker Lamb, Jr., in 1961. A. Anthony Toprac founded the Structures Fatigue Research Laboratory in 1962, conducting crucial studies on highway and bridge design. Gloyna, who had earned a national reputation for his development of the Environmental Health Engineering Laboratory together with Malina, who had joined the faculty in 1961, organized the Center for Research in Water Resources in 1963, initiating a much broader scope of study for engineering. The Electrical Engineering Research Laboratory continued its studies in radio telescopes directed by Archie W. Straiton, a project that had been named by the Associated Press as one of the three most significant accomplishments of this century for the United States.[57]

The engineering faculty in the 1960s encountered one problem they could not solve: undergraduate enrollment in the College under Hagerty declined sharply. The fall was due to several factors, both internal and external: a drop in the number of births during World War II; the establishment of new engineering programs in the state, especially at Lamar State College and Arlington State College; development of the community college system; and the higher admission standards imposed by the College. Some small effect was already being felt from a growing antipathy toward technology in general. Dean Woolrich left a program with the largest undergraduate and graduate enrollment in the South and Southwest, ranked third nationally in daytime enrollment and eighth in total registration in all classes. By 1963, The University ranked twenty–third in daytime enrollment and had slipped from fourteenth to twentieth in the number of bachelor's degrees awarded among ECPD accredited schools, commensurate with a decline from 631 engineering baccalaureates granted by The University in calendar year 1958 to 374 in 1963. The College ranked fortieth in master's degrees awarded in 1963, down almost ten positions from 1957, despite an increase in the number of master's degrees granted by The University from 73 to 80 over the same period. Although the College generally maintained its regional prominence in the production of engineers with master's degrees, within the state of Texas it had slipped to third by 1963.[58]

Dean Hagerty and the College tried numerous measures to correct the decline in enrollment. One of the most innovative efforts was a series of television programs entitled "Paths to Progress," sponsored by channel KTBC in Austin and the Travis County Chapter of the Texas Society of Professional Engineers. Through these fifteen–minute presentations on the achievements of engineers in Texas, the faculty attempted to counteract a noticeable public apathy toward scientific and technological disciplines. More directly, the Engineering Foundation began funding scholarships to attract better high–school students following the initiation of a more active recruitment effort by the College. In September 1959, Dean Hagerty announced the first Fellows of the College of Engineering: twenty–two exceptional undergraduate students from all departments. Each received a fellowship from the Louis C. Wagner Scholarship Fund, endowed by an alumnus of the College, and they were encouraged to take special courses that would expedite their progress toward graduate study. The awards became annual; the next year the College recognized its first female Fellow, Peggy Jean McClain of Aerospace Engineering.[59]

Falling engineering enrollment in the early 1960s was a national problem; The University of Texas was not alone in being unable to find a solution. There were a few bright spots. The retention of freshmen improved every year, while the overall percentage of enrollees who graduated from the College of Engineering under the stricter admission requirements and scholastic standards steadily rose, presenting a record of efficiency that caught the attention of important sponsors and organizations. The number of doctoral candidates rose rapidly, advancing The University nationally from seventeenth in 1957 to tenth in enrollment in 1963, and from twenty–first to fourteenth in doctoral degrees granted. The College maintained its dominant position in graduate study within the state and region, and increased its prestige on the national level.[60]

Dean Hagerty and the engineering faculty realized that their efforts would have little impact if they were not advertised to industrial leaders and educators outside Austin. The publication system of the College had been greatly curtailed during Dean Woolrich's last years, due to budget restrictions, but with funds from the Engineering Foundation, Dean Hagerty expanded the annual report and had it printed for distribution. The Foundation itself published a series of reports on its activities and on research at The University of

The Engineering Laboratories Building, completed in 1959, was later renamed in honor of former Dean of Engineering Willis R. Woolrich. [College of Engineering, The University of Texas at Austin]

Texas. The College responded to a notable increase in Texas electronics manufactures by organizing a media campaign to publicize the advantages available in Austin for such industry, particularly the research and education provided by the College of Engineering at The University. William W. Hartwig, a noted member of the Department of Electrical Engineering and editor of the *Analog*, a journal produced by the local section of the Institute of Radio Engineers, devoted an entire issue to the subject, copies of which were distributed across the United States. Unfortunately, corporate and state leaders failed to act on the opportunity.[61]

The ECPD, in 1960, reaccredited the College of Engineering for an addtional three years, in recognition of its achievements in teaching and research. When Dean Hagerty had presented President Wilson with his ambitious plan for developing the College shortly after his arrival in 1958 and told him it would be done in five years, Wilson was incredulous. After studying the charts for a few more moments, the president then allegedly replied, "Brother Hagerty, if you take five years to do this, you'll be President and I'll be famous." Wilson did indeed win recognition for the progress made by The University of Texas during his tenure and was appointed to the National Research Council. Dean Hagerty accepted an appointment to be president of Drexel Institute in Philadelphia almost five years to the day after he arrived in Austin.[62]

Dean Hagerty left behind a College that was much improved by his brief tenure. The engineering science trend would fade, but the measure of prestige he had introduced in the engineering program lingered, along with great pride. A vice–president of a Chicago firm visited The University for the first time soon after Dean Hagerty left, recruiting doctorates to aid in a major expansion of his company's research and development program. He spoke with a number of the faculty and students in the College and expressed his amazement at the atmosphere of purpose that he encountered. He congratulated some of the senior professors, remarking, "I have never seen a school in which both faculty and students have as enthusiastic and as confident a view of its future as you have here. It has been a real inspiration because I didn't know this kind of spirit existed in any school today." Dean Hagerty had effected a similar change at the University of Delaware, and would follow the same course of action as president of Drexel Institute where he remained for twenty years after leaving The University of Texas in 1963.[63]

# THE DRIVE FOR
# TEACHING EXCELLENCE:

*Dean John J. McKetta, Jr., and the College of Engineering, 1963–1969*

P ublic perceptions about technology in the 1960s seemed to cast a pall over the future development of engineering education in the United States. Prejudice against technological enterprise grew in large measure from the vocal protest against the apparent corporate support for the war in Vietnam, the related demand for nuclear disarmament, and from the more widespread concern about environmental conservation. Enrollments in nontechnical degree programs climbed sharply from 1965 to 1970, but students stayed away from disciplines such as engineering, which barely held its own during the same period. The federal government, which had vigorously supported research since the end of World War II, became more restrictive in its grants and contracts, forcing engineering colleges to look elsewhere for development funds. Some institutions discontinued certain engineering degree programs when the flow of new students and revenue slowed to a trickle.[1]

Engineering education during the latter half of the decade had to develop new purposefulness as a reaction to the stigma attached to industry and technology. Just as the preceding deans dealt with the problems of their times, John J. McKetta, Jr., provided strong leadership for the College during a difficult period. He placed renewed emphasis on teaching excellence and the importance of working with students, bringing more support from industrial leaders, University administration, and alumni than that enjoyed by many engineering colleges. As a result, the College survived the slump with its degree programs, faculty, and research centers stronger than ever before.

McKetta officially became the dean of the College of Engineering on September 1, 1963. Selected by the dean's advisory council and approved by the regents, he was the first dean selected by the College from within its own ranks. Dean McKetta earned his doctoral degree from the University of Michigan, then joined the Chemical Engineering faculty in 1946. He served three separate terms as chairman of the department and won respect for himself and the program with his innovative research and administration as well as effective teaching style. He left the faculty briefly, from 1951 to 1953, to be editorial director for Gulf Publishing Corporation, but could not remain away from the classrooms and laboratories he enjoyed. Dean McKetta returned to the College and further acclaim: in 1962, after three years as national director of the American Institute of Chemical Engineers, he was elected president of that organization. As dean, McKetta maintained the drive for excellence in teaching and research he had initiated in the Department of Chemical Engineering.[2]

Dean McKetta continued the semimonthly meetings of the chairmen, but there were many changes in personnel. He relinquished the chairmanship of Chemical Engineering to Howard F. Rase, who in turn gave the position to Eugene H. Wissler in 1968. Lymon C. Reese succeeded Walter L. Moore as chairman of Civil Engineering in 1965. Burns N. Gafford, chairman of Electrical Engineering for nineteen years, stepped down in 1964 and was replaced by Clarence L. "Ben" Coates, who joined the faculty in 1963 and initiated further research in microelectronics. When Coates became involved with the Joint Services Electronics Project in 1966, Archie W. Straiton chaired Electrical Engineering. Carl Gatlin, chairman of Mechanical Engineering, followed Hagerty to Drexel Institute, so the direction of that department was given to William R. Upthegrove, a Michigan graduate who had come to the College in 1964. Ben H. Caudle earned a doctorate from The University of Texas in 1963 after working in the oil–refining industry for fifteen years, and became chairman of Petroleum Engineering that fall. He was succeeded in 1966 by Kenneth E. Gray.[3]

Departmental consolidation effected the balance of the changes made in chairmanships. The mergers of Engineering Drawing into Mechanical Engineering, and Architectural Engineering into Civil Engineering, along with the combination of Engineering Mechanics with Aerospace Engineering, were part of a pattern of academic economy approved by President Norman Hackerman in response to falling enrollments and tighter budgets. Engineering Drawing was reorganized within the Department of Mechanical Engineering as engineering graphics when James D. McFarland retired in 1968 after serving seventeen years as chairman. The Department of Architectural Engineering, under the chairmanship of Franklin B. Johnson, merged with the Department of Civil Engineering in 1969, where it continued as a degree–granting program. Lyle G. Clark chaired Engineering Mechanics in 1968, when it combined with the Department of Aerospace Engineering. Byron D. Tapley succeeded Milton J. Thompson as chairman of the latter department in 1966, and continued as chairman of the joint Department of Aerospace Engineering and Engineering Mechanics until 1977.[4]

The College continued its program of selectively employing new faculty to improve its growing national reputation. The regents in 1965 approved a sizable University budget that included 113 new faculty positions as well as across–the–board increases in salary for current faculty. The increase in appropriations for engineering was three times larger than for most other divisions of The University. The greater pay helped to compensate for the loss of faculty income after the abolition of the overtime rule whereby they could work on re-

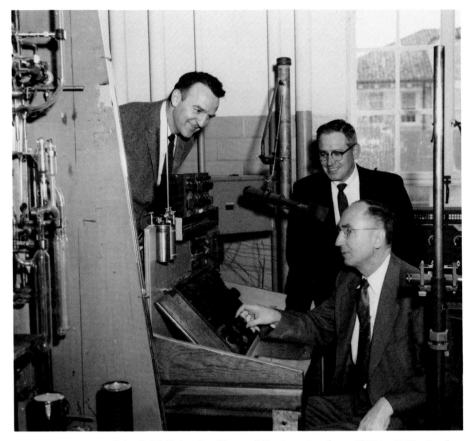

John J. McKetta, Jr., Dean of Engineering from 1963 to 1969, stands with Matthew Van Winkle, center, and Kenneth A. Kobe, seated, of the Department of Chemical Engineering. [College of Engineering, The University of Texas at Austin]

search projects and earn up to an additional fourth of their base pay. Most of the openings were created to attract high–ranking academics who would be paid above the average, many in engineering and the sciences. Dewitt C. Greer joined the Department of Civil Engineering in 1968. The following year, Governor John Connally appointed Greer to the Academy of Texas for outstanding contributions to the state, and Governor Preston Smith selected Greer to chair the Texas Highway Commission. Ilya Prigogine received a dual appointment as Professor of Physics and Chemical Engineering in 1967. He established the Center for Studies in Statistical Mechanics and won the Nobel Prize for Chemistry in 1977. Many others joined the College faculty under the expanded budget, increasing the teaching staff from 107 professors and lecturers in 1964 to 185 in 1969, 91 percent of whom held doctorates in their field. Each contributed to the remarkable growth in professional recognition accorded the College.[5]

One of the College's most notable achievements was its leadership in minority employment. The University of Texas, the first in the former

Confederacy to integrate both its graduate and undergraduate programs, adopted a strong policy in 1964 against racial discrimination in employing faculty. Dean McKetta read the statement to the chairmen in May, emphasizing that administrators expected action to be taken to correct bias, but the Department of Civil Engineering went a step further. In May 1964, Erwin S. Perry, a recent doctoral graduate of The University, became its first black faculty member as an assistant professor of civil engineering. Public praise greatly outweighed the few protests over his appointment, but it was not intended to be a "blow for liberty" nor a statement of an ideology. Perry was simply the best of the engineering graduates in his specialty to be had anywhere. As a contemporary remarked, "Engineering had carried the torch and made it all look easy." Augusto L. Podio, who arrived in 1968 with less fanfare, became the first Hispanic engineering professor to be tenured. Margaret R. Baker, an instructor in Engineering Drawing since 1954, received tenure as an assistant professor of mechanical engineering in 1967. The rank of assistant professor ordinarily does not merit tenure; Baker's accomplishment, therefore, is quite remarkable, and indicative of her outstanding ability as a teacher.[6]

Renewed efforts at professionalism accompanied the changes in administration and faculty within the College. A strongly worded statement from Phil M. Ferguson of Civil Engineering, a former President of the Texas Society of Professional Engineers, to the assembled engineering faculty in 1963 initiated a strong movement for registration. J. Neils Thompson served as president of the National Society of Professional Engineers in 1965–1966, and Ferguson followed him as the national director of that society from 1966 to 1969. Within the College, the faculty, led by a committee composed of Howard F. Rase, Byron E. Short, and Walter L. Moore, formally established a set of rules and regulations codifying administrative procedures and points of order for the first time.[7]

In the fall of 1964 the College of Engineering adopted a formal set of goals. Supported by a grant from the National Science Foundation, a committee of five—Billy H. Amstead, Caudle, Upthegrove, Straiton, and chairman Rase—proposed a resolution embodying many of the important trends in engineering education. "The objective of the College of Engineering," it began, "is to develop the intellectual capabilities of individuals so that through their profession they can make the greatest possible contribution to society." The immediate task was to expedite development while acknowledging The University's responsibility for continuing education and service to the industrial community. The effort would require at least a 20 percent growth in graduate enrollment for the next five years, with a parallel increase in the number of undergraduate students and an acceleration of education programs for those already at work. New sources of funds would have to be found, and new faculty and staff added on a selective basis. Another committee, chaired by Dougal and including Upthegrove, Tapley, Reese, and Earnest F. Gloyna, was selected by Dean McKetta in 1966 to incorporate these goals into a long–range plan through 1975.[8]

The goals adopted by the engineering faculty contained many elements endorsed by a variety of academic organizations. The Panel on Engineering Education of the Engineers' Joint Council reported in 1966, "The engineer must assume an ever increasing concern and broadened obligation in assuring the positive and constructive integration of technological change and the improvement of the human condition throughout the world." A review board appointed by the American Society for Engineering Education added that for engineers to reach their objectives, "education . . . must be as dynamic and rapidly changing as the profession of engineering itself." The simple resolution of the engineering faculty was endorsed by The University and broadcast to an even larger audience. Chancellor Harry H. Ransom, speaking to a meeting of chemical engineers in Houston in December 1963, stated, "The engineer's education of others is paramount," adding, "The simple fact is that unless this generation produces a mobile, adaptable, intelligent, socially responsible, and completely altruistic group of engineers, the rest of us are sunk." Ransom and President Norman Hackerman often attended the seminars on research and teaching sponsored by the engineers and actively supported their plans for expansion.[9]

Dean McKetta proudly announced the new goals at the dedication of the Engineering Science Building in October 1964. Concrete action taken by the College, he asserted, would effect the "creation of an environment where teacher and student can engage in the free unhampered pursuit of knowledge and achievement." Continuing to speak on the objectives of the faculty, McKetta added, "Our aim is to train the students so their knowledge will be useful for the future, which is even now more rapidly changing." Curricula would be made more flexible in order to instill broad functional education rather than segmented and stratified training. The primary stress would be on the application of theory to practice, the utilization of results achieved through scientific research for the good of society at large.[10] His words were a clear signal of the faculty's rejection of the trend toward research for its own sake and engineering science as the dominant ideal, and a return to the basic engineering tenet of applicability based on sound scientific principles.

The most immediate effect of the new resolve to work more closely with students and the public was McKetta's reorganization of the dean's office. Amstead continued as assistant dean, but John A. Focht retired as counselor in 1964 and was replaced by Clayton W. Chance, an assistant professor of drawing since 1956. Following Chance's departure in 1968, Leonardt F. Kreisle, a professor of mechanical engineering and a member of the faculty since 1943, became counselor, remaining until 1977. Kreisle was assisted initially only by Peter Mansbendel, Jr., but McKetta thought every engineering faculty member should serve two years in the counseling office to become better acquainted with students. Two members of the Department of Civil Engineering served in turn: Ned H. Burns in 1968, followed by Carl W. Morgan in 1970. Clyde S. Carman was employed to accelerate the Industrial Associates program in 1966, doubling participation in his first year. Dean E. Griffith came that fall as director of Continuing Education. Joe L. Bruns directed the Cooperative Education program, begun in 1967, in addition to his duties as director of the Placement Office, rounding out a program of academic support for industry and students.[11]

The College, working toward its professed goals, led a national trend in engineering education to improve teaching methods. Dean Woolrich had presided over the establishment of the first formal awards for engineering teaching excellence in 1956, sponsored by the Consolidated Vultee Aircraft Corporation of Fort Worth, later a division of General Dynamics. Dean McKetta further developed procedures to poll both students and faculty for rewarding good teachers in 1964. The Teaching Effectiveness Colloquia began that year as informal luncheons, during which the faculty held discussions or listened to visiting lecturers. The budget for speakers increased through the sponsorship of the Engineering Foundation; by 1967 the climax of each annual program was a day–long series of meetings. The engineering faculty attended regularly along with teachers from almost every department of The University. Ransom and Hackerman came often and lent their support for developments introduced there. Chance organized the initial meetings, then was succeeded by Kreisle and later by James E. Stice, who came in 1968 as a member of the Department of Chemical Engineering and served as director of the new Bureau of Engineering Teaching. Stice expanded the use of television monitors and computers for in-struction and evaluation of teaching methods. Morgan, who initiated the use of video in the College, became the first member of the engineering faculty to hold a dual appointment at The University—as a professor of education and of civil engineering. Because of its achievements, the College was chosen to host a Teaching Institute for the American Society for Engineering Education (ASEE) in the fall of 1969 and conducted three Effective Teaching Institutes for the Gulf Southwest section of the ASEE in 1969 and 1970.[12]

The dean's office coordinated the acquisition and disbursement of an increasing amount of government funds after Dean McKetta took office. The creation of the National Academy of Engineering (NAE) and passage of the National Defense Education Act (NDEA) in 1964 brought an increase in federal support for technical education. The NAE was established on December 10, 1964, bringing greater recognition to the vital contributions of engineers to so-ciety and initiating greater public interest in funding more research and develop-ment. The National Science Foundation (NSF) increased its grants to the Col-lege, providing $300,000 to the Committee on Goals and nearly $140,000 for research and teaching equipment in 1964 alone. The College that year received five out of seven Faculty Initiation Grants from the NSF, the most of any school in the country, to help new faculty begin research. The National Aeronautics and Space Administration (NASA) gave $100,000 for a three–year period to fund ten students through a doctoral degree in various fields. By early 1964, seventy of the College faculty were receiving government grants or research contracts. The NDEA moved more slowly, but in 1967 it funded 6,000 fellowships for graduate students, over 100 at The University of Texas.[13]

Government support alone was not enough to effect the devel-opment envisioned by the engineering faculty. The College initially depended on fellowships and low–cost loans from the NDEA to bring a great increase in graduate enrollment, but in 1968 Congress cut the project's budget in half. Be-cause the College diversified its sources of financial support, it continued to expand. As early as 1964, Dean McKetta told the chairmen and the Advisory Council of the Engineering Foundation that further development could not be supported primarily from government sources. The Foundation responded strongly: the annual contributions from the Advisory Council "snowballed," from $99,600 in 1963–1964 to $343,200 in 1969–1970. Support from the Council for the period of McKetta's deanship increased more than threefold from the total for Dean Hagerty's tenure, from $351,200 to almost $1.2 million. Funds for graduate students increased every year; in 1968, McKetta's last year as dean, the College awarded 116 fellowships and assistantships. Through the diversified support of outside sources, the College budget increased from a little over $3 million in fiscal year 1964 to over $8.2 million by the end of fiscal year 1969.[14]

The departments also supplied much of their own support through loyal alumni and the departmental visiting committees. The regents approved a new teaching associate position to aid graduate students in the last year of study for the doctoral degree, and the departments were able to fund the higher–paying and more responsible awards. Petroleum Engineering, in particular, reaped the benefits of a recovering oil industry. Phillips Petroleum, Gulf Oil, and Esso, among others, donated funds to the Department and the Engineering Foundation to support advanced study. Chemical Engineering also benefited from the recovery of the petrochemical industry from its slump early in the decade, and other departments to a lesser degree profited from a stronger state economy.[15]

The expanding microelectronics industry gave funds and equipment to the Department of Electrical Engineering, which also received millions of dollars from the Joint Services Electronics Program (JSEP). The JSEP was initiated by the federal government during World War II to encourage research useful to the military, and involved some of the most prestigious engineering schools, such as MIT and Columbia. In 1965, The University of Texas became the first institution in the Southwest selected for inclusion in the JSEP. Dougal served as the first director of the JSEP in the College of Engineering, and was succeeded by

The Engineering Science Building, on the left, was completed in 1964. In the background can be seen the W. R. Woolrich Laboratories. [College of Engineering, The University of Texas at Austin]

Coates in 1967. The project provided support for young faculty to begin research in some of the most advanced areas of engineering, particularly in materials science and microelectronics, and employed graduate students in all fields of study. The Texas Atomic Energy Research Foundation gave an additional $1.2 million to The University to initiate research in controlled thermonuclear fusion for power generation. Dougal and William C. Duesterhoft of Electrical Engineering worked with faculty from the Department of Physics to lay the groundwork for experiments with the Texas Experimental Torus, the second TOKAMAK built at The University.[16]

Two separate efforts demonstrated the diversity and strength of the revitalized financial support for the College. A Year of Development, from 1967 to 1968, in which faculty members would attend courses and seminars, was partly funded through the dean's office by the Ford Foundation and the Engineering Foundation. The latter primarily relied on the Industrial Associates program, led by Carman, who reported receipts of $150,000 in 1967 and $210,000 the following year. Over half of the money for the Year of Development, however, originated with the individual or department involved in each project. In addition, The University during this period approved seven professorships in engineering. The Henry Beckman Professorship in Chemical Engineering became the first endowed position in the College on March 13, 1965. It was awarded to Matthew Van Winkle in 1971 upon completion of its funding. In 1968, Joe J. King endowed another professorship, the first engineering alumnus to do so. McKetta became the initial appointee to the position, named by the College in King's honor, when he finished his term as dean that fall. The University also endorsed positions in 1968, although funds were not available, in honor of two former deans: the T. U. Taylor Professorship and the W. R. Woolrich Professorship. Phil M. Ferguson received the Taylor Professorship in 1969 when funds were made available on an annual basis by the Engineering Foundation; Byron D. Tapley was awarded the Woolrich Professorship upon completion of its endowment in 1974. Three annually funded positions lent additional support: the honorary Engineering Foundation Professorship for Engineering Practice, awarded to Dewitt C. Greer; the Alcoa Professorship in Chemical Engineering, awarded to Joel O. Hougen, then suspended in 1975; and the Halliburton Education Foundation Professorship, first assigned to Kenneth E. Gray, then continued on a rotating basis.[17]

The expansion of The University of Texas system presented unique problems in administration and financial aid to the engineering faculty in Austin. Texas Western University and Arlington State University were accepted as The University of Texas at El Paso and Arlington respectively in 1967. The College of Engineering forged close relations with each school, but an attempt to fully integrate the degree programs met with determined resistance from the faculty. They recognized that awarding engineering degrees without a clear indication of where the student had completed his or her studies would result in a reduction of the national reputation that the faculty in Austin had worked so hard to win, especially on the graduate level. Free transfers between the Texas schools would hinder student development by decreasing the opportunities for those from more prestigious schools outside the state to come to The University of Texas at Austin. A complete merger would dilute the financial support accrued for the College and obstruct future attempts to qualify for federal support. Ransom and Hackerman agreed; the College for this period in history continued to provide independent graduate programs, although it extended a great amount of support to its sister institutions through continuing education and research.[18]

The College, with its growing national reputation and new goals for professionalization, increasingly became a catalyst for the development of engineering programs in the United States and abroad. The University hosted a number of councils for the engineering deans of the Southwest to acquaint them with the College goals and advances in research and teaching techniques. Members of the engineering faculty traveled to many schools within Texas, helping those with new curricula ready themselves for accreditation by the Engineering Council for Professional Development. Perry, who served a one–year internship with the American Council on Education, worked along with Dean McKetta and William A. Cunningham to upgrade the programs at Prairie View A&M University and Huston–Tillotson College in Austin, which were seeking to rid themselves of the segregated status historically attached to their background. The faculty also extended their inspection visits to institutions in Venezuela and Mexico, aiding those countries through technical advice and shared research. Extension courses in Texas high schools and classes taught by the College for nonengineering students at The University served the dual purpose of demonstrating the need for greater engineering development and returning support to the College by increasing familiarity with its activities.[19]

The engineering faculty achieved their goal of increasing support for research and teaching under Dean McKetta and added many new members who would improve its national reputation, but could not correct the problem of depressed enrollment. They anticipated an annual increase of 20 percent annually in graduate enrollment in five years, but the total increase for the period fell short of the mark. In 1964, the College awarded 96 master's degrees and 36 doctoral degrees; the figures rose to 162 and 74 respectively in 1969, for an increase of about 79 percent during Dean McKetta's tenure. Undergraduate degree production grew even more slowly: 332 took a degree in 1964, then 410 in 1969, for an increase of less than 25 percent. Engineering enrollment increased slightly under Dean McKetta, but did not rise as dramatically as he and the faculty had anticipated. Engineering, as a technological discipline, suffered from the stigma attached to all technology during that turbulent decade. Falling enrollments were a problem in many engineering institutions and were particularly acute in disciplines experiencing a marketing slump, such as petroleum engineering. The College actually fared better than most; its increase in the number of students earning doctorates pushed it from thirteenth nationally in 1964 to sixth in 1968.[20]

The Advisory Council of the Engineering Foundation sponsored many programs to help boost enrollment. A movie, "Heads You Win," was filmed at the College in 1964 and shown at 132 schools in Texas. A new film, "Engineering—The Challenge of the Future," adapted from one produced by Eta Kappa Nu, the national honor society for electrical engineers, was adopted in 1968. An experimental project for recruitment sponsored by the Engineering Foundation was the "Engineer," a tractor–trailer unit fifty–five feet in length containing an exhibit from each department in the College. It took to the road in the fall of 1967, visiting more than 200 junior and senior high schools in Texas where over 70,000 students and parents toured its displays.[21]

This recruitment program was supplemented by a concerted effort on the part of the engineering faculty at the close of the decade to encourage minority enrollment. Dean McKetta organized courses to be taught in San Antonio to graduating high school seniors in order to reach the large Hispanic population as well as any other interested students who might need a head start. The Engineering Foundation provided the funds for this project. New efforts in tutoring, counseling, and housing for black engineering students were initiated under Amstead as acting dean in the spring of 1970. Amstead also oversaw the first stages of Future Engineering Women, or Operation FEW, in 1969, which had greater success than previous College projects in bringing women into the profession, traditionally practiced almost exclusively by men.[22]

Depressed enrollment in engineering schools in the United States during the 1960s was intensified by a spiraling attrition rate, especially in the first two years of study. A reviewer for the ASEE reported, "The entering student heading toward engineering should find the first year in college an exciting initiation into his chosen profession, whereas in actual fact he is typically placed in limbo during this period." A faculty committee in the College of Engineering, chaired by John E. Breen, reached similar conclusions, and a freshman engineering program, supervised by Amstead, was initiated in 1968 to cope with the problem.[23]

Entering students attended lectures on the history of engineering and current opportunities and challenges in special classes, but, more important, they began learning engineering measurement and data analysis using a computer and attempting problem formulation and solution in the first year. By becoming more deeply involved earlier in the program, the student became more aware of the engineer's role in society and of his or her own capabilities and chances for success. Distinguished visiting lecturers from all fields spoke to the freshmen, and separate counseling, advising, and tutoring services were made available by Kreisle in his role as counselor. Stice coordinated lecture and laboratory activities for the first–year study program, which granted three hours of credit. Response was overwhelming: 742 freshmen enrolled in the course in the fall of 1968, taught by twenty–six visiting lecturers. Stice assumed personal direction of the class from Amstead in 1969. The retention of new students contributed to an increase in undergraduate enrollment from 2,380 in the fall of 1963 to 2,785 six years later. The College–wide freshman course was discontinued after 1970 because enrollments became too large, but the individual departments continued similar efforts. Another class, entitled Engineering—The Manmade World, was initiated by the College for Plan II students in the College of Liberal Arts in the fall of 1968, establishing a basis for the later adoption of a dual degree program.[24]

To further increase retention of superior students, the College of Engineering began recognizing individual student achievement through an honors program. Rase suggested a freshman curriculum in which better students would be able to take more advanced technical course work, and it was eagerly accepted by the rest of the faculty. Intended for those who graduated in the top 5

The Engineer, a mobile display on the College of Engineering, conducted a successful tour of the state in 1967. [College of Engineering, The University of Texas at Austin]

percent of their high school class, the Freshman Engineers Honor Program began in the fall of 1964. It enjoyed great initial success, and has since been expanded through all four years in almost every engineering department. In 1968 the name was changed to First Year Engineering Honors Program and a number of special courses were instituted for qualified students. The faculty were more reluctant to award superior academic performance by giving distinguishing degrees, but in 1968 they approved the awarding of undergraduate certificates for "highest honors" to students with a grade point average of 2.75 and above on The University's three–point scale, and "high honors" to those with an average between 2.25 and 2.75.[25]

       The College during Dean McKetta's tenure extended its curricula within new areas of research and reshaped more traditional fields of study to be of greater use to students. The educational lead time for engineering, the period during which the new engineer would be useful without further training, was quickly dwindling. Assistant Dean Amstead had a favorite story to reinforce this fact. He would tell each graduating class, "Gentlemen, I have a confession to make—one–half of what we taught you while you were here is wrong," then add, "Unfortunately, we don't know which half is wrong." The faculty, led by

Dean McKetta, acted to solve the problem. Degree programs were limited to 130 hours and classes were grouped more closely into option blocks to be chosen on the basis of a future career. Professors changed the content rather than the title of their course work, adhering to the goal of economy. The first two years of study were reformed into a common curriculum rather than a rigid core of classwork, as the faculty recognized differences between fields made the latter impossible. Programs for cooperative and continuing education stressed the importance of both practical experience and keeping abreast of engineering developments. The visiting committees of each department were consulted at each step, and the ECPD gave its stamp of approval in 1969.[26]

Dean McKetta lessened the emphasis on engineering science as a discipline initiated by Dean Hagerty. The program achieved its goal of placing a higher percentage of its students in graduate school than the more established curricula, but encountered some opposition when it began attracting the best students from other fields into its hybrid effort, which focused more on theoretical research than practical engineering. Support for the curriculum was not eliminated and the number of block options and courses remained constant, but the tenets of flexibility and a sound background in mathematics and science were incorporated more strongly than before in other degree programs, and students were encouraged to earn more traditional degrees that would be more acceptable to future employers. The undergraduate program in engineering science remained a degree–granting division of the College of Engineering, offering an interdisciplinary approach for those students whose plans do not fit into an established mold.[27]

Course offerings in the Department of Aerospace Engineering were limited because of small enrollments. Many schools in the United States, due to lack of student interest, had combined or reduced their aerospace departments during the 1960s because positions in industry were limited. To support its faculty, the Department at The University of Texas merged with the graduate program in Engineering Mechanics in 1968. The joint Department of Aerospace Engineering and Engineering Mechanics has worked quite well as an academic unit, continuing to recruit both students and faculty while graduating better–qualified engineers for industry and education. Among those who joined the Department during this period was Eugene B. Konecci, a doctorate from the University of Bern, Switzerland. Konecci received the Kleberg Professorship, a joint appointment in Aerospace Engineering and the College of Business Administration. Despite the restrictions, the Department expanded its curriculum into fields such as astronautics, inviting guest speakers from the Manned Space Center in Houston to speak with undergraduate and graduate students.[28]

The Department of Chemical Engineering initiated the structured blocks system in 1953 when McKetta was chairman and they remained the most active in changing curricula, stressing the flexibility of the block option arrangement. The Department began with six curricula in 1966: engineering analysis, engineering operations, engineering management, engineering chemistry, engineering materials, and engineering physics. In 1968 engineering physics was discontinued in favor of environmental engineering, which combined some of the civil engineering course work with classes in organic chemistry. Chemical Engineering began a unique radio tutorial program in the spring of

1966. The broadcast was a cooperative effort between the College of Engineering and KUT–FM, the campus station. Chairman Rase directed the project, which gave reviews of daily lectures for the students who needed help. The response was enormous, and air time doubled after the first year. Similar programs were initiated in other departments, and the Bureau of Engineering Research (BER) taught a computer course on the radio.[29]

The list of block options for Civil Engineering reflected the growing concern for both academic economy and service to the public. Reorganization in 1964 eliminated the undergraduate option in environmental health engineering for a degree in civil engineering, but engineering science continued to offer water resources and environmental science as a degree program. Civil Engineering offered seven additional options: general civil engineering, surveying and photogrammetry, highway engineering, soil mechanics and foundation engineering, hydraulic engineering, structural engineering, and materials. Architectural Engineering, which merged with the Department in 1969 as a degree–granting program, added four blocks to the curriculum: building structures and engineering, industrial building design, general building construction, and environmental systems.[30]

Electronics and information systems increasingly became the focus of study in electrical engineering. The Department of Electrical Engineering offered seven curricula blocks by 1966—analytical methods, biomedical electronics, fields and waves, management and production, physical electronics, information science, and power systems and energy conversion—then added an option in computer systems for a total of eight in 1968. The options in computer systems, analytical methods, and information science were merged into a new program, called computer, information, and control engineering, in 1969. Five years earlier, the master of science degree in communication engineering had been discontinued; only one student, in 1955, had ever completed the program. Coates received a substantial grant for continued development of an information sciences program, so that field benefited from even greater attention in the second half of the decade. Course work in electronics and information systems has continued to expand and now constitutes the single largest portion of the curricula in electrical engineering.[31]

Much effort was spent on the developing biomedical engineering program, which settled, as at many schools, in the Department of Electrical Engineering. Biomedical engineering at The University of Texas as a formal effort began in 1966 when McKetta appointed Eugene A. Ripperger, of Engineering Mechanics, as the director of the Bio-Engineering Laboratory to initiate a graduate program in bio-engineering. The project involved several faculty members from diverse fields, such as Eugene H. Wissler from Chemical Engineering and Fred B. Vogt, M.D., from Electrical Engineering, as well as other medical doctors from the community. The relation between engineering and medicine had existed informally for years. It was natural that electrical engineers should dominate the discipline: one of the earliest joint accomplishments was the electrocardiograph, perfected in 1903, and electronics remained the primary focus of the engineering effort in medicine. In 1970, the program became an undergraduate option in engineering science and continued to expand as one of the most rapidly developing curricula at The University of Texas in the next decade.[32]

Mechanical Engineering began with four blocks in 1964, but by 1969 had redefined its curricula to include six option programs: general mechanical engineering, materials engineering, mechanical systems, nuclear engineering, operations research and management, and energy systems. The Department resumed responsibility for nuclear engineering from engineering science in 1966, when the Department of Chemical Engineering declined the opportunity in favor of continuing its focus on petrochemicals. Concurrently, Dean McKetta was selected to be vice–chairman of the Southern Interstate Nuclear Board (SINB), under the Southern Governor's Conference, in 1966 following an initial appointment to that organization and the Texas Atomic Energy Advisory Committee by Governor Connally in 1964. The SINB was the only nonfederal, publicly supported, interstate advisory and development agency in the fields of nuclear energy and related technologies. Seventeen southern states pooled their resources to develop nonmilitary uses for nuclear energy. Their impetus through the dean's office helped the Department of Mechanical Engineering, along with other public schools and programs, to initiate further research in peaceful uses for nuclear power. In 1968, Stephen J. Gage of Mechanical Engineering added fuel elements to the TRIGA reactor, a teaching unit, upgrading it from a steady state of 10 Kw to 250 Kw, and under the supervision of the Atomic Energy Commission installed a battery of cobalt 60 rods, totaling 8,400 curie, for research in materials irradiation.[33]

Curriculum development in the Department of Petroleum Engineering remained closely tied to the fortunes of that industry in Texas. The Department had suffered a sharp drop in enrollment during the first half of the decade when oil production in the state went into a deep slump, but rebounded strongly as business recovered. The faculty established seven blocks in 1966: drilling and rock mechanics, mathematics, design and technology, natural gas engineering, reservoir engineering, production engineering, and finance–economics–management. The curriculum in mathematics was dropped in 1968, and a block in the analytics of reservoir engineering was added, indicating both the research interests of the faculty and the changing demands of industry.[34]

In response to growing demand, the College of Engineering in 1969 began offering a master of science degree without a thesis along with the established graduate programs. An ASEE report in 1967 indicated that only one–fourth of the major engineering schools still required a thesis. Most of the engineers who earned a master's degree sought only to increase their "broad professional competence," while those who pursued a career in research and development went on to complete a doctorate. The engineering faculty assured the Graduate School that the curriculum would provide a "full and diversified program of advanced professional training for engineering practitioners." The candidates, instead of generating "new knowledge" through original research, would solve engineering problems through "innovative application" of existing data and better "enlightened engineering judgement." The Departments of Electrical, Civil, and Mechanical Engineering, as well as Aerospace Engineering and Engineering Mechanics, were permitted to initiate the program, which required six additional hours of class work instead of a thesis for a total of thirty–six hours for the degree.[35]

The College of Engineering, in order to combat the encroachment of technical obsolescence in engineers once they graduated, began a continuing education effort. Only the largest corporations could afford an education staff to retrain employees, but most could share the costs of a program in a public university. The College became one of the first schools to assume responsibility for a "fourth student body": professionals who periodically return to replenish their knowledge, but who have needs and goals different from the graduate, undergraduate, and correspondence students. The primary source of financial support and students were the members of the Industrial Associates program, under the direction of Carman. Dean McKetta appointed William H. Hartwig of Electrical Engineering as part–time supervisor of the project in 1964. Dean E. Griffith became the full–time director of the Office of Engineering Programs in 1966, assisted by James A. Johnson. Enrollment nearly doubled again in two more years, permitting an increase in the selection of courses from fifteen in 1965–1966 to thirty in 1969–1970. Supported entirely by fees, the program continued after this period as the Engineering Institutes section of the Division of Extension at The University of Texas.[36]

Dean McKetta renewed discussion of cooperative education when he took office in 1963; Dean Woolrich had established the first such project with General Dynamics in 1955, but little had been done to further its development. The increasing complexity of engineering tasks in industry made it desirable for many students to acquire on–the–job experience as part of their education. Such a program would also help economically deprived students meet rising tuition and housing costs; it was no accident that the push for cooperative engineering education had begun in the South at the turn of the century. Industry leaders, particularly the Advisory Council of the Engineering Foundation, eagerly supported the plan because it would produce engineering graduates who already had vital practical experience. About three–fourths of the engineering schools accredited by the ECPD in 1966 had such programs; NASA, with whom the College had an informal cooperative education arrangement for several years, was the official sponsor of nearly forty projects. Joe Bruns became the director of the Cooperative Engineering Education Program, which began placing students in February 1967. Thirteen enrolled in the semester–on, semester–off five–year degree program in 1967; by 1969 the number had grown to sixty each semester. Initially placement included only undergraduates, but in 1968 NASA agreed to take graduate students into its program, creating a new source of support for those pursuing a career in advanced engineering research and development.[37]

Research by the engineering faculty during this period emphasized the traditional responsibilities of teaching and public service once more, reversing the trend toward pure scientific inquiry. This reaction was part of a national trend sparked in part by the creation of the NAE. The new organization promoted engineering research through coordination of government research grants. The BER, like the dean's office, also relied on an increasing amount of industrial support in addition to federal and state funds. The Engineering Foundation and other private sources provided an important supplement for research that eventually rivaled the more restrictive government grants. Contract research by the College increased from less that $4 million in 1963 to over $5.4 million in 1969. Industry, because it responds to consumer needs, also provided the engineers with greater opportunity for public service. Cunningham continued as director of the BER, overseeing the relocation of many research operations to the Balcones Research Center (BRC) as space on campus became harder to find. There they expanded through the efforts of J. Neils Thompson, the professor of civil engineering who served as the director of the BRC in addition to conducting his own research units.[38]

The Defense Research Laboratory merged with the Military Physics Research Laboratory in 1964. The combined operation became known as the Applied Research Laboratory, indicating the shift from classified defense research into more declassified studies with broader applications. The laboratory on campus closed in 1967 and relocated to the BRC. The Applied Research Laboratory staff soon dominated the north Austin location; with over 400 employees, it was by far the largest single research unit. Freed from the restrictions of their cramped campus facilities, the engineers on the staff diversified their focus, incorporating their findings into classroom lectures. The retention of a strong emphasis on classified research in many fields lent impetus to the effort to move to the "cutting edge" of new technological research. Engineering graduate students as well as faculty extracted the findings of such work into the civilian sphere, gaining vital technical experience.[39]

The Department of Electrical Engineering, in addition to the Joint Services Electronic Program, continued to develop the Electrical Engineering Research Laboratory. Straiton remained the director, reorganizing the operation in 1965 into separate divisions devoted to different fields of research. Kenneth H. Jehn supervised the Atmospheric Science Research Laboratory, which became a fully independent unit in 1966. Studies were initiated on flight problems within the stratosphere, under the sponsorship of the Department of the Army's White Sands Missile Range. The NSF, along with other government agencies and private industries, sponsored new research on the upper sea breezes along the Texas coast. The University became one of six schools to form the Gulf Universities Research Corporation, devoted to studies of oceanographic phenomena and air–sea interactions in the Gulf of Mexico. Straiton, appointed an Ashbel Smith Professor by The University in honor of his work, served as vice–president of the new organization. Charles W. Tolbert directed the division for research in millimeter wave sciences, perfecting methods for astronomical observation and satellite communication. Much of this group's work took place at the Millimeter Wave Observatory, located near the McDonald Observatory at Fort Davis. The geomagnetics division, led by Harold W. Smith, focused its study on the electromagnetic waves in the ultra low frequency portion of the spectrum. Alfred H. LaGrone, as director of the antennae and propagation section created in 1965, continued to develop research in microwave broadcasts, applying this technology to instrument landing systems for aircraft, weather prediction, and wildlife migration, as well as a variety of other devices.[40]

Research development in Civil Engineering meant the application of advanced computer techniques to older problems in structures, materials, design, and soil mechanics. A new Center for Highway Research (CHR) began in June 1963 as a cooperative effort between the College of Engineering and the Texas Highway Department. Funded initially with five interagency contracts worth $134,000, the CHR won legislative approval in 1965 and expanded rapidly. By 1970 the program conducted seventeen projects, worth $630,000, on subjects ranging from computerized traffic control to new designs for long–span bridges. Clyde E. Lee, as director, emphasized, "We feel that our first responsibility is in teaching." All staff members taught at least half–time, while nine dissertations and twenty–one theses were completed through the CHR between 1963 and 1970. John E. Breen, together with his graduate students, contributed to the analysis and design of the first long–span bridge built in the United States using the precast concrete box girder method. Funded through the CHR, this work was carried out at the expanding Civil Engineering Structural Engineering Laboratory, which was later renamed for former director Phil M. Ferguson, whom Breen succeeded in 1967. The highly economical bridge was erected across the intracoastal canal at Corpus Christi.[41]

The Center for Research in Water Resources (CRWR) moved from the campus to the BRC in 1966, where it worked with the Environmental Health Engineering Laboratory, active at the site since 1952. Earnest F. Gloyna continued as director of the joint operation, stressing the primacy of graduate education. The CRWR became a University–wide research effort involving al-

This radio telescope, originally constructed at the Balcones Research Center under the direction of Professor Archie M. Straiton of Electrical Engineering, was transported to the Millimeter Wave Observatory on Mount Locke near the McDonald Observatory in 1967 for continued research in astronomical observation. [College of Engineering, The University of Texas at Austin]

most all colleges, schools, and special organizations having interests in water, such as the Marine Science Institute. Research varied from the disposal of radioactive waste to the possible reuse of municipal discharges. As the projects began to encompass water problems across the state, the "Engineer," the trailer used in 1967–1968 to recruit students for the College, was converted into a mobile water–sampling laboratory.[42]

The Structural Mechanics Research Laboratory, directed by J. Neils Thompson, was chosen in 1968 to take part in an intensive research project to determine the most suitable type of shelter for federal housing projects. The Department of Housing and Urban Development sponsored the study, recruiting builders from every state and giving $360,000 to The University of Texas to support its participation. Thompson coordinated the efforts of more than twenty faculty members from Architectural, Civil, and Mechanical Engineering, as well as Architecture, Sociology, and Psychology. One innovation was the use of plastic piping for the plumbing, developed in part from polymer studies by the faculty of Chemical Engineering. The crash program in two years produced ten low–cost units and was cited by President Hackerman as another example of The University working with the government for the public welfare.[43]

The BRC sheltered many new engineering research programs because of restricted space on campus. Ronald O. Stearman of Aerospace Engineering led the Aerospace Thin Shell Structures Laboratory, begun in 1967 with support from the Department of the Air Force and NASA to study the dynamic behavior of airborne structures exposed to extreme environments. Gray, of Petroleum Engineering, supervised the Center for Earth Sciences and Engineering, an interdisciplinary program for graduate students initiated in 1968 that focused on the recovery of minerals and the interaction of human beings with their environment, dubbed "inner space." Other research groups moved in with existing laboratories, expanding their focus.[44]

Engineering research on campus continued to flourish even as the effort at BRC expanded. The Institute of Statistical Mechanics and Thermodynamics, begun as a combined effort of the Departments of Chemical Engineering and Physics in the Engineering Science Building in 1967, employed one of the most prestigious of the new engineering faculty members, Ilya Prigogine. A native of Russia, Prigogine, was considered "one of the outstanding irreversible thermodynamists in the world." He had been brought to Austin in 1960 as a visiting speaker by the Engineering Foundation, but was teaching at the University of Brussels when he accepted the joint appointment. The Institute became a "think tank," continuing the theoretical scientific research necessary as a foundation for practical application in many engineering fields. Prigogine became the first foreign–born scientist ever elected to the National Academy of Science, and in 1977 won a Nobel Prize for his work.[45]

To facilitate research and enhance instruction, the engineers invested in establishing a computation center that would be open to engineering students and faculty. Teletype consoles connected to The University's Control Data 6600 were installed in each engineering building in 1967, and in 1970 the College purchased a Sigma V unit to provide faster exchanges with the mainframe. An IBM 1620 was installed for undergraduate use in 1967, the only such unit available for students at The University. When it quickly became obsolete, the BER allowed students to work with its Pace analog machine until the Sigma V computer became operational.[46]

The College of Engineering, as part of its drive to build a national reputation, stressed the importance of publications to advertise the efforts of the faculty. Although Dean McKetta's recommendation that the engineers begin yet another magazine was not acted upon, the departments submitted bulletins and reports to the Engineering Foundation for distribution to industrial supporters and contributed to the *Texas Engineering and Science Magazine,* a student publication begun in 1965. Amstead served on the editorial advisory board of the publication, but the staff was recruited from the entire University, with student representatives from every technical field. The engineers also experimented with video, filming several shorts for television. When Amstead became acting dean, the Engineering Foundation sponsored the publication of *Engineering Brief Case,* a biweekly magazine written to expose engineering seniors to methods of accounting, decision making, and general business matters that would be useful to them after graduation.[47]

McKetta stepped down as dean of the College of Engineering in the fall of 1969 and became Executive Vice–Chancellor for Academic Affairs for The University of Texas System, in recognition of his talent as an administrator and educator. Dean McKetta took his work seriously, but not himself; in a typically modest fashion he later summed up his contribution as a member of the faculty and dean of the College of Engineering as an ability to stay out of the way of those colleagues who were developing faster than he. In 1970, he and Gloyna were elected to the National Academy of Engineering, the highest honor for a professional engineer in the United States.[48]

Amstead presided as acting dean from September 1969 through March 1970. William R. Hudson, who joined the Civil Engineering faculty in 1965, served as assistant dean, and Dougal replaced Cunningham as the director of the BER. Amstead continued the emphasis on industry–sponsored research for solutions to the problems of contemporary society, especially pollution, transportation, and urban overcrowding. His efforts received wide recognition, and in January 1970 he became the first president of The University of Texas in the Permian Basin. Dean McKetta, in his final annual report, had written, "It may go down in UT Austin annals that I was the 'last of the transitional engineering deans,' those who have spanned the explosive years of the technological change between 1938 and 1969. Those years have culminated in a turning point for all of us, with the landing of man on the moon. Now it is a time for designing a bridge to the future."[49] As acting dean, Amstead provided the link between Dean McKetta, who steered the College through a trying period of low enrollment and unsure financial support, and Dean Gloyna, who directed an unprecedented expansion in facilities, faculty, and students wih an accelerated program of outside monetary and academic sponsorship in the next decade.

Earnest F. Gloyna became Dean of Engineering at The University of Texas on April 1, 1970, the same date as his election to the National Academy of Engineering. [College of Engineering, The University of Texas at Austin]

# TOWARD A POSITION OF ACADEMIC LEADERSHIP:

*Dean Earnest F. Gloyna and the College of Engineering, 1970–*

As The University of Texas at Austin matured into a position of academic leadership, the College of Engineering contributed by materially upgrading the quality of its faculty, student body, and teaching facilities. During the 1970s, American society, as well as that of other countries, became increasingly dependent upon new technology, requiring more versatile innovation at a constantly accelerating pace. The United States, immersed in a global competition for economic and military security in a new era of space travel and computer networks that can transfer information at the speed of light, relied on engineers to conduct vital research and direct renovation of the nation's municipal and industrial infrastructure. At the same time, a growing recognition of the necessity for protecting the environment characterized the efforts of industry around the world, creating a greater need for engineers who embrace in their educational background a greater diversity of skills in science, management, public policy, and engineering design.

Earnest F. Gloyna was appointed dean after more than two decades of exemplary professional and academic service to the College of Engineering. Following a tour of duty during World War II as an Engineer Officer for the U. S. Army, which included engineering construction and six campaigns in Europe, Gloyna completed the requirements for a baccalaureate in civil engineering from Texas Technological College in 1946. He was employed by the Texas Highway Department and Magnolia Petroleum Company, then became an instructor in civil engineering at The University of Texas in 1947. At The University, Gloyna followed the then common practice of teaching while undertaking graduate study, which brought him a master's degree in civil engineering in 1949. A leave of absence allowed him to obtain a doctor of engineering degree in sanitary and water resource engineering from Johns Hopkins University in 1952. He subsequently served as the director of the Environmental Health Engineering Laboratories and the Center for Research in Water Resources at The University.[1]

Gloyna is widely recognized for his leadership in the accelerated development of the College during a deanship that has spanned the service of five presidents—Norman Hackerman, Stephen H. Spurr, Lorene L. Rogers, Peter T. Flawn, and William H. Cunningham—as well as the *ad interim* presidency of Bryce Jordan. President Hackerman appointed Gloyna as dean effective April 1, 1970, the same day as his election to the National Academy of Engineering (NAE). An internationally known author and an active consultant in the United States and abroad, Gloyna has also been elected a Fellow and Honorary Member of the American Society of Civil Engineers (ASCE) and a member of the Academy of Sciences of Venezuela and the National Academy of Engineers of Mexico. Other selected honors include the Harrison Prescott Eddy Medal from the Water Pollution Control Federation (WPCF); the Gordon Maskew Fair award from the American Academy of Environmental Engineers and the WPCF; the 1977 Environmental Quality Award from the U.S. Environmental Protection Agency; the Order of Henri Pittier, National Conservation Medal, from the Republic of Venezuela; the National Environmental Development Award from the National Environmental Development Association; and the Si Freese Medal from the ASCE. With a single–minded devotion to the College, Dean Gloyna has directed its academic, professional, and fiscal development into a recognized position of excellence.

The College under the direction of Dean Gloyna undertook a broad program of improvement, expanding into new areas of research and teaching as funds and enrollment rapidly increased. Dean Gloyna stressed teamwork, just as he had done as director of the Center for Research in Water Resources and the Environmental Health Engineering Laboratory, both of which he helped to develop into international prominence. Significant development required departments as well as individuals to pool their resources and establish cooperative enterprises to conduct research and disseminate information. Gloyna established a goal that has remained clear through nearly two decades of academic progress: "The basic thrust of our College is to develop the best possible professional base for future engineering practitioners, for those who later choose to direct their leadership capabilities toward the management of public and private enterprise, and for those who wish to add to basic knowledge through research." By working toward that end, the College would not only enhance the natural leadership of its students, but also establish itself as a model for the development of other engineering institutions.[2]

A revolution in the management structure of The University, in part accelerated by the academic turmoil of the 1960s, effected a consolidation of administration in the deans' offices. The primary responsibility for budgets, personnel, and curricula was generally transferred from the department chairmen to the deans. This change in University and College management policy removed many of the problems of diffuse leadership, but placed a strain on the existing administrative structure that was exacerbated by increasing requirements from governmental agencies for stricter management of contract research and program development. Swelling enrollment and establishment of broader research and teaching operations added to the need for reorganization in an ongoing effort to provide for both astute direction and continued expansion. In order to forestall academic stagnation, a program of intensive planning and continuous reevaluation was initiated, a concept that has intensified with time.[3]

Dean Gloyna initially divided the administrative duties of the office of the dean of engineering in two: Assistant Dean William R. Hudson remained as the Associate Dean for Advanced Programs, and Eugene H. Wissler, then chairman of Chemical Engineering, became Associate Dean for Academic Affairs. Hudson supervised the Bureau of Engineering Research (BER), Continuing Engineering Education, and the Engineering Foundation, while Wissler oversaw those divisions directly concerned with student matters, such as the Office of Engineering Counselor, the Bureau of Engineering Teaching, and the Engineering Career Assistance Center. As the responsibilities of the dean's office multiplied under pressure from swelling enrollments and increasing demands for qualified engineering graduates, this reorganization proved flexible enough to provide for each situation.[4]

Associate Dean Hudson became director of the Council for Advanced Transportation Studies in 1971. Lymon C. Reese, formerly chairman of Civil Engineering, succeeded him and ably expanded efforts in planning and research. With him, Frank P. Wood, a Distinguished Graduate of the College, served as associate director of the BER after his retirement as a U.S. Air Force general in 1970. Reese also oversaw a rapid expansion of Continuing Engineering Studies during the 1970s—his own seminar on the design of offshore structures became one of the most popular and enduring short courses, attracting engineers from all over the world—and supervised production of the first planning document for the College. Thomas W. Kennedy, who had inherited the Council for Advanced Transportation Studies from Hudson, succeeded Reese in 1981 and served under the expanded title of Associate Dean for Advanced Programs, Research, and Planning, directing the BER and coordinating production of the annually updated planning document and other College research publications.[5]

Associate Dean Wissler served a productive term, then turned over direction of academic affairs to J. Parker Lamb, Jr., chairman of Mechanical Engineering, in 1976. Recognizing his abilities, The University appointed Wissler to be an associate dean in the Office of the Vice–President and Dean of Graduate Studies in 1978, although he continued his teaching and research in chemical and biomedical engineering. Lamb placed the Equal Opportunity in Engineering program for minority students, as well as other student support organizations, on a sound footing, then accepted an appointment to chair the Department of Aerospace Engineering and Engineering Mechanics in 1981. Charles A. Sorber, who joined the dean's staff in 1980 as Associate Dean for Professional Education and Career Development, assumed the title of Associate Dean for Academic Affairs the following year, retaining oversight over Continuing Engineering Studies and the Engineering Career Assistance Center on his list of responsibilities for the latter position.[6]

Sorber's able direction of a greatly expanded effort in academic affairs became evident to engineering educators in his native state; the University of Pittsburgh appointed him as its dean of engineering in July 1986. This key vacancy in the dean's office along with the expansion of the research capability of the faculty prompted Dean Gloyna to adjust the administrative tasks of the associate deans in June 1986. Herbert H. Woodson, former chairman of the Department of Electrical Engineering and director of the Center for Energy Studies as well as the Center for Fusion Engineering, joined the dean's office as Associate Dean for Development and Planning. Kennedy remained as Associate Dean for Research and Facilities, retaining primary responsibility for the BER. The position formerly held by Sorber was filled with the appointment of Mario J. Gonzalez, Jr., as Associate Dean for Academic Affairs. Gonzalez, a professor of electrical and computer engineering, previously had directed the Engineering Division at The University of Texas at San Antonio.

The College devoted particular attention to the special problems of students. Participation by students where applicable gained early acceptance from Dean Gloyna, and a new concept of student leadership was born. A primary factor in the nationwide campus unrest of the 1960s had been the students' mistrust of academic administration. The College took a major step to incorporate students into the management learning process. Several served on the committee that selected Gloyna to be dean, the first time student opinion had been sought in such an important decision at The University. The College established a Graduate Engineering Council to work together with the existing Student Engineering Council, expanding student participation. Student leaders were appointed to relevant administrative committees and the advisory council for each associate dean, who sought their input whenever possible. The first appointments were remarkably effective both for student morale and for better management of College affairs, so the practice has been continued. To implement an even more effective dialog between student leaders, College administrators, and others, weekly discussions were initiated that developed into an organized course on leadership. Attendance is required of all students who serve as officers of an approved campus organization and register for the course. All student leaders are invited to attend, and most have participated since the class was initially offered in 1970. Under the direction of Dean Gloyna they obtain hands-on experience in evaluating administrative challenges in the College.[7]

Reorganization and expansion included enhanced placement efforts for alumni and graduating students. Carl W. Morgan of Civil Engineering became director of the placement program, officially renamed the Engineering Career Assistance Center by Acting Dean Amstead, after the retirement of Joe Bruns in 1972. Morgan in turn was succeeded by Anthony L. Franzolino following his own retirement in 1981. The Center in 1985–1986 hosted recruiters from 372 companies who conducted over twelve thousand interviews, talking with more than fifteen hundred students who registered for placement. The organization's functions have expanded to include career counseling, resume preparation, and publication of the *Placement Manual*, with information for graduating seniors and College alumni on techniques to enhance employability.[8]

Leonardt F. Kreisle continued to direct the Office of Engineering Counselor from 1968 to 1977, when Bob M. Fannin joined the dean's staff. Margaret R. Baker from the Department of Mechanical Engineering has served continuously as an associate counselor since 1972, when Morgan's two–year term as assistant counselor expired. Kreisle directed the scholarship foundation established by Taylor, but following his return to full–time teaching in 1977 its supervision passed from the counselor to a new office for engineering scholarships, now managed by Ed D. Davis in addition to his responsibilities as director of the Equal Opportunity in Engineering effort. Davis has also assumed direction of the Engineers' Loan Fund, supervised in the past by senior faculty including Morgan, James D. McFarland, H. Grady Rylander, Jr., and William C. Deusterhoeft. The amount of financial support available to engineering students from the College has increased rapidly during the past decade due to the generosity of industry and alumni, coordinated through the Engineering Foundation. The Office of Engineering Scholarships disbursed approximately $813,717 in aid to undergraduates in 1985–1986, including about $61,275 in minority opportunity grants. This amount was the largest for any undergraduate program at The University of Texas. Tom Backus, on loan from the IBM Corporation, coordi-

Executive Vice President and Provost Gerhard J. Fonken and Dean Earnest F. Gloyna meet with the dean's staff and the department chairmen at Conoco Ranch, or Purple Sage, near Bandera, Texas, for the 1985 Chairman's Advance, in which plans are laid for the coming year. Sitting, from left: Edward J. Powers, Jr., Barbara Powers, Ida Malina, Joseph F. Malina, Jr., and J. Parker Lamb, Jr. Standing, from left: Thomas W. Kennedy, Thomas F. Edgar, Donna Edgar, Paul F. McClure, Fonken, Carolyn Fonken, Agnes M. Gloyna, Linda Sorber, Gloyna, Charles A. Sorber, W. Thomas Reeder, Marilyn Reeder, Betty Rylander, Nancy Lamb, H. Grady Rylander, Jr., and Gary A. Pope. [College of Engineering, The University of Texas at Austin]

nates many other projects to enhance minority enrollment, including tutoring, counseling, and Pi Sigma Pi, a minority service organization.[9]

The Bureau of Engineering Teaching lost its mentor in 1973 when James E. Stice became the director of the new Center for Teaching Effectiveness for The University, tutoring the entire campus on the instructional methods developed in the BET. Billy V. Koen, of Mechanical Engineering, assumed direction of the BET, expanding the application of the Keller Personalized System of Instruction (PSI) initiated by Stice and sponsored since 1972 by a $340,000 grant from the Alfred P. Sloan Foundation. The BET periodically hosted Effective Teaching Institutes for the Gulf Southwest Conference of the ASEE during the 1970s, demonstrating the PSI and other techniques to improve engineering teaching.[10]

Wallace T. Fowler of Aerospace Engineering became director of the BET in 1976. He presided over increases in the number and amount of awards given to engineering faculty to encourage greater professionalism and recognize substantial achievement, and began a program to reward graduate students who excelled as teaching assistants with funds from the Engineering Foundation in 1977, the first such effort at The University. William G. Lesso, as Assistant Dean for Special Projects, took control of the BET in 1981. He expanded the use of videotape, primarily for use in the graduate courses given by College of Engineering faculty at The University of Texas at San Antonio. Associate Dean Sorber and a faculty committee assumed direction of the continuing graduate programs in San Antonio and the BET in 1982. With their aid, The University of Texas at San Antonio initiated an undergraduate engineering program in that year.[11]

In the College's quest for national prominence, it became obvious that well-defined goals had to be established and communicated to all participants in the expanding engineering effort. Coordinated objectives and strategic central planning had to be devised and implemented. Thus, Dean Gloyna initiated an ambitious project to facilitate effective and efficient administration. He called for the creation of a six-year, annually upgraded plan, much as a successful corporation might produce, to serve as a guideline for the development of the departments and research centers into a position of academic leadership. By 1975, the first publication was anticipated "in response to and in consonance with" a similar University document. The annual report of the College that year contained a clear statement of the spirit behind the effort: "The mission of the College of Engineering is to provide a superior educational experience for men and women of the state of Texas, to help develop professional academic leadership for this region of the country and to establish a nationally recognized center of academic excellence in engineering at The University of Texas at Austin." The six-year planning document, annually revised with departmental input, has been hailed as a milestone in academic administration, and has served as a model for publications by other institutions across the United States.[12]

The yearly planning document is only one part of an accelerated publication effort within the College. *Engineering*, published quarterly, serves as an interorganizational newsletter, offering information on faculty and student accomplishments to interested readers both in academia and in industry. Each department is now responsible for producing an annual report for distribution and incorporation into the College statement. Each major research center produces its own prospectus and activity reports, to be summarized in *Engineering Research*, first published by the College in 1971. *Vector,* printed by a student staff, keeps the student body apprised of professional and social events. The Clint W. Murchison, Sr., Chair of Free Enterprise, as part of its role as a link between the business community and The University, began publishing *Nexus* shortly after

AWARDS AND HONORS IN THE COLLEGE OF ENGINEERING

| National Academy of Engineering Members | Department | Year Elected |
|---|---|---|
| Earnest F. Gloyna | Civil Engineering | 1970 |
| John J. McKetta, Jr. | Chemical Engineering | 1970 |
| Gerard A. Rohlich* | Civil Engineering | 1970 |
| Phil M. Ferguson† | Civil Engineering | 1973 |
| Willis A. Adcock | Electrical and Computer Engineering | 1974 |
| James R. Fair | Chemical Engineering | 1974 |
| Claude R. Hocott | Chemical Engineering | 1974 |
| Leo R. Beard† | Civil Engineering | 1975 |
| Lymon C. Reese | Civil Engineering | 1975 |
| Herbert H. Woodson | Electrical and Computer Engineering | 1975 |
| John E. Breen | Civil Engineering | 1976 |
| John B. Goodenough | Mechanical Engineering | 1976 |
| Robert S. Schechter | Chemical Engineering | 1976 |
| Archie W. Straiton | Electrical and Computer Engineering | 1976 |
| Harvey G. Cragon | Electrical and Computer Engineering | 1978 |
| Robert Herman | Civil Engineering | 1978 |
| Lincoln F. Elkins | Petroleum Engineering | 1980 |
| Irwin W. Sandberg | Electrical and Computer Engineering | 1981 |
| Victor G. Szebehely | Aerospace Engineering and Engineering Mechanics | 1982 |
| Raymond C. Loehr | Civil Engineering | 1983 |
| Ernest T. Smerdon | Civil Engineering | 1985 |

* Deceased
† Retired

Nobel Laureate

Ilya Prigogine, Professor of Chemical Engineering and Physics, Nobel Prize in Chemistry, 1977.

Dr. Prigogine's study of self-organization in nonequilibrium structures led to the development of the theory of dissipative structures. These structures occur when a set of conditions sufficiently distant from equilibrium and at a minimum level of dissipation are satisfied. Dr. Prigogine's contributions in the field of nonequilibrium dynamics have led to a deeper understanding of chemical, biological, physical, and sociological processes and have been a seminal influence in the development of modern scientific and philosophical pathways.

its establishment by the Engineering Foundation in 1976. In addition to these periodic productions, the College also publishes an increasing number of special reports and informational pamphlets designed to publicize its accomplishments as an academic leader in the drive to create a "university of the first class."

Academic leadership by the College of Engineering required the development of a faculty with nationally recognized stature in every department. Despite a restrictive employment policy and strong competition from both industry and other institutions of higher education, the College conducted an active recruitment campaign which increased the teaching staff to 283 by 1986. The tenured faculty reflect a high degree of professionalism: 96 percent hold doctorates and more than 90 percent are registered as professional engineers. As of 1986, 21 faculty members had been elected to the NAE, beginning with Dean Gloyna and former Dean McKetta in 1970. The College now employs more members of the NAE than all other Texas engineering colleges combined. Ilya J. Prigogine, of Chemical Engineering and Physics, won a Nobel Prize on October 11, 1977, further enhancing the stature of the College with which he is associated.[13]

The College recognizes the accomplishments of its faculty

---

**GENERAL DYNAMICS AWARD FOR EXCELLENCE IN ENGINEERING TEACHING, 1956–1986**

| | | | |
|---|---|---|---|
| 1956 | James W. Turnbow | 1972 | Joseph A. Yura |
| 1957 | Carl W. Morgan | 1973 | Wallace T. Fowler |
| 1958 | William C. Duesterhoeft | 1974 | Charles H. Roth, Jr. |
| 1959 | Kermit E. Brown | 1975 | David W. Fowler |
| 1960 | Harold W. Smith | 1976 | Ben H. Caudle |
| 1961 | Howard F. Rase | 1977 | Donald R. Paul |
| 1962 | Phil M. Ferguson | 1978 | John J. Bertin |
| 1963 | Cyrus O. Harbourt | 1979 | John J. McKetta, Jr. |
| 1964 | Leonardt F. Kreisle | 1980 | James E. Stice |
| 1965 | Ned H. Burns | 1981 | Victor Szebehely |
| 1966 | Roy R. Craig | 1982 | Kenneth M. Ralls |
| 1967 | Eugene H. Wissler | 1983 | Philip S. Schmidt |
| 1968 | Francis X. Bostick | 1984 | John C. Westkaemper |
| 1969 | Harry L. Kent, Jr. | 1985 | Ian B. Thomas |
| 1970 | John E. Breen | 1986 | Anthony M. Bedford |
| 1971 | Richard R. Ensminger | | |

---

**JOE J. KING PROFESSIONAL ENGINEERING ACHIEVEMENT AWARD, 1976–1986**

| | | | |
|---|---|---|---|
| 1976 | John J. McKetta, Jr. | 1982 | Earnest F. Gloyna |
| 1977 | Lymon C. Reese | 1983 | B. Frank McCullough |
| 1978 | Herbert H. Woodson | 1984 | J. Parker Lamb, Jr. |
| 1979 | H. Grady Rylander, Jr. | 1985 | Edward J. Powers, Jr. |
| 1980 | J. Neils Thompson | 1986 | John E. Breen |
| 1981 | Donald R. Paul | | |

---

**BILLY AND CLAUDE R. HOCOTT DISTINGUISHED ENGINEERING RESEARCH AWARD, 1984–1985**

| | |
|---|---|
| 1984 | Robert S. Schechter |
| 1985 | Jason L. Speyer |

through awards of its own. To complement the General Dynamics Award for Teaching Excellence initiated in 1956, the Engineering Foundation established the Joe J. King Engineering Achievement Award to honor professional leadership and the Billy and Claude R. Hocott Distinguished Engineering Research Award. In recognition of the College's achievements, the National Society of Professional Engineers bestowed upon it the prestigious Education Professional Development Award in 1985 and the coveted Koerper Engineering College Professional Development Award in 1986.

During the 1970s and 1980s, the search for oustanding faculty became acutely competitive. Faculty who were motivated to teach and to develop into a role of professional leadership were sought from every sector of the population. Recruitment by the College included a concerted attempt to employ the best female and ethnic minority engineering graduates, historically poorly represented in the profession. Associate Professor Linda H. Hayes, who earned a doctoral degree in applied mathematics, joined Aerospace Engineering and Engineering Mechanics in 1973 as an instructor; then, after earning a master's degree in engineering, she took a permanent position with the College in 1978 to teach and develop finite–element techniques for modeling. In Civil Engineering, Assistant Professor Priscilla Nelson conducts important research in the Geotechnical Engineering Center. Associate Professor Ramon Carrasquillo researches the properties of high–strength concrete. Associate Professor Dan Wheat, the second black faculty member of Civil Engineering, coordinates research in structural mechanics. His wife, Harovel Wheat, was appointed an associate professor of materials science and engineering in Mechanical Engineering in 1986, becoming the first black woman on the engineering faculty. Mechanical Engineering benefits also from the work of Assistant Professors Melba M. Crawford and Ilene J. Busch–Vishniac, the former in multivariate time series analysis, the latter in transducers. Margaret M. Maxey, appointed professor of bioethics in 1982, directed the innovative conferences supported by the Clint W. Murchison, Sr., Chair of Free Enterprise, providing educational support and ethical direction to University faculty, the professional community, and the public as a whole. Ekwere J. Peters became the first black associate professor of petroleum engineering in the United States in 1980; he works in enhanced oil recovery and received the Ex–Students' Award for Teaching Excellence in the College for 1983–1984.[14]

Faculty recruitment was accomplished through an expansion of the College budget between 1970 and 1986. Funds expended during the 1970 fiscal year totaled over $9 million, but just sixteen years later annual expenditures exceeded $38 million, an increase which far exceeded the inflation rate and expedited a broad development effort. The College received more financial support in fiscal year 1985 than under the first three deans of engineering at The University combined. A significant proportion of the increase came from the private sector, especially from industrial sponsors through the Engineering Foundation. Expenditures by the latter organization for the College in fiscal year 1970 totaled only $343,200; in 1986 the Foundation spent about $4 million. During the same period, its endowments increased from $255,200 to more than $37 million in 1986. The federal government remains the greatest single contributor to research in the College, but the support of private industry has increased markedly through the efforts of the Engineering Foundation. The legislature has also increased its financial contribution following reinstatement of the BER as a line item in the state budget in the fall of 1979. Research in civil and chemical engineering, for example, now depends more on funds from the state and private industry than federal support.[15]

In his first annual report, Dean Gloyna anticipated the greater role of the Engineering Foundation, saying: "We are entering a new decade of challenge, change, and growth . . . The help of the Engineering Foundation is needed today as never before." The organization was streamlined, and fund management was placed under the direction of the dean's office. Paul Hollingsworth came from the Center for Research in Water Resources to facilitate the development of the expanded Foundation activities. Following his retirement in 1984, Paul F. McClure, who joined the Department of Aerospace Engineering and Engineering Mechanics in 1974 and later worked for Tracor, assumed Hollings-

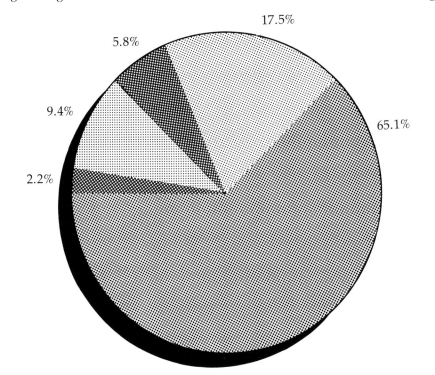

CUMULATIVE BUDGET OF THE COLLEGE OF ENGINEERING, 1888–1986

| Dean | Fiscal Years* | Cumulative Expenditures[†] | % of Total |
|---|---|---|---|
| Thomas U. Taylor | 1888–1936 | $ 17.6 million | 2.2% |
| Willis R. Woolrich | 1937–1958 | 72.1 | 9.4 |
| William W. Hagerty | 1957–1963 | 44.2 | 5.8 |
| John J. McKetta, Jr.** | 1964–1970 | 134.6 | 17.5 |
| Earnest F. Gloyna | 1971–1986[††] | 499.3 | 65.1 |
| Total | 1958–1986 | $767.8 million | 100.0% |

*Fiscal year 1986 began September 1, 1985, and ended August 31, 1986.
[†]In 1985 dollars (instruction, research, and other income exclusive of endowment).
**Includes period during which Billy H. Amstead served as acting dean, September 1969–March 1970.
[††]Budget for 1985–1986 estimated.

worth's duties. As Assistant to the Dean for Development, McClure supervised the affairs of the Foundation during the period of its greatest growth, as its expenditures and activities increased at a rapid pace. In July 1986, John C. Halton became the Assistant Dean for Development, replacing McClure, who returned to private enterprise.[16]

Much of the Engineering Foundations' growth can be attributed to the support accorded by alumni through special programs such as the Friends of Alec, established in 1973 to encourage alumni donations to endow teaching positions in the College. Directed during its first year by Joe J. King, the project exceeded all expectations and continues to be a reliable source of financial support. As of 1986, 1,032 alumni had become Friends, an increase of more than 10 percent over the previous year. These supporters have facilitated the establishment of endowed positions in every field of engineering, either directly by their own donations or indirectly by inspiring others to follow their example and contribute to the College. The success of the Friends of Alec has led to the revival of

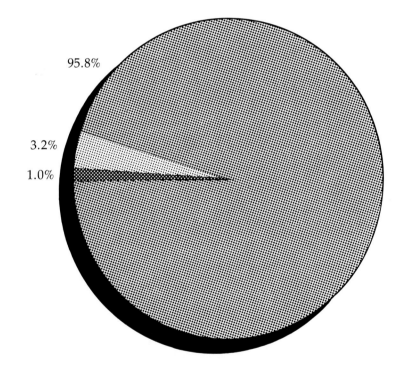

CUMULATIVE ENGINEERING FOUNDATION EXPENDITURES, 1957–1986*

| Dean | Fiscal Years | Cumulative Expenditures | % of Total |
|------|-------------|------------------------|-----------|
| William W. Hagerty | 1957–1963 | $     264,000 | 1.0 |
| John J. McKetta, Jr.[†] | 1964–1970 | 914,000 | 3.2 |
| Earnest F. Gloyna | 1971–1986** | 27,124,800 | 95.8 |
| Total | 1958–1986 | $28,302,800 | 100.0 |

*Fiscal year 1986 began September 1, 1985, and ended August 31, 1986.
†Includes period during which Billy H. Amstead served a acting dean, September 1969–March 1970.
**Expenditures for 1985–1986 are estimated; all figures are rounded off to the nearest $1,000.

departmental alumni clubs and the revitalization of the system of class secretaries, through which each engineering graduate can continue to participate in the development of the College. These groups serve not only as sources of financial aid, but also forums for exchanging ideas and disseminating vital information.[17]

Some of the most important contributors to the Foundation remain the Industrial Associates, renamed the Industrial Participants, who subscribe within a structure of nine levels of contribution. Each receives benefits through academic participation and the communication of research from the College. The members of this program consistently supply most of the revenue available to the Engineering Foundation each year. Like the alumni organizations, they also impart vital information to the College on the needs of the

ENGINEERING FOUNDATION RECEIPTS AND EXPENDITURES, 1958–1986

| Fiscal Year* | Contributions $ | Income on Investments $ | Total Receipts $ | Total Expenditures $ |
|---|---|---|---|---|
| 1958 | 86,900 | 300 | 87,200 | 40,500 |
| 1959 | 71,500 | 400 | 71,900 | 36,000 |
| 1960 | 53,500 | 1,800 | 55,300 | 51,300 |
| 1961 | 79,200 | 3,200 | 82,400 | 59,100 |
| 1962 | 113,400 | 6,700 | 120,100 | 76,800 |
| 1963 | 105,500 | 5,900 | 111,400 | 87,500 |
| 1964 | 89,000 | 10,500 | 99,500 | 99,600 |
| 1965 | 136,400 | 7,700 | 144,100 | 89,300 |
| 1966 | 162,300 | 1,300 | 163,600 | 114,700 |
| 1967 | 218,800 | 3,000 | 221,800 | 141,900 |
| 1968 | 259,900 | 11,700 | 271,600 | 207,400 |
| 1969 | 242,700 | 15,100 | 257,800 | 174,000 |
| 1970 | 319,000 | 7,400 | 326,400 | 343,200 |
| 1971 | 328,800 | 20,500 | 349,300 | 384,100 |
| 1972 | 320,700 | 13,100 | 333,800 | 300,540 |
| 1973 | 289,900 | 29,600 | 319,500 | 289,200 |
| 1974 | 408,900 | 39,300 | 448,200 | 355,600 |
| 1975 | 659,400 | 45,100 | 704,500 | 518,600 |
| 1976 | 622,900 | 85,600 | 708,500 | 622,900 |
| 1977 | 765,900 | 116,600 | 882,500 | 607,400 |
| 1978 | 640,700 | 148,100 | 788,800 | 800,700 |
| 1979 | 1,245,000 | 247,000 | 1,492,000 | 1,278,700 |
| 1980 | 1,478,200 | 453,800 | 1,932,000 | 1,446,900 |
| 1981 | 1,461,100 | 705,000 | 2,166,100 | 2,048,400 |
| 1982 | 1,979,800 | 1,318,000 | 3,297,800 | 2,813,300 |
| 1983 | 2,239,000 | 1,821,000 | 4,060,000 | 3,377,000 |
| 1984 | 2,639,300 | 2,225,000 | 4,864,300 | 4,281,400 |
| 1985 | 2,808,300 | 2,817,200 | 5,625,500 | 3,656,400 |
| 1986** | 2,950,200 | 3,100,000 | 6,050,200 | 4,000,000 |

*Fiscal Year 1958 began September 1, 1957, and ended August 31, 1958.
**Estimated.

Tom Backus, coordinator of the minority services program in the College, consults with students on a project. [College of Engineering, The University of Texas at Austin]

By 1986, 1,032 alumni had joined the Friends of Alec program, established to expedite the endowment of additional faculty positions. [College of Engineering, The University of Texas at Austin]

marketplace along with their financial support. With this constant exchange of viewpoints, the College is better able to keep abreast of the changing demands of American society and help its students by preparing them in a pragmatic and up–to–date manner to take their place in a position of leadership.[18]

The Engineering Foundation solved the most pressing problem of the College during the 1970s—faculty salaries—by funding a variety of salary supplements. Annual awards were given for merit but could not be relied upon as a source for faculty development. The endowment of a number of professorships for The University minimum of $100,000 provided a partial solution. Foundation members Joe J. King and C. W. "Tex" Cook funded two in their own names, then suggested the creation of a Giver's Club to sponsor more. Ashley H. Priddy gave the idea definite form, and the Friends of Alec completed the endowment of three professorships for the College, named for Taylor, Woolrich, and Schoch, in 1979, then supported the creation of another for each department, to be named after a prominent member of the faculty. These were fully funded by 1981, bringing the total to twenty–four professorships in the College, most of them partially or completely supported by the Foundation until fully endowed. In addition, the Foundation created three faculty chairs, which require a minimum endowment of $500,000, during this same period.[19]

The stellar achievement of the Engineering Foundation during this period was the Chair of Free Enterprise. Conceived and initiated under the chairmanship of Robert L. Parker, Sr., with the able assistance of Z. D. Bonner, R. Earle Wright, Bob R. Dorsey, Frank W. McBee, Jr., and other Engineering Foundation Advisory Council members, the chair became the first fully endowed position of its kind at a major state university. Dean Gloyna served as director of the chair's executive council, which initially included the deans of the College of Education, the College of Business Administration, and the Lyndon Baines Johnson School of Public Affairs. The chair reached its first level of funding of $500,000 by 1976 and commenced operations, directed by a committee led in turn by Archie W. Straiton, Hudson, and Martin L. Baughmann from the College of Engineering. The chair operated without a faculty director for its first six years, printing literature on the free enterprise system and sponsoring guest speakers and symposia to guide Texas public school teachers in fulfilling the legislative mandate to educate their students on the merits of the American free–enterprise system.[20]

The most successful means of instruction for the Chair of Free Enterprise became the Summer Practicum for Secondary Teachers, in which the participants actually worked for a corporation for four weeks. The annual Symposium on Teaching Free Enterprise brought similar praise, and Parker was elected national director of the Association of Chairs of Free Enterprise in 1978. That year the chair completed an endowment of $1 million, enabling its first visiting professor, William Linvill, chairman of the Department of Engineering–Economics at Stanford, to teach a graduate course in the College of Engineering on technical entrepreneurship, with the assistance of Baughmann. Margaret M. Maxey, professor of bioethics, became director of the activities supported by the chair in 1982. After graduating from Union Theological Seminary, she had taught at the University of Detroit from 1970 to 1979, then came to Austin from the Energy Research Institute in Columbia, South Carolina, where she had won na-

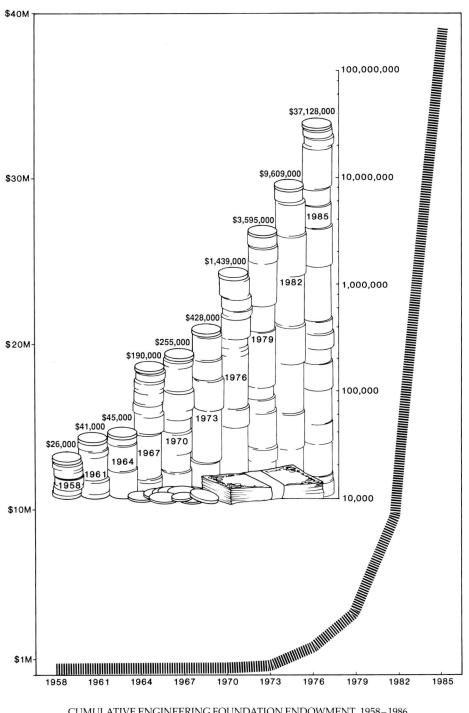

$40M

$30M

$20M

$10M

$1M

100,000,000

$37,128,000

$9,609,000

10,000,000

$3,595,000

1985

$1,439,000

1982

1,000,000

$428,000

1979

$255,000

$190,000

1976

100,000

$45,000

$41,000

1973

$26,000

1970

1967

1964

1961

1958

10,000

1958    1961    1964    1967    1970    1973    1976    1979    1982    1985

CUMULATIVE ENGINEERING FOUNDATION ENDOWMENT, 1958–1986

Endowments for 1986 are estimated; all figures are rounded off to nearest $1,000.

tional recognition for her lectures on ethics in the modern world of technology. Maxey continued the practicum and the symposium, adding more programs to enhance the teaching of technical entrepreneurship and to further improve The University's contact with industry. Academic support expanded to include the deans of the Colleges of Liberal Arts and Natural Sciences.[21]

To further the efforts of the Chair for Free Enterprise, Virginia L. Murchison donated an additional endowment of $500,000 in 1985, expediting the creation of the Center for Technology Development and Transfer (CTDT), which was established through an act of the Texas legislature during the 1983–1984 session. Jack J. Locy, a graduate of the Department of Electrical Engineering and a noted businessman, provided initial leadership by organizing the CTDT and

ENGINEERING FOUNDATION ENDOWMENT, 1958–1986

| Fiscal Year* | Endowment (Cumulative Total) $ |
|---|---|
| 1958 | 26,300 |
| 1959 | 27,300 |
| 1960 | 40,800 |
| 1961 | 40,800 |
| 1962 | 40,800 |
| 1963 | 40,800 |
| 1964 | 44,700 |
| 1965 | 144,200 |
| 1966 | 158,300 |
| 1967 | 190,400 |
| 1968 | 217,200 |
| 1969 | 225,200 |
| 1970 | 255,200 |
| 1971 | 271,700 |
| 1972 | 321,300 |
| 1973 | 428,000 |
| 1974 | 574,900 |
| 1975 | 745,000 |
| 1976 | 1,439,000 |
| 1977 | 1,901,500 |
| 1978 | 2,730,800 |
| 1979 | 3,594,600 |
| 1980 | 6,100,100 |
| 1981 | 9,335,300 |
| 1982 | 9,608,600 |
| 1983 | 18,250,000 |
| 1984 | 26,096,300 |
| 1985 | 37,127,800 |
| 1986** | 41,100,000 |

*Fiscal Year 1958 began September 1, 1957, and ended August 31, 1958.
**Estimated.

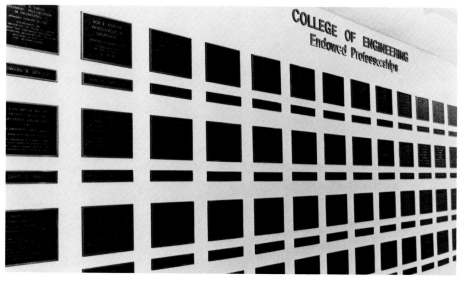

The College of Engineering has established 34 endowed chairs, 58 funded professorships, and 47 faculty fellowships to enhance its drive for academic leadership. [College of Engineering, The University of Texas at Austin]

The completion of the Chemical and Petroleum Engineering Building in 1986 climaxed a construction drive of more than a decade during which the College of Engineering also completed Ernest Cockrell, Jr., Hall and Engineering Teaching Center II. [College of Engineering, The University of Texas at Austin]

initiating a popular graduate seminar on technological entrepreneurship. The Chair of Free Enterprise was renamed in honor of Virginia L. Murchison's grandfather, Clint W. Murchison, Sr., a successful entrepreneur in the natural gas industry. In 1986, Stephen A. Szygenda, the first holder of the Clint W. Murchison, Sr., Chair for Free Enterprise, assumed direction of the CTDT, while Locy remained as assistant director.[22]

The Engineering Foundation's achievements during the decade of the seventies were indeed impressive but were overshadowed by the expanded activities of the next five years. Under the sponsorship of The University's matching funds effort, the Centennial Endowed Teachers and Scholars Program, which was followed by the Regents' Endowed Teachers and Scholars Program, the College between 1981 and 1985 received thirty endowed chairs, twenty–seven named professorships, forty–seven permanent faculty fellowships, and ten endowed lectureships. The greatest gain came with the funding of thirty–two chairs endowed for a minimum of $1 million each in engineering and natural science at The University. The regents, by combining private donations, most notably the gift of $8 million from Peter O'Donnell, a Dallas investor, with matching funds provided by the Cockrell Foundation and others, established or extended sixteen chairs for the College in the fields of computer engineering, microelectronics, manufacturing systems engineering, and materials science and engineering.[23]

By 1986, the College had completed the endowment of four chairs for $1.4 million each, nine of thirteen chairs for $1 million apiece, fourteen of seventeen chairs for $500,000 each, fifty–three of fifty–eight funded professorships, twenty–nine of forty–seven faculty fellowships, and five of ten lectureships. The Cockrell Foundation, established by the family of alumnus Ernest Cockrell, Jr., who was a founder of the Engineering Foundation and who remained active on the University Development Board until his death in 1972, donated $3.3 million to complete the endowment of these faculty positions. The Engineering Foundation played an active role in their establishment, coordinating donations and pledging support for those endowments not yet fully funded. Along with the support provided for engineering students, this burst of activity provided a fitting climax to President Peter T. Flawn's War on Mediocrity, initiated in 1979.

The teaching facilities of the College also benefited from the expansion of the endowment program. The engineering library, renamed in honor of Richard W. McKinney (RWM), who generously supported its development, received several endowments, enabling it to become a useful component in the eighth largest academic library in the country. By 1985, the RWM Library contained more than 105,000 books and bound journals, 1,800 subscriptions to periodicals, and 500,000 technical reports on microfiche. Its collections are supplemented by the endowments of McKinney for $100,000, Dresser Laboratories, Inc., for $100,000, which is dedicated to development of the John J. McKetta Collection, and alumni who support the Alec Center for Creativity. Alumni and other sponsors also donated or pledged funds for the endowment of fifteen laboratories and thirteen classrooms in the new Chemical and Petroleum Engineering Building that opened in December 1985. In all, the College in 1986 had seventeen endowed laboratories, supported by an endowment of $626,800, and eighteen endowed rooms, funded for a total of $181,207, which are available to students in every department.[24]

The construction of the endowed laboratories and rooms capped a decade of construction for the College, during which a total of $60 million, exclusive of endowments, were spent for construction on campus and at the BRC. Engineering Teaching Center I, named in honor of Ernest Cockrell, Jr., was dedicated October 18, 1974, in a ceremony that featured Robert C. Seamans, then president of the NAE, as a guest speaker. The new building added 198,145 square feet of offices, classrooms, and laboratories to the engineering physical plant, but was more than matched nine years later with the completion of Engineering Teaching Center II in the fall of 1982, which contained 224,664 square feet. The first building cost almost $7 million to erect; the second over $18 million, far eclipsing the original estimate of less than $10 million for both. The two buildings provide modern teaching and research facilities for undergraduate and graduate instruction in civil and mechanical engineering respectively.[25]

Dedication of the new Chemical and Petroleum Engineering Building (CHE–PE) in February 1986 marked a climax in efforts to upgrade facilities for the College in both quantity and quality. Built at a cost of nearly $20 million, the CHE–PE Building became the flagship of a campus engineering plant of 835,249 square feet, valued at over $51 million, all built since 1958. The Department of Aerospace Engineering and Engineering Mechanics occupies the W. R. Woolrich Laboratories Building, finished in 1959, and the Department of Electrical Engineering is housed in the Engineering Science Building, completed in 1964. In moving forward, the College outgrew its old quarters in T. U. Taylor Hall, E. P. Schoch Laboratories, and the Petroleum Engineering Building, each of which will be occupied by other University departments that are also expanding in the drive to establish a "university of the first class." The alumni will mourn the absence of the engineers from Taylor Hall and the Taylor T–Room, dug by the students and named in honor of the first dean, but the new space will expedite greater academic development.[26]

Engineering expansion at the BRC during this period included construction of a facility containing both the Center for Energy Studies and the Center for Electromechanics, encompassing a total of nearly 145,000 square feet at a cost of over $23.2 million for the structure and equipment. Two–thirds of the space in the Electromechanics and Energy Building is taken up by laboratories, including a five–story experimental bay the length of a football field. A large–scale system for testing distillation and extraction devices and techniques has been installed, as well as a VAX 11/750 computer to aid in research. Completion of this building at the BRC increased the engineering plant there to about 260,910 square feet with a carrying value of over $9.3 million. Computer facilities there were greatly enhanced in 1986 by the installation of a "supercomputer," a Cray X–MP/24, which will become an integral element in the systemwide Center for High–Performance Computing.[27]

An unprecedented explosion in student numbers necessitated many of these increases in engineering staff and teaching facilities. Initially, undergraduate engineering enrollment repeated the slump that characterized

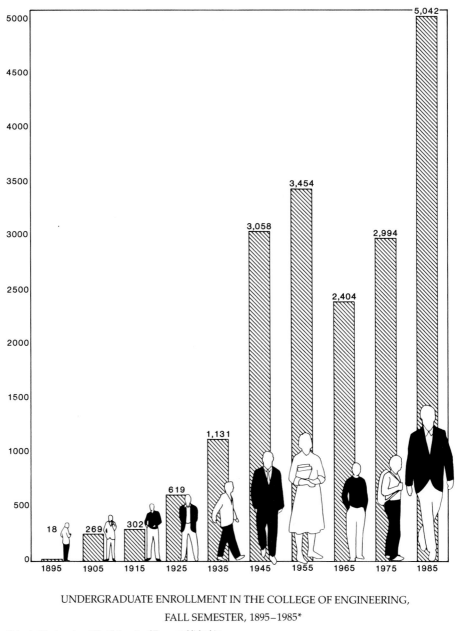

UNDERGRADUATE ENROLLMENT IN THE COLLEGE OF ENGINEERING,

FALL SEMESTER, 1895–1985*

*School of Engineering at The University of Texas established in
1895; first engineering student enrolled in 1883.

the tenure of former deans Hagerty and McKetta. During those years the College had fared better than most of the engineering schools in the United States, but it did not escape the doldrums of the early 1970s. The College between 1966 and 1970 increased its enrollment 22 percent, while national totals declined sharply after 1967. Freshman entering the College increased 36 percent in this same period, foreshadowing the boom in the next decade. College enrollment in the fall of 1970 was 2,816, then, pushed by a nationwide curtailment in engineering employment, fell to 2,319 in the fall of 1973, the lowest level in twenty years for The University. The economy soon recovered strongly, however, and by the fall of 1982 enrollment reached a new record of 6,426. Electrical Engineering attracted the greatest proportion of students as opportunities in electronics expanded. The balance between undergraduate and graduate numbers in the College closely approximated the national situation in the fall of 1985, reflecting both a tremendous expansion in each sector since 1974 and a relative increase in graduate enrollment. The latter proved to be the most dependable student population for the College during the 1970s: their overall numbers steadily increased through the decade, in contrast to the national decline in doctoral–level enrollment in engineering.[28]

The total number of degrees granted by the College between 1970 and 1985 reflects the rapid growth of the engineering profession. The sum of the diplomas awarded during this fifteen–year period, 14,549 graduate and undergraduate degrees, nearly matches the sum granted previously. The number of graduate degrees earned by students in these same years, 4,172, is more than half again as many as that awarded before 1970. Among Texas institutions, the College awarded the greatest number of master's and doctoral degrees, which ranked it tenth and eighth respectively among all engineering colleges in the United States. More than a fourth of the students who graduated from the College in 1984, the last year for which data are available, took a graduate degree, higher than the proportion awarded nationally that year. In the number of bachelor's degrees granted in Texas in 1984, it remained second only to Texas A&M, whose graduate degree total did not place among the top ten nationally. Led by The University, Texas has become a national leader in the production of educated engineers, ranking fourth in the number of bachelor's degrees granted in 1984, third in master's, and fifth in doctorates, the only Southwestern state in the top five in each category. In the College, as across the country, the greatest number of graduating students in 1984 were in electrical and computer engineering, in response to employment opportunities presented by an increasingly technology–oriented society.[29]

Even as engineering enrollments multiplied, the overall quality of the student body increased. The College benefited from the consistent recruitment of freshman who averaged at least fifty points higher on the Scholastic Aptitude Test than the balance of those entering The University. The Engineering Scholars project continued to strengthen and grow, and a greater proportion of the graduating seniors passed their Engineer–in–Training examinations each year. As individuals and within their organizations the engineering students achieved greater national recognition for their accomplishments. The College, recognizing the advantages to be gained from an increasingly profession–oriented student body, initiated methods to reward outstanding achievement.

## ENROLLMENTS IN THE COLLEGE OF ENGINEERING, 1883–1985

Undergraduate Fall Enrollment

| Year | Men | Women | Total | Year | Men | Women | Total |
|------|-----|-------|-------|------|-----|-------|-------|
| 1883 | 1 | | 1 | 1935 | 1,115 | 16 (1%) | 1,131 |
| 1884 | * | | * | 1936 | 1,429 | 14 (1%) | 1,443 |
| 1885 | * | | * | 1937 | 1,676 | 23 (1%) | 1,699 |
| 1886 | 15 | | 15 | 1938 | 1,783 | 23 (1%) | 1,806 |
| 1887 | 18 | | 18 | 1939 | 1,723 | 10 (1%) | 1,733 |
| 1888 | 19 | | 19 | 1940 | 1,693 | 10 (1%) | 1,703 |
| 1889 | 21 | | 21 | 1941 | 1,610 | 11 (1%) | 1,621 |
| 1890 | 27 | | 27 | 1942 | 1,679 | 15 (1%) | 1,694 |
| 1891 | 26 | | 26 | | | | |
| 1892 | 24 | | 24 | 1943 | 2,227 | 29 (1%) | 2,256 |
| | | | | 1944 | 1,989 | 62 (3%) | 2,051 |
| 1893 | 21 | | 21 | 1945 | 2,988 | 70 (2%) | 3,058 |
| 1894 | 20 | | 20 | 1946 | 4,253 | 59 (1%) | 4,312 |
| 1895 | 18 | | 18 | 1947 | 3,971 | 35 (1%) | 4,006 |
| 1896 | 21 | | 21 | 1948 | 3,452 | 38 (1%) | 3,490 |
| 1897 | 15 | | 15 | 1949 | 2,794 | 37 (1%) | 2,831 |
| 1898 | 24 | | 24 | 1950 | 2,212 | 30 (1%) | 2,242 |
| 1899 | 40 | | 40 | 1951 | 1,655 | 13 (1%) | 1,668 |
| 1900 | 56 | | 56 | 1952 | 1,914 | 12 (1%) | 1,926 |
| 1901 | 93 | | 93 | | | | |
| 1902 | 126 | | 126 | 1953 | 2,307 | 9 (0%) | 2,316 |
| | | | | 1954 | 2,987 | 12 (0%) | 2,999 |
| 1903 | 153 | | 153 | 1955 | 3,427 | 27 (1%) | 3,454 |
| 1904 | 214 | | 214 | 1956 | 3,750 | 21 (1%) | 3,771 |
| 1905 | 269 | | 269 | 1957 | 3,801 | 23 (1%) | 3,824 |
| 1906 | 316 | | 316 | 1958 | 3,566 | 25 (1%) | 3,591 |
| 1907 | 315 | | 315 | 1959 | 3,117 | 25 (1%) | 3,142 |
| 1908 | 271 | | 271 | 1960 | 2,769 | 15 (1%) | 2,784 |
| 1909 | 236 | | 236 | 1961 | 2,538 | 13 (1%) | 2,551 |
| 1910 | 270 | 1 (0%)** | 271 | 1962 | 2,413 | 15 (1%) | 2,428 |
| 1911 | 239 | 1 (0%) | 240 | | | | |
| 1912 | 299 | 10 (3%) | 309 | 1963 | 2,370 | 10 (0%) | 2,380 |
| | | | | 1964 | 2,380 | 14 (1%) | 2,394 |
| 1913 | 296 | 8 (3%) | 304 | 1965 | 2,386 | 18 (1%) | 2,404 |
| 1914 | 284 | 12 (4%) | 296 | 1966 | 2,438 | 22 (1%) | 2,460 |
| 1915 | 287 | 15 (5%) | 302 | 1967 | 2,431 | 22 (1%) | 2,453 |
| 1916 | 265 | 14 (5%) | 279 | 1968 | 2,572 | 29 (1%) | 2,601 |
| 1917 | 181 | 11 (6%) | 192 | 1969 | 2,753 | 32 (1%) | 2,785 |
| 1918 | 478 | 13 (3%) | 491 | 1970 | 2,772 | 44 (2%) | 2,816 |
| 1919 | 566 | 22 (4%) | 588 | 1971 | 2,503 | 48 (2%) | 2,551 |
| 1920 | 582 | 29 (5%) | 611 | 1972 | 2,290 | 42 (2%) | 2,332 |
| 1921 | 608 | 17 (3%) | 625 | | | | |
| 1922 | 578 | 20 (3%) | 598 | 1973 | 2,558 | 61 (3%) | 2,319 |
| | | | | 1974 | 2,363 | 124 (5%) | 2,487 |
| 1923 | 576 | 19 (3%) | 595 | 1975 | 2,746 | 248 (8%) | 2,994 |
| 1924 | 591 | 16 (3%) | 607 | 1976 | 3,106 | 343 (10%) | 3,449 |
| 1925 | 601 | 18 (3%) | 619 | 1977 | 3,501 | 406 (10%) | 3,907 |
| 1926 | 613 | 15 (2%) | 628 | 1978 | 3,951 | 505 (11%) | 4,456 |
| 1927 | 681 | 23 (3%) | 704 | 1979 | 4,406 | 636 (13%) | 5,042 |
| 1928 | 718 | 28 (4%) | 746 | 1980 | 4,755 | 757 (14%) | 5,512 |
| 1929 | 811 | 46 (5%) | 857 | 1981 | 5,214 | 882 (15%) | 6,096 |
| 1930 | 913 | 46 (5%) | 959 | 1982 | 5,433 | 993 (16%) | 6,425 |
| 1931 | 972 | 37 (4%) | 1,009 | | | | |
| 1932 | 884 | 27 (3%) | 911 | 1983 | 5,198 | 909 (15%) | 6,107 |
| | | | | 1984 | 4,776 | 849 (15%) | 5,625 |
| 1933 | 829 | 25 (3%) | 854 | 1985 | 4,280 | 762 (15%) | 5,042 |
| 1934 | 943 | 20 (2%) | 963 | | | | |

*No students listed as engineering majors.
**0% indicates less than 1/2% women enrolled.

Dean Gloyna presided over the establishment of annual awards for student leadership in public service and academic excellence beginning in 1970. At the instigation of the Student Engineering Council, the College held its first Awards Day Convocation in May 1970, when the guest speaker was Distinguished Graduate Alan L. Bean, the Texan who walked on the moon. The College expanded the event into an annual tradition as the students and faculty continued to earn national commendations for their contributions.[30]

The centerpiece of the Awards Convocation has become the Joe J. King Lecture, presented by the faculty member being honored as having contributed most notably during the previous year to the development of the engineering profession. In addition, the General Dynamics Teaching Award and the special recognition given to both a nontenured professor and teaching assistants continue as rewards for outstanding teaching. Students share the limelight with their teachers, accepting awards for their own contributions to the professional development of their chosen discipline. For example, the Engineering Scholars are introduced during the convocation and presented with the now traditional mug.

The College not only increased its enrollment but also broadened the demographic base of the student body. Although the University charter had been amended after heated debate to admit women as well as men, historically females had shunned engineering. The first significant change came when the number of women registered in the College swelled dramatically during the enrollment surge that began in 1973, paralleling the national increase in female attendance in all institutions of higher education. In Austin, women engineering undergraduates increased from 61 in the fall of 1973, 3 percent of the total, to 762 in the fall of 1985, or 15 percent of the undergraduate engineering students. The

DEGREES GRANTED BY THE COLLEGE OF ENGINEERING, 1888–1986

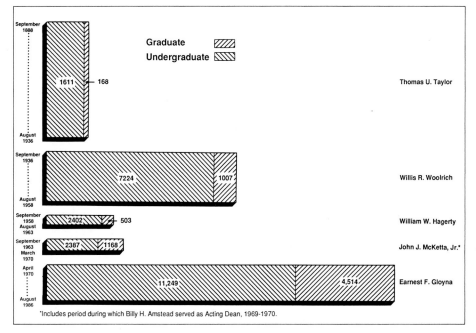

'Includes period during which Billy H. Amstead served as Acting Dean, 1969-1970.

College initiated a number of projects to attract women into engineering, but the most successful have originated with the female students themselves. The Society for Women Engineers' student chapter conducts an annual high school outreach program, talking to their peers about their experiences and successes in engineering. The women have competed easily, often ranking higher academically than male classmates. Teresa Gail Sipes, a Chemical Engineering senior, became the first woman named an Outstanding Graduate of the College in 1976, and usually a greater proportion of females qualify as Engineering Scholars, the top 5 percent of each class, than males. Currently, opportunities for women in industry preclude the retention of many for graduate study, but as the number of role models in engineering education and research increase, that situation should change rapidly.[31]

An increase in the proportion of minority students in engineering reflects a similar effort in recruitment and retention. Hispanic students have always been represented in the engineering student body, but blacks have had to overcome some impressive obstacles. The first black to graduate from the College

GRADUATE ENROLLMENT, 1972–1985

| Academic | M.S. | | Ph.D. | | | |
|---|---|---|---|---|---|---|
| Year | Men | Women | Men | Women | Total | Women (%) |
| 1972 | 406 | 10 | 271 | 4 | 691 | 2.0 |
| 1973 | 454 | 15 | 260 | 8 | 737 | 3.1 |
| 1974 | 503 | 19 | 247 | 3 | 772 | 2.8 |
| 1975 | 518 | 22 | 253 | 8 | 801 | 3.7 |
| 1976 | 526 | 31 | 258 | 9 | 824 | 4.9 |
| 1977 | 583 | 39 | 247 | 6 | 875 | 5.1 |
| 1978 | 612 | 44 | 257 | 13 | 926 | 6.2 |
| 1979 | 662 | 54 | 271 | 15 | 1,002 | 6.9 |
| 1980 | 623 | 61 | 289 | 14 | 987 | 7.6 |
| 1981 | 745 | 69 | 352 | 16 | 1,182 | 7.2 |
| 1982 | 839 | 79 | 390 | 17 | 1,325 | 7.2 |
| 1983 | 880 | 97 | 391 | 17 | 1,385 | 8.2 |
| 1984 | 871 | 99 | 431 | 27 | 1,428 | 8.8 |
| 1985 | 901 | 132 | 441 | 33 | 1,507 | 10.9 |

GRADUATE MINORITY AND FOREIGN ENROLLMENT, 1976–1985

| Academic | Minority | | Foreign | |
|---|---|---|---|---|
| Year | No. | % | No. | % |
| 1976 | 43 | 5.2 | 270 | 32.0 |
| 1977 | 53 | 6.1 | 271 | 30.0 |
| 1978 | 53 | 5.7 | 329 | 35.5 |
| 1979 | 48 | 4.8 | 338 | 33.0 |
| 1980 | 49 | 5.0 | 393 | 39.8 |
| 1981 | 71 | 6.0 | 526 | 44.5 |
| 1982 | 79 | 6.0 | 625 | 47.2 |
| 1983 | 87 | 6.3 | 575 | 41.5 |
| 1984 | 98 | 6.9 | 538 | 37.7 |
| 1985 | 105 | 7.0 | 576 | 38.2 |

was John Hargis, who earned his baccalaureate in chemical engineering in 1959. Hargis attended Morehouse College in Atlanta, Georgia, before deciding to return to his home in Austin and enroll in The University. He was accepted for admission in 1954, but just a few days before registration he was informed that President Logan R. Wilson had announced that The University would continue to refer blacks to other colleges within the state. Hargis was sent to Prairie View A&M, then returned to The University with four other blacks during the summer of 1955, a year before official integration. Of these five, only he and Marcel Haywood, an architect, graduated. Housing and other support programs remained a problem through the majority of the 1960s; it was only during the next decade that integration began to really take effect at The University.[32]

While nationally the number of native Americans, blacks, and Hispanics attending college declined during the 1970s, minority enrollment in The University increased dramatically. The American Council on Education found that the number of black students attending The University increased by 92 percent between 1976 and 1985, while Hispanic enrollment rose 56 percent. The College has led the way in providing services to augment minority recruitment and retention, increasing its minority undergraduate student population from 3.7 percent of the undergraduate engineering student body in the fall of 1971, when 94 enrolled, to 14 percent by the fall of 1985, when 705 registered as engineering majors. In 1983–1984 the number of minority students graduating from the College increased for the twelfth year in a row, placing it among the top 10 percent of engineering schools in the United States for undergraduate degrees earned by minorities. This record has remained constant through 1986, but the enrollment of minority students in graduate degree programs remains negligible due to both the usual delay for working engineers to return for more advanced study and the greater demand on minorities to fill roles in industry.[33]

Much of the increase can be directly attributed to the Equal Opportunity in Engineering (EOE) program, which offers support through financial aid, tutoring, and counseling. Initiated in 1972 under the direction of Phillip S. Schmidt of Mechanical Engineering, EOE has expanded through donations

UNDERGRADUATE MINORITY AND FOREIGN ENROLLMENT, 1973–1985

| Academic | Minority | | Foreign | |
|---|---|---|---|---|
| Year | No. | % | No. | % |
| 1973 | 83 | 3.6 | 390 | 16.0 |
| 1974 | 167 | 6.7 | 372 | 13.0 |
| 1975 | 261 | 8.7 | 377 | 12.0 |
| 1976 | 363 | 10.5 | 480 | 13.6 |
| 1977 | 427 | 10.9 | 479 | 12.8 |
| 1978 | 516 | 11.6 | 497 | 11.2 |
| 1979 | 635 | 12.6 | 399 | 8.4 |
| 1980 | 649 | 11.8 | 367 | 6.7 |
| 1981 | 695 | 11.4 | 463 | 7.6 |
| 1982 | 790 | 12.3 | 657 | 10.2 |
| 1983 | 780 | 12.8 | 794 | 13.0 |
| 1984 | 756 | 13.4 | 701 | 12.5 |
| 1985 | 705 | 14.0 | 544 | 10.8 |

from corporate and individual sponsors. Revenue for the first year approached $4,000; in 1985–1986 contributions for tutors, scholarships, recruitment, and administration totaled over $400,000. Under Thomas F. Edgar of Chemical Engineering, Schmidt's successor, minority enrollment doubled, but the program really expanded under its first full–time director, Jack Robottom, who came in 1976 and stayed three years. The EOE, under the direction of Davis and Backus, continues to ensure that "no qualified student, regardless of ethnic origin, [will] be denied an engineering education due to financial need." Pi Sigma Pi, established as a service organization by engineering minority students in 1973, takes an active part in visiting high schools across Texas, demonstrating the opportunities for education and employment in industry. The World of Engineering exposition, sponsored by Pi Sigma Pi and friends of the College, attracted more than 850 students to the campus in 1986 to hear about the possibilities open to them. Pi Sigma Pi at The University remained one of the largest minority academic organizations in the United States in 1986.[34]

Foreign students constitute a significant portion of engineering enrollment. While the nonnative percentage of the undergraduate student body never exceeded 13 percent, their proportion of the graduate population grew to over 47 percent in the fall of 1982. The implementation of incentive programs for American engineering students who enter graduate school made much progress toward the reestablishment of a more reasonable balance, however, and the introduction of enrollment management reduced the foreign student body in proportion to the overall numerical consolidation. Highly motivated foreign students continue to be welcome in the College, whose expanded programs attract scholars from more than sixty countries where they can contribute greatly to the development of both academic research and industrial applications. The number of nonnative students remains close to the national average, lending a cosmopolitan flavor to engineering education in Austin.[35]

The expanded student body required a commensurate increase in financial aid. Nearly a fourth of the support for undergraduates in 1984–1985 came from the Cooperative Engineering Education Program. Directed from 1973 to 1981 by Carl W. Morgan, who also served as director of the Engineering Career Assistance Center, then by Anthony L. Franzolino, the program expanded quickly in response to the needs of engineering students, becoming the most rapidly developing source for undergraduate aid. The greatest increase in participants came after the imposition of enrollment management in the fall of 1982; many students viewed the program as a good way to enhance their technical course work, and their numbers and earnings tripled in one year. Morgan started with 26 students in the field; in 1985–1986, 390 students worked for 79 employers, earning $2.5 million to continue their education and laying the foundation for a career after graduation. They were employed all over Texas and from coast to coast in some of the most important government agencies and private corporations. A greater number of co–op students attended classes, rounding out a program that involved over a thousand future engineers. Graduate students benefited from a similar arrangement inspired by the success of the co–op program; designated the Graduate Research Internship Program, it allowed engineers already on the job to work toward an advanced degree and provided full–time graduate students with another means of financial aid through professional employment.[36]

Burgeoning engineering enrollment forced the implementation of restrictions on new admissions and candidates for undergraduate degrees. Dean Gloyna and the faculty discussed such measures from the onset of the rapid expansion, which became evident in 1974. The tripling of student numbers in the following eight years severely taxed even the growing capacity of a developing staff and physical plant. Pressed hard by deteriorating student–teacher ratios and laboratories filled to overflowing, the faculty agreed that something had to be done. It was a difficult decision to make; as Dean Gloyna explained: "On the one hand, we have a whole world that is technologically oriented, a nation that has recognized the value of an engineering education, and a backlog of orders for more engineers. On the other hand, we have a budgetary constraint." Faculty committees and the University administration formulated the plan, implemented in the fall of 1982 to coincide with a campuswide enrollment restriction effort initiated by President Flawn as a response to a flood of new admissions into all disciplines as the "baby boomers" grew up in the 1970s.[37]

In addition to reinstating higher College admission standards, which had been dropped in 1975, the program organized engineering curricula into a basic and major sequence. All students would henceforth be required to maintain a grade–point average of 2.0 in their basic sequence, approximately the first two years of study, before petitioning and being allowed to take classes in their major sequence, corresponding to the junior and senior curricula. The minimum acceptable grade in any engineering course would be a C. Through restriction, the College intends to decrease undergraduate enrollment to manageable dimensions while increasing the number of graduate students, thereby matching the student body with available facilities. Efforts to recruit women and minority engineers continue; these students decreased less in proportion to their total number than the traditional white male student body in the first four years of enrollment management. In order to facilitate further enrollment deflation, two departments initiated additional grade restrictions. In 1982, the Department of Electrical and Computer Engineering required a minimum grade–point average of 2.5 for admission into the major sequence that begins with the junior year of study. The Department of Aerospace Engineering and Engineering Mechanics instituted an identical requirement in 1986.[38]

Enrollment management accomplished a second major revision of the engineering curriculum. The first occurred within the context of the administrative consolidation initiated by Dean Gloyna upon assuming office, in tandem with a University policy of academic economy requested by President Bryce Jordan. Each engineering department for 1972 had a roster of new or revised courses, from a high of fourteen in Mechanical Engineering to five in Petroleum Engineering. In all, the College made forty–nine changes in one year, setting a pattern of constant change and development for the future. Graduate degree programs were consolidated into a single master of science or doctor of philosophy framework, with specializations becoming "fields of concentration" within the new alignment. The College presently offers fourteen graduate degree programs: aerospace, architectural, biomedical, chemical, civil, electrical, mechanical and petroleum engineering, environmental health engineering, materials science and engineering, energy and mineral resources, engineering mechanics, manufacturing systems engineering, and operations research and industrial engineering. Within eight undergraduate degree plans, the engineering faculty teach fifty–two engineering fields. The core of classes common to all disciplines, in response to diversifying interests, shrank from fifty–eight hours in 1970 to forty–four, the heart of the new basic sequence for enrollment management.[39]

Extending the desire for teamwork into the academic sphere, the College under Dean Gloyna entered into a number of joint degree programs. In 1973–1974, Huston–Tillotson College in Austin began a short–lived 3/2 degree program in which undergraduates could earn a bachelor of science from that school and from the College of Engineering in five years of study. Response was poor, and the idea was abandoned. An extension program in engineering at The University of Texas at San Antonio (UTSA) met with similar delays in implementation and even poorer initial attendance, but survived to provide for the creation of an engineering division there. Faculty from the College of Engineering in Austin taught graduate courses beginning in 1978 by closed–circuit television with two–way video and audio communication to students in San Antonio, traveling every three weeks to meet with their pupils. Petroleum engineering courses met at The University of Texas in the Permian Basin (UTPB). Howard F. Rase of the Department of Chemical Engineering initiated a dual degree program for honor students enrolled in either the Plan II curriculum of the College of Liberal Arts or the College of Engineering; those who finished the five–year course received a degree in both disciplines. It has become quite popular with freshmen honor students faced with the restriction of the basic engineering curriculum. Graduate students can earn two master of science degrees, in engineering and public affairs, in a two–year program, begun under Associate Dean Wissler. This program is conducted by the College in conjunction with the Lyndon Baines Johnson School of Public Affairs.[40]

The Continuing Engineering Education program embodied the spirit of cooperation between disciplines and between academics and the corporate world. It continued to provide a means for the renewed education of engineers already on the job and supplied the basis for the graduate programs at UTSA and UTPB, which began as a way to reach technical employees at sites far from Austin. Dean E. Griffith remained director of the program while it served as the Engineering Institutes section of The University's Division of Extension from 1967 to 1974, and after its relocation back to the dean's office in the College of Engineering. He left the College in 1978. Assistant Dean Lesso directed the reorganized Office of Continuing Professional Engineering Education, later shortened to Continuing Engineering Education, from 1978 to 1981, supervising the use of videotape and closed–circuit television for extension courses. Under these men and Associate Dean Sorber, the office expanded to provide a broader variety of educational experiences. Associate Dean Reese taught on the design of fixed offshore drilling platforms in 1972; the only course of its kind in the world, it was overenrolled, attracting participants from as far away as France, Canada, England, and Venezuela. It remains one of the most popular annual seminars, balancing a menu with many diverse academic choices, including other favorites such as the advanced water pollution course that has been taught each year for over a decade. More than 2,700 people attended the courses and seminars in 1985–1986, indicating the demand for continuing engineering education.[41]

Among the departments of the College of Engineering, Aerospace Engineering and Engineering Mechanics endured perhaps the most diverse history in the 1970s. Enrollment dipped to just above one hundred in the early part of the decade but slowly increased thereafter. With the space shuttle flights covered intensely by the national media, many engineering freshmen began to enroll in aerospace engineering in the early 1980s. By 1985, the total undergraduate enrollment had reached nearly seven hundred, which was beyond the capability of physical facilities and faculty. A control plan was established for the fall of 1986 to gradually reduce student numbers to about five hundred; it was estimated that this enrollment would result in about eighty undergraduate degrees each year, a target figure approved by the faculty.[42]

Byron D. Tapley served as chairman until 1977, followed by Victor G. Szebehely, then Lamb, who came to the position in 1981 after five years as associate dean. The first visiting committee was formed in 1974 and has continuously supported the chairmen in the effort to establish a program with a national reputation. The undergraduate curriculum in aerospace engineering has always been characterized by breadth since a typical graduate may be employed in a wide range of technical areas. Each student was required to take a group of courses in three major areas: aerodynamics and propulsion, flight and orbital mechanics, and structures and materials. Since the early 1980s a fourth major technical area, guidance and control, has emerged, and the baccalaureate program has been restructured to permit every student to obtain more background in this field as well. Together with the foregoing development came an increased demand by industry and government for graduates with a strong knowledge of space technology. Because of limitations on curriculum length, it was not possible for any additional material to be added, so in 1984 a dual–track technical option program was instituted in which a student could choose either an atmospheric flight or a space flight option. The establishment of the Strategic Defense Initiative project, as well as the continued glamor of NASA's space shuttle and plans for an orbiting space station, have focused national attention on aerospace engineering, lending added vitality to the College program. In the past few years, the Department has ranked among the top five schools nationally in graduate degrees granted, and in the top fifteen in undergraduate degrees awarded.[43]

Robert S. Schechter became chairman of the Department of Chemical Engineering with the appointment of Wissler as Associate Dean for Academic Affairs in 1970, and in turn was succeeded by David M. Himmelblau in 1973. Donald R. Paul then chaired the Department from 1977 to 1985, when Thomas F. Edgar took over. The curriculum under each leader has reflected a renewed emphasis in development while retaining and expanding upon the innovation of the previous chairmen. Schechter developed important research and courses in surface phenomena and enhanced recovery of petroleum and other minerals. Himmelblau extended the curriculum in process analysis. Under the direction of Paul, along with James R. Fair, research and courses on separations processes, especially those utilizing polymer membranes, have been greatly advanced. Edgar has expanded an emphasis on fuels, exploring new sources of energy and methods for improved recovery.[44]

By 1986 the faculty in Chemical Engineering had won international recognition for accomplishments in areas as diverse as catalysis, separations processes, polymers, process control and simulation, chemical processing for microelectronics, and many others. They also have contributed to development of the interdisciplinary biomedical engineering program. Robert P. Popovich initiated a cooperative effort that pooled the talents of the Departments of Chemical and Electrical Engineering with a number of physicians and other medical personnel in Austin to conduct research for the improvement of artificial internal organs, biotechnical devices, and techniques for treating disease states. Fred B. Vogt oversaw the establishment of a graduate program in biomedical engineering in 1970, which recruited many students and became one of the most rapidly developing curricula in the College. Expanding enrollment caused congested classrooms and laboratories for several years, necessitating the construction of a new home for the Department of Chemical Engineering, but a contraction of chemical industries in the United States brought a welcome decrease in new student admissions during the early 1980s.[45]

The deterioration of the national transportation and public utility infrastructure, much of it constructed between 1932 and 1966, provided continuing opportunity for civil engineers. The Department of Civil Engineering underwent constant change under Reese, chairman from 1965 to 1971, L. Hudson Matlock, who succeeded Reese in 1972, and Joseph F. Malina, Jr., who became chairman in 1976. A visiting committee was organized in conjunction with the dedication of Ernest Cockrell, Jr., Hall, the new home for the Department beginning in 1974. Nine faculty are members of the NAE, and the Department's developing expertise is reflected in the diversity of graduate degrees offered. Along with master's degrees in architectural, civil, and environmental health engineering, it also awards doctorates in seven fields: construction engineering and project management, environmental engineering, geotechnical engineering, structural engineering and materials, ocean and offshore engineering, water resources engineering, and transportation engineering. The increasing emphasis on environmental protection and revitalization of the national infrastructure has expanded the opportunities for civil engineering graduates and added more impetus to the development of academic programs at all levels. The Jones–Lindzey report in 1982 recognized the doctoral program in civil engineering at The University as having made the greatest improvement during the previous five–year period among seventy–three institutions evaluated in the United States and ranked the program sixth in the nation.[46]

The Department of Electrical Engineering, renamed Electrical and Computer Engineering in 1984 in recognition of its involvement in computer development, experienced the highest enrollments and the broadest outside support during the past two decades. Herbert H. Woodson succeeded Archie F. Straiton as chairman in 1971, serving until 1981. Also the director of the interdisciplinary Center for Energy Studies, Woodson supervised the creation of a graduate curriculum in energy systems. Under Woodson's direction, the Department invested in improved equipment and more faculty for computer course work and teaching laboratories after initiating an undergraduate program on computers in 1973.[47]

Edward J. Powers, Jr., followed Woodson as chairman in 1981. Powers, along with Ben G. Streetman and others in the spring of 1983, was instrumental in the selection of Austin as the site for the Microelectronics and Computer Technology Corporation (MCC), which provided new opportunities for research and education in those fields. The recruitment of MCC was the result of a concerted effort by universities, state government, and the private sector. An important component of this successful event was the strength of The University of Texas, particularly its electrical and computer engineering and computer sciences program on the Austin campus. The University pledged a major increase in its research and education effort, including substantial commitments of new faculty positions and more endowed chairs in microelectronics, computer engineering, and computer science, as well as graduate student fellowships, annual research support, and equipment. As a result of these commitments, the Department of Electrical and Computer Engineering has undergone substantial expansion in microelectronics and computer engineering, with the establishment of new curricula and the recruitment of more faculty. Although these areas became the most popular, students and faculty have also continued to develop strong options in power generation and transmission, communications, and biomedical engineering.[48]

Lamb was the chairman of the Department of Mechanical Engineering until 1976, when H. Grady Rylander, Jr., took over. Lamb, whose interests lay in fluid mechanics and heat transfer, proved to be an important catalyst, revitalizing the curricula and directing inquiry into new areas of research, including advanced energy technology and electronics. Rylander focused on one objective, "productivity:" the education of engineers who can complete a project more quickly at a better cost than their competitor. The curriculum remained in every sense "miscellaneous engineering," embracing a variety of diverse fields such as materials science under Harris L. Marcus, biomedical engineering under Kenneth R. Diller and George B. Thurston, electromechanical systems under Rylander and William F. Weldon, and solar energy under John R. Howell, who succeeded Rylander as chairman in September 1986. Despite uncertain public support, the nuclear engineering program continued to develop under Dale E. Klein as the faculty involved themselves in research for the application of fusion technology along with other alternative energy sources. They hosted an international conference on controlled nuclear fusion during November 1972, signalling the new focus on energy research for the future. Work also continued with the TRIGA fission reactor, which was scheduled to be moved from Taylor Hall to a facility under construction at the BRC in 1986.[49]

The Department of Mechanical Engineering initiated two innovative interdisciplinary graduate degrees in response to industry needs: Operations Research, which required course work in business and plant management, and Manufacturing Systems Engineering (MSE), which combined classes in mechanical, electrical, and aerospace engineering with those taught by the Graduate School of Business and the Department of Computer Science to provide an education for those who will design and manage the computer–integrated manufacturing systems of the future. Roy Harris, a mechanical engineer and former chairman of the Department of Management in the College of Business Administration, became the first director for MSE. Robert H. Flake from the Department of Electrical and Computer Engineering took charge of the graduate curriculum. New faculty have added more complexity to the effort, such as Delbert Tesar's work in robotics. Computer–aided designs were introduced in all sections of engineering graphics by Walter S. Reed in 1977, and with the new facilities Davor Juricic was able to rapidly expand course work, enhancing the utility of this modern medium of engineering communication.[50]

Petroleum Engineering as a department and as a discipline went through turbulent times in the past two decades, but the overall characteristic has been an enormous surge in academic activity due to the boom in domestic oil wells after 1973. This growth concentrated on the undergraduate level as industry recruited students almost before they could finish their examinations, and Robert S. Schechter, who succeeded Kenneth E. Gray as chairman in 1975, responded to additional demand by expanding the master's curriculum from a research orientation to a professional focus because of the flow of graduates into engineering practice rather than doctoral study. The number of active domestic wells fell precipitously after 1981. Undergraduate enrollment declined as a consequence, which alleviated the problem of overcrowding and brought the student–teacher ratio closer to the College goal. A fiscally conservative industry holds more promise for doctorates trained in advanced methods of locating, recovering, and refining dwindling oil reserves, but in the immediate future affords little room for a large number of undergraduates. By the 1990s, demand for petroleum engineers at the bachelor level will rise in response to an increase in crude oil prices. Since it requires at least four years to complete the undergraduate curriculum, today's freshman will probably have excellent job prospects.[51]

The long–term solution to this "feast and famine" problem seems to lie in the concept behind a plan initiated by Schechter and Myron H. Dorfman, chairman from 1978 to 1985, which calls for an expansion of program content, including more studies in recovery processes and other mineral resources. A master of arts degree program in energy and mineral resources, approved by the regents in February 1981 and now directed by Willem C. J. van Rensberg, requires courses in geological science, petroleum engineering, economics, and resource management to produce graduates skilled in the many techniques for the conservative use of energy. It was the only program of its type in the state at its inception. The Department plans to continue to develop new courses to teach methods for recovering not only primary fuel sources, such as petroleum, coal, and uranium, but also many other minerals of use to industry. The program will be more than conventional mining engineering as such techniques will require the use of technology that has yet to be developed. As the Department of Petroleum Engineering has produced more than half of the world's doctorates in petroleum engineering and supports the largest graduate degree program in its field, its prospects for continued development in its new home, under the leadership of chairman Gary A. Pope, who took over in September 1985, remain excellent.[52]

Engineering science continued to serve as a flexible major for those students whose interests lay outside the curricula of the more structured disciplines. The enrollment management program implemented in the fall of 1982 allowed students to take courses only as a major sequence, into which they could enter from any basic sequence after their first two years. Specializations included atmospheric science (discontinued in 1986), biomedical engineering (coordinating curricula offered by faculty in the Departments of Electrical, Chemical, and Mechanical Engineering for those who will attend medical school), computer applications engineering, environmental engineering, engineering science and mechanics, geological engineering, nuclear engineering, ocean engineering, and materials science and engineering. Degrees are granted through the dean's office, where the program has been directed by the Associate Dean for Academic Affairs.[53]

Research in the College remained an even more important tool for curriculum development and teaching as it diversified through fifteen years of increasing budgets and reorganization. College efforts to tailor its research to public needs began in response to the federal initiative supplied through the Research Applied to National Needs (RANN) project. The focus on solving public problems without deemphasizing the need for basic scientific research received new impetus from a directive promulgated by the NAE, which criticized RANN for not including enough consideration of social and economic impacts. The College retained the overall goal of public service in establishing objectives for individual research effort. In 1985–1986, the faculty conducted over five hundred projects in nineteen organized research units, supported by a 67 percent increase over the previous year in financial aid. Since 1975 the research funds available through the College have tripled, increasing to almost $40 million in 1986. The University in 1985 spent more on engineering–related research than all of the other schools of engineering in Texas combined, despite receiving less than a fifth of the state financial support given to Texas A&M University. Like most institutions, the College obtains the greatest proportion of its research funds from the federal government, but recent efforts have increased the grants from industry.[54]

A revitalized BER coordinates most of the research on campus and at the BRC. Wood became the first full–time associate director of the BER in 1970. He consolidated the engineering research laboratories and groups in concert with a University effort to create a more efficient funding structure. At the same time, J. Neils Thompson, director of the BRC since its inception, created the Balcones Institute for Research and Development, empowered to contract with private industry and government agencies for new research projects that would enhance the BRC, especially in its facilities for graduate study. The organization received little support from a skeptical University administration and expired after the elimination of the position of director for the BRC in 1978. This action placed the responsibility for each research operation back in the deans' offices and, along with a decline in overall financial aid for engineering research, revived efforts within the Office of the Dean of Engineering to achieve line–item status for the BER. The Bureau appeared once more in the state budget for fiscal year 1980. Project funding has supplemented individual grants, fostering teamwork and interdisciplinary research projects.[55]

The Department of Aerospace Engineering and Engineering Mechanics sponsors three research centers formally recognized by the BER and three other active groups which are not currently formalized. The Center for Aeronautical Research (CAR), founded by Ronald O. Stearman but now directed by Lamb, focuses on problems of applied aerodynamics, structures, and materials which relate to aircraft and spacecraft. Faculty in the field of applied aerodynamics include Lamb, John J. Bertin, and John C. Westkaemper; those in structures and materials include Stearman, Ching–Hsie Yew, Roy R. Craig, Jr., and Stelios Kyriakides, chosen by the NSF in 1983 to receive a Presidential Young Investigator Award. Ably directed by Tapley, the Center for Space Research and Applications(CSRA) studies uses for nonmilitary earth resource satellites as well as potential unclassified military applicants. Faculty associated with the CSRA include Bob A. Schutz, Roger A. Brouke, Wallace T. Fowler, Raynor L. Duncombe, and Victor G. Szebehely. J. Tinsley Oden directs the Texas Institute for Computational Mechanics (TICOM), which studies the numerical simulation and analysis of physical properties and processes. This center employs several faculty including Eric B. Becker, Graham F. Carey, Linda J. Hayes, and Morris Stern. In September 1986, TICOM hosted the First World Conference on Computational Mechanics.[56]

Three additional research groups serve as adjuncts to the formal centers. The Engineering Mechanics Research Laboratory operates closely with the CAR, emphasizing nonaeronautical applications of composite materials, fluid and solid mechanics, and acoustics to marine, petroleum, and semiconductor industries along with various government agencies. Associated faculty include Anthony M. Bedford, Lyle G. Clark, Lawrence R. Mack, John W. Porter, and Eugene A. Ripperger. The Celestial Mechanics Group, directed by Szebehely, is an ancillary of the CSRA. Its research focus is on fundamental problems of dynamical astronomy that have an impact on the development of space technology. Szebehely, a member of the NAE, has earned international recognition for his research in orbital mechanics and space dynamics, and even has an equation for determining the relative gravitational pull of orbiting bodies named in his honor. Other faculty in this group include Brouke, Duncombe, and Paul E. Nacozy. The Guidance and Control Group, led by Jason L. Speyer with David G. Hull, has further expanded the research program through its focus on applying contemporary control and system theory to problems of guidance and control in missiles, aircraft, and orbiting vehicles.[57]

Research in Chemical Engineering focuses on a variety of areas related to industrial processes but there has been a growing interest in three prominent areas. Paul directs the Center for Polymer Research, which seeks new applications for polymers, incorporating them into media as diverse as thin membranes in protective medical and industrial barriers to large structures built of concrete and other durable materials. Associated faculty include Joel W. Barlow and William J. Koros, recognized by the NSF as a Presidential Young Investigator in 1983. Polymers are incorporated into the Separations Research Program (SRP) directed by Fair, elected to the NAE in 1974. The SRP seeks new methods of distillation and extraction for medical and industrial processes, especially in the petrochemical industry. This program benefits from the research of Keith P. Johnson, Douglas R. Lloyd, and Gary T. Rochelle. Additional work for the petrochemical and other derivative industries is done by Himmelblau, Edgar, John G. Eckerdt, and Howard F. Rase in process analysis and catalysis, and Wissler and

James R. Brock in aerosol physics and chemistry as they relate to atmospheric disturbance. Hugo Steinfink and Isaac Trachtenberg contribute to the micro-electronics industry through work in solid state and electrochemistry. The Bio-medical Engineering Research Group, initiated by Vogt and Popovich, continues through the involvement of faculty from almost every department. Projects include the use of polymer membranes for a system of peritoneal dialysis created by Popovich that eliminates the dangers of frequent hemodialysis at a third of the cost, which has been adopted by clinics around the world.[58]

The Department of Civil Engineering focused its research in five distinct fields: construction, geotechnical engineering, water and environmental resources engineering, structural engineering, and transportation. B. Franklin McCullough is director of the Center for Transportation Research, a merger of the Center for Highway Research, founded under the direction of Clyde E. Lee, with the Council for Advanced Transportation Studies, which had originated in 1972 to combine the talents of sixty–nine faculty from twenty–five disciplines for research under the direction of Associate Dean Reese. Both the earlier organizations were primarily funded by the state of Texas and the federal government to revitalize public transportation networks, and the CTR today continues that initiative. Associated faculty include Lee, Kennedy, former CATS acting director William R. Hudson, Randy B. Machemehl, Hani S. Mahmassani, Alvin H. Meyer, C. Michael Walton, and Robert Herman, elected to the NAE in 1978.[59]

Reese, elected a member of the NAE in 1975, led the Geo-technical Engineering Center (GEC), expanding research in soil mechanics into broader applications for roads, buildings, and industrial structures. The GEC is a broad research effort which benefits from the work of numerous faculty, such as Richard W. Miksad, Priscilla P. Nelson, Roy E. Olson, José M. Roesset, Kenneth H. Stokoe II, and Stephen G. Wright. Much of the work in the GEC complements the research on materials and design done by the Structural Engineering Laboratory, renamed in honor of Phil M. Ferguson (PMFSEL). Under the direction of John E. Breen, elected to the NAE in 1976, the PMFSEL underwent extensive renovation and now continues crucial structural analyses directed by James O. Jirsa for public and private construction projects. Structural mechanics research is conducted by David W. Fowler, together with Dan L. Wheat. Richard E. Klingner studies structural responses to dynamic loads, work aided by the design research of Richard W. Furlong and the analysis of C. Philip Johnson. The properties of concrete aggregates absorb the attention of Fowler, Ned H. Burns, and Ramon L. Carrasquillo. Joseph A. Yura and Karl H. Frank focus their research on steel structures. The Construction Industry Institute, established by Richard L. Tucker in 1984 with the aid of fifty companies engaged in construction, is funded by industry to enhance the cost–effectiveness of building contractors through research and education in materials and labor management. Active faculty include John D. Borcherding, James T. O'Connor, Calin M. Popescu, and David B. Ashley, selected as a Presidential Young Investigator in 1983.[60]

Finally, the Center for Research in Water Resources (CRWR), first organized by Dean Gloyna as a University–wide effort, continued to explore methods of water pollution control and conservation under William Butcher, Leo R. Beard, and Neal E. Armstrong during the 1970s. Joseph F.

Malina, Jr., took over the Environmental Health Engineering Laboratory, also under Dean Gloyna's previous direction, in 1970, paralleling studies in the CRWR until their consolidation in 1984. Under the direction of Ernest T. Smerdon, like Beard and Gloyna a member of the NAE, the expanded CRWR completes a research effort in civil engineering devoted to public service. Environmental engineering problems involving water and wastewater treatment, contaminant transport, solid waste disposal, and health effects continue to be the subject of studies by Gloyna, Malina, Armstrong, Sorber, Edward R. Holley, Randall J. Charbeneau, Howard M. Liljestrand, and Desmond F. Lawler, chosen to receive a Presidential Young Investigator Award in 1984. David R. Maidment and Larry W. Mays focus on systems analysis and hydrology. Other topics including the disposal of hazardous wastes are being researched by David E. Daniel, Jr., and Raymond C. Loehr, a member of the NAE. Miksad, along with E. Lothar Koschmeider and Norman K. Wagner, continues to provide fundamental support in studies of fluid mechanics, wind structure, and atmospheric instability.[61]

The Department of Electrical and Computer Engineering, along with its vital contributions to interdisciplinary programs such as biomedical engineering, continued to develop research into the field of microelectronics and energy under Powers and Woodson, elected to the NAE in 1975. The Joint Services Electronics Program celebrated its twentieth anniversary in 1984 without any sign of slowing down. Research topics included information electronics, with Powers, Stephen I. Marcus, and J. K. Aggarwal; solid state electronics, by Michael F. Becker, Robert W. Bené, and Rodger M. Walser; and quantum electronics, with Becker and Walser. The Electrical Engineering Research Laboratory (EERL) at BRC continued to explore new areas of inquiry with Tatsuo Itoh as director, along with former director Harold W. Smith, Francis X. Bostick, John R. Cogdell, John H. Davis, Bob M. Fannin, and William C. Duesterhoeft. Several engineering faculty actively contribute to the biomedical engineering program, including H. Grady Rylander, III; Jonathan W. Valvano; Ashley J. Welch; Lee E. Baker, the current director; and John A. Pearce, selected as a Presidential Young Investigator in 1984. Other research includes acoustics by Elmer L. Hixson; computer–aided design by M. Ray Mercer, who received a Presidential Young Investigator Award in 1985; digital process control by Robert H. Flake; cybernetics by Baxter F. Womack, and power systems by Woodson, Baughman, and W. Mack Grady.[62]

Expansion in the field of microelectronics brought MCC to Austin, initiating an entirely new phase of rapid development. MCC was established in 1982 in response to a general need in industry for a cooperative basic research project. Nineteen companies pooled their financial resources for the enterprise, then chose Austin from fifty–seven possible sites. A statewide task force of business leaders raised $23.5 million for a plant at the BRC, and the program has already begun to attract talented scientists and engineers from all over the world to Texas. Financial aid has been disseminated to the Department's other research centers: the Electronics Research Center, under Powers, with A. Bruce Buckman, Terry J. Wagner, Gary L. Wise, and Dean P. Neikirk, who received a Presidential Young Investigator Award in 1985; the Microelectronics Research Center, directed by Streetman, along with Charles H. Roth, Jr.; the Center for Fusion Engineering, led by Woodson; and the Computer and Vision Research Center, under

J. K. Aggarwal. G. Jack Lipovski has devised a prototypical high–speed parallel computer, the Texas Reconfigurable Architecture Computer, an ongoing project which utilizes studies by Chuan–Lin Wu and Harvey G. Cragon, a member of the NAE and the first member of the faculty to be appointed to one of the chairs sponsored in part by MCC. Al F. Tasch, Jr., joined the faculty from Motorola in July 1986 to enhance the research effort in microelectronics. NAE members such as Willis A. Adcock and Irwin W. Sandberg, a pioneer in electronic communications, will contribute to the revitalization of the Texas economy by placing the state at the forefront of technological research.[63]

Woodson directs the Center for Energy Studies (CES), an ambitious interdisciplinary research project in the College of Engineering. Established in June 1972 by President Spurr as The University of Texas at Austin Energy Research Group, the program initially included eighteen members of academic departments with research interests. Renamed in 1973, the CES with Woodson as director operates with support from about forty corporate subscribers. Research topics encompass almost every conceivable source of energy. In 1978, the CES initiated an extensive probe into the geothermal resources along the Texas coast, a project supervised by Dorfman of Petroleum Engineering. The CES also houses the separations research project in chemical engineering, which has applications in many industries. The budget in 1985–1986 exceeded $1.8 million, but the development of Austin as a site for technological enterprise should accelerate subscriptions from industry to spark even greater expansion into broader areas of energy research in the new building finished in 1985.[64]

Research in Mechanical Engineering primarily depends on three organizations. The Center for Electromechanics (CEM), led by William F. Weldon, strives to develop methods and applications for pulsed electric power technology. The previous director, Rylander, designed and constructed a compact homopolar generator capable of pulsing a thermonuclear reactor. Current research in pulsed power focuses on the compulsator, which provides multiple bursts of intense energy for application in many projects, such as the CEM's own railgun. Much of the research in the CEM is now supported by the Strategic Defense Initiative organization for possible incorporation into a space–based defense system and other more peaceful uses. The Center for Materials Science and Engineering (CMSE), directed by Harris L. Marcus, participates in a variety of research into the microstructure of materials, with applications in areas as diverse as the reduction of friction in machinery and solid–state transport. Associated faculty include David L. Bourell, Zwy Eliezer, John P. Stark, and Kenneth M. Ralls. Led by Dale E. Klein, the Nuclear Engineering Teaching Laboratory (NETL) provides facilities for fission experiments within the CMSE and also conducts its own graduate research and teaching. Faculty include Koen and Nolan E. Hertel. Like the CEM, the NETL will relocate to the BRC soon, where expanded facilities will permit graduate students to become familiar with all phases of electrical power generation by fission.[65]

Mechanical engineering research in addition to that of the major centers reflects a broad spectrum of interest and a renewed push for development. Computer graphics and computer–aided design studies are conducted by Davor Juricic, Margaret R. Baker, Ronald E. Barr, and Walter S. Reed. The biomedical engineering research group includes Kenneth R. Diller and George B.

Thurston. Lesso, J. Wesley Barnes, Charles S. Beightler, and Paul A. Jensen make up the core of an innovative operations research team. Energy use is the focus of a diverse range of efforts: Jerold W. Jones in heat transfer and dynamics; John R. Howell and Gary C. Vliet in solar energy; Ronald D. Matthews and Ronald L. Panton in topics concerned with combustion; Glenn Y. Masada in power systems; and Philip S. Schmidt in energy systems engineering. Alfred E. Traver and Joseph J. Beaman, elected a Presidential Young Investigator in 1983, focus on dynamic systems. Additional topics include mechanical design analysis, conducted by Kurt M. Marshek, and thermosciences, by H. Alan Walls. Delbert Tesar directs a rapidly growing research effort in robotics. Many of the active faculty in the Department of Mechanical Engineering are relatively young as a result of its program of redevelopment. The election of three more of its faculty as Presidential Young Investigators—Ilene Busch–Vishniac, Theodore L. Bergman, and Mark F. Hamilton—indicates the great progress made, and foreshadows the greater development to be experienced in the immediate future. Prominent new faculty such as John B. Goodenough, a member of the NAE who specializes in magnetism and ceramics conduction, will provide the necessary elements of leadership and reputation.[66]

Research in Petroleum Engineering reflects the growing concern for the world's oil reserves. Pope, chairman of the Department beginning in September 1985, established the Center for Enhanced Oil and Gas Recovery Research (CEOGRR), which now has an annual fund of over a half million dollars to continue inquiry into more efficient means of exploiting known deposits of petroleum and its byproducts. Studies by faculty involved in the CEOGRR include modeling improved reservoirs and developing tertiary recovery techniques of bringing up oil from fields abandoned when existing methods proved unprofitable. Research topics include well logging by Dorfman; enhanced oil recovery by Kamy Sepehrnoori, Peters, Pope, and Schechter, elected to the NAE in 1976; well completion and production by Augusto L. Podio; and reservoir modeling and engineering by NAE member Claude R. Hocott, Ben H. Caudle, and Larry W. Lake, who became director of the CEOGRR in 1985. Similar research in secondary recovery is funded by the Texas Petroleum Research Council; Irwin H. Silberberg served in 1985–86 as the associate research director for The University of Texas. The CEOGRR also cooperates with the CES in exploring the geothermal resources of Texas, a multimillion–dollar project sponsored by the Department of Energy and a number of private companies. Gray remained the sole director of the Center for Earth Sciences and Engineering, a comprehensive effort in rock mechanics that has grown beyond applications for the petroleum industry into new mineral resources. Associated faculty include Podio and van Rensberg. Support from industry for this study is increasing; the present interest of the Petroleum Engineering faculty in such research may produce the energy resources for the technological world of the future.[67]

During the 1970s and 1980s, the College of Engineering has grown into a position of leadership. Industry in Texas now looks to The University in Austin for outstanding engineers and world–class research. Individual departments in the College have won well–deserved reputations for academic leadership and public service. This stature is to a large degree attributable to the remarkable rapport established with the employers of engineers and friends of the

College. Much credit should be given to the Engineering Foundation Advisory Council (EFAC), the six Departmental Visiting Committees, the Industrial Associates, and other donors. Without the dynamic support of EFAC chairmen such as Bob R. Dorsey, John E. Kasch, Melvin H. Gertz, John W. Sheehan, Robert L. Parker, Sr., Ernest H. Cockrell, Paul D. Meek, R. Earle Wright, Perry G. Brittain, John T. Files, Charles M. Simmons, Lewis A. Beecherl, Jr., and Bobby R. Inman, the College could not have developed its excellent faculty, endowment programs, or its state–of–the–art teaching and research facilities on campus and at the BRC.

The Jones-Lindzey report in 1982 reflected the trend toward excellence by the College. The poll, sponsored by the American Council on Education, National Research Council, American Council of Learned Societies, and Social Sciences Research Council, reviewed 2,700 doctoral programs in thirty–two fields at 228 universities in the United States. The Department of Civil Engineering at The University of Texas ranked sixth overall and third among public institutions, while Electrical and Chemical Engineering placed thirteenth and seventh respectively. Mechanical Engineering ranked sixteenth nationally and

Bobby R. Inman, chairman of the Engineering Foundation Advisory Council in 1986, congratulates M. Ray Mercer, of Electrical Engineering, following his selection by the National Science Foundation as a Presidential Young Investigator. [College of Engineering, The University of Texas at Austin]

ninth among state–supported schools, but ranked first in improvement among all colleges. Mechanical, Electrical, and Civil Engineering were recognized as the best in the Southwest, while Chemical Engineering came in second only to the University of Houston, whose strong support from the petroleum industry pushed it to tenth nationally.[68]

Development has continued apace in the College since 1982, as indicated by some simple statistics. Graduate student enrollment increased to 1,507 by the fall of 1985, while the undergraduate population stablilized at 5,042. At the same time, the relative proportion of minority enrollment has increased. These students benefit from the service of an outstanding faculty that numbered 283 by 1986, including twenty–one members of the prestigious NAE and eleven NSF Presidential Young Investigators. The quality of the educational experience available at the College has also been enhanced by the expansion of the operating budget in the past two decades, to more than $38 million in 1985–1986, accompanied by an increase in support for research to almost $40 million during the same period. This fiscal development has been supplemented by the establishment of 149 endowed faculty positions, forty–six endowed laboratories and classrooms, and thirty–three fellowship and scholarship funds. The number of graduate and undergraduate degrees conferred in 1985—399 and 942 respectively—ranks the College among the top ten in the United States in the production of engineers. With the continued teamwork of faculty and students and the sponsorship of loyal alumni and corporate sponsors, the College of Engineering should find itself without peer in the Southwest, if not in the nation, as it continues to develop on the leading edge of the drive for a "university of the first class."

# ENGINEERING LEADERSHIP THROUGH RESEARCH:

## *The College of Engineering and the State of Texas*

The College of Engineering is proud of its record of effective teaching, classroom and laboratory instruction, and academic research. Through this effort, the College has made important contributions to the economic development of the state of Texas. Its more than 80,000 engineering graduates include leaders in design, engineering management, academia, and research. Many of these engineers have become businessmen, heads of corporations, bankers, government officials, entrepreneurs, physicians, clergy, and attorneys. It has been the policy of the College to enhance a broad rigorous scientific classroom experience with an exposure to the state of the art in engineering practice. This effort has produced better engineers cognizant of the needs of a growing state and capable of doing their share to improve the quality of life and develop a strong economic future.

Research in the academic environment brings out the best in both the faculty and students. The continuous exercise of new talent results in an ever–expanding body of knowledge. Over fifteen hundred strong in 1986, the graduate student population in the College has greatly facilitated the development of a center of research excellence in Texas. After graduation, they have led in the development of technological industry in Texas and in the construction of the necessary infrastructure for a safer and more prosperous tomorrow. Research in engineering education materially improves teaching effectiveness, and the students who have earned a degree within the graduate program at The University, which is dedicated to continuing development, have served the state well through their product innovation, entrepreneurship, and public service.

Today engineering research at The University of Texas at Austin has become a forty–million–dollar operation under the direction of a well–organized Bureau of Engineering Research (BER). As the graduate student body has expanded and the faculty has initiated the research necessary for a greater national reputation, the BER has developed in a commensurate fashion. The greatest expansion in personnel and facilities occurred during the 1970s and 1980s, and rapid growth is expected to continue through the next decade. By 1991, the research budget of the College of Engineering will exceed sixty million dollars. Through a constant search for new solutions to the engineering problems of the present, the College will enable Texas to remain at the cutting edge of technological research for the future.

The goals of faculty and students have remained constant during the one–hundred–year history of the College. Beginning with the efforts of Dean Thomas U. Taylor before the turn of the century, engineering research at The University has facilitated greater use of the natural and human resources in the region and led the way to more diverse industry as technology progressed rapidly after World War II. Both the public and private sectors of the state economy benefited immeasurably from the innovations of the engineering laboratories in Austin during the tremendous growth and change that characterized an industrializing Texas in the twentieth century. This progress initially set the pace for engineering research at The University, but during the last decade the necessity for greater leadership in the industrial development of Texas led to the reorganization of the BER and the creation of the Center for Technology Development and Transfer.

Dean Taylor's research interests focused primarily on road and bridge construction, water power, and irrigation. His first book, *Prismoidal Formulae and Earthwork*, drew from both his graduate work at Cornell and personal experience, and received lavish praise from engineering journals in the United States and Britain. He became an early activist for better roads in Texas, conducting some of the first surveys of roadway conditions in the state and later directing construction of the Oakcliff Viaduct in Dallas. Like many Austinites, he welcomed the completion of the Austin Dam as a source of cheap power to improve life and attract industry. Shocked by the structure's collapse on April 7, 1900, Dean Taylor conducted a number of studies during the next four decades on stream flow, impoundment silting, and dam structure, both as district engineer for the Water Resources Branch of the U. S. Geological Survey (USGS) and as a consultant for the state, and served as supervising engineer for the final reconstruction of the dam near Austin. His reports on the flow rates of Texas streams were the first ever published on the subject, revealing important information on the depletion and replenishment of the state's most valuable natural resource. The USGS also funded a study of rice irrigation in Texas by Dean Taylor that aided in the development of that nascent enterprise by demonstrating its profitability if properly managed.[1]

As the Department of Engineering grew, the faculty and students shared the sense of responsibility for Texas. Projects underway on campus in 1910 included surveying the site for a new library, now Battle Hall; demolition of the old Power Plant's smokestack and other renovations so that the building could be used for classrooms; and Bantel's ambitious attempt to survey the entire Forty Acres into two–hundred–foot squares, marking each quadrant with concrete and steel boundary pins after the style of the U. S. Coast and Geodetic Survey. Engineering students obtained additional practical experience that year by designing an oil pipeline for the State Lunatic Asylum in Austin, planning a new water supply system for The University, and grading the east campus and peripatos areas. John M. Bryant was particularly active on campus, installing the first streetlight systems in 1926. Hal C. Weaver designed the present University power plant, which bears his name, and served as the first director after its completion in 1927. Werner W. Dornberger, who earned bachelor's degrees in architecture and architectural engineering from The University in 1922 and became the first full–time faculty member for Architectural Engineering in 1945, worked for the supervising architect of The University from 1922 to 1944, overseeing many projects, including the construction of McDonald Observatory. Charles E. Rowe drew the plans adopted for Taylor Hall, and other engineering faculty served on building committees during the busy years when The University spent its new–found oil revenues on an expansion program.[2]

Creation of the Division, later Bureau, of Engineering Research (BER) in 1915 through a reorganization of the Bureau of Economic Geology and Technology (BEGT) lent greater purpose and a broader scope to the effort in engineering research. James P. Nash, a "testing engineer" for the BEGT, worked together with Richard G. Tyler of Civil Engineering to evaluate paving materials for Texas roads. They cooperated with the Bureau of Municipal Research and Reference (BMRR) in a similar task and sponsored one of the first statewide conferences on paving materials and road construction during Municipal Engineers' Week in February 1917. Because of their efforts and location in Austin, the Texas Department of Highways, created in 1917, relied on The University for much of its testing.[3]

Tyler developed the first short course on highway engineering at The University in 1919, but when he left for Cornell University the curriculum was discontinued. Tyler's departure also suspended research efforts in sanitary engineering, which had been expanded by him after initial work by the BMRR. John A. Focht revived highway studies and, along with Raymond F. Dawson, established the first soil mechanics laboratory in the Southwest in 1930 to research the properties of road foundations. The Thirty–Eighth Legislature of Texas mandated standardization of headlights in Texas and chose C. Read Granberry of Electrical Engineering to test available devices for compliance. Frederick E. Giesecke and Stanley P. Finch expanded earlier studies of concrete aggregates for application in construction, publishing one of the first attempts at precise measurement of building materials.[4]

Dean Willis R. Woolrich revived the BER after the fiscal straits of the Depression enforced a period of near dormancy. Byron E. Short had continued a study of heat transfer in commercial heat exchangers through the 1930s and now expanded his research for applications in refrigeration. Dean Woolrich, Howard E. Brown, and Luis H. Bartlett patented innovative methods for preserving foodstuffs by freezing and dehydration developed for the military before and during World War II. Dean Woolrich also continued the research on air conditioning conducted by Howard E. Degler. Along with James D. McFarland, Dean Woolrich designed systems combining forced–air ventilation with evaporative and ice cooling primarily for intermittent service. Successful units were installed in some churches and other municipal buildings in Texas, but continued low energy costs brought disfavor on his ideas. As cheap sources of power have declined, public interest has again increased for mixed air-conditioning systems, especially economical evaporative cooling units. Carl J. Eckhardt, Jr., published the first reports on his study of the utility of lignite in 1942, providing early information on an abundant alternative fuel source in Texas. The effort of the BER enjoyed greater publicity as the College hosted conferences on traffic engineering, air conditioning, foodstuff preservation, and soil mechanics and circulated the contributions in their own independently produced publications.[5]

The Division, later Bureau, of Industrial Chemistry (BIC) also originated with the reorganization of the BEGT in 1915. Eugene P. Schoch served as its director during its active life of almost forty years, using the BIC as a fulcrum to establish a curriculum in chemical engineering at The University. Schoch felt a deep obligation to the people of his adopted state, and focused his research on the development of the natural resources within the region. He published the first full compilation of existing data, including a lengthy bibliography, in 1918. Water treatment, lignite, potash minerals, and natural gas came under his scrutiny and that of the legions of graduate students he tutored. Natural gas became the subject of his major project as he tried to devise a process to economically convert hydrocarbons, primarily methane, to acetylene and other more useful materials through electrical discharge. He succeeded, but not in a commercially viable manner, although the Schoch Electric Discharge Process was purchased by the Esso Research and Engineering Corporation. His early study of the thermodynamic relationships between hydrocarbon liquids and vapors and his interpretation of such data, however, led directly to the current legal distinction between oil and gas wells and to sound conservation measures.[6]

Four factors combined to effect a rapid expansion of engineering research at The University following World War II. The first was the increased emphasis within the United States on the need for graduate education for competent technological research. Industry now moved much too fast to rely on the accumulation of personal experience for innnovation; engineering researchers required the background afforded by graduate education, preferably at the doctoral level, in order to contribute effectively. Secondly, the federal government, realizing the necessity for accelerating such studies, began funding organized technological research programs on an unprecedented level, spurred in part by the new Engineering College Research Council. Later renamed the Engineering Research Council, this organization played a strong role in determining the close relationship between the national government and the institutions of engineering education and research represented by its members. In Texas, a third factor shaping the course of new research was an increase in electronic development and related enterprises. The state ranked eighth nationally in the value of its electronics production in 1959, but by 1980 it had the third largest share of electronics manufacturing employment in the United States. Finally, the development of the Balcones Research Center (BRC) afforded a more spacious home for rapidly expanding engineering research. Under the management of J. Neils Thompson, of Civil Engineering, the BRC came to be dominated by engineers intent upon forging a new future for themselves and Texas.[7]

Industry had been the primary sponsor of research in the United States after World War I, but during the second global conflict the federal government took the lead in financial support. In 1940 industry contributed 68 percent

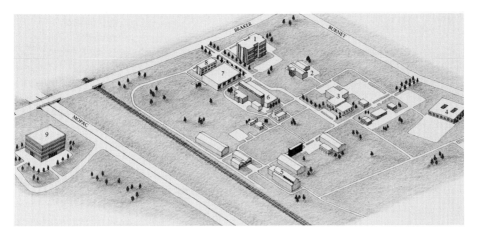

The Balcones Research Center: 1. Bureau of Economic Geology, 2. Center for Research in Water Resources, 3. Commons Building, 4. Applied Research Laboratory, 5. Phil M. Ferguson Structural Engineering Laboratory, 6. Center for Electromechanics and Center for Energy Studies, 7. Well Sample and Core Library, 8. Mineral Studies Laboratory, 9. Microelectronics and Computer Technology Corporation (MCC). [Illustration by Pam Fuller]

of the national investment of $345 million in technical research and development, while the federal government donated only 19 percent. Between 1941 and 1945 the national government provided 83 percent of the funds invested in scientific and engineering research as industry's support fell to 13 percent of the total of $600 million. The initiative in research did not end with the surrender of Germany and Japan in 1945; the war effort had made American scientists and engineers acutely aware of their weakness in basic research. The Europeans had proven to be far superior in the fundamentals of technology, and the United States had relied too greatly on their work for applied research.[8]

Americans after World War II embarked on their greatest era of engineering promise: the war had ruined the nations of Western Europe, the nearest competitor, and new organizations such as the National Science Foundation (NSF) provided unprecedented funding for research and development. By 1947 the national research budget for science and engineering had swelled to more than $1 billion. Industry, recovering from its wartime preoccupation with military production, contributed 39 percent of this total, but the federal government donated 54 percent, setting a pattern for funding that persisted through the next four decades for the nation as well as the College, even after the reorganization of the BER as the central administrative agency for fund management and its reinstatement as a line item in the state budget.[9]

By 1986, engineering research at The University encompassed a broad spectrum of topics. Faculty from the six departments of the College, which offer a total of eleven graduate programs, conduct research within nineteen organized research centers and an interdepartmental research effort, biomedical engineering, under the aegis of the revitalized BER. Faculty and students from the College also continue to contribute to two University research organizations: the Applied Research Laboratory (ARL), the first government–

sponsored research center founded at The University; and the Center for Energy Studies (CES), dedicated to exploring new solutions for the energy problems of today and the future. Through their research, the faculty and students of the College have earned greater recognition for themselves and have expedited the development of a stronger economic base and a higher standard of living for Texas.

The aerospace industry played a crucial role in the development of a more diverse economy in Texas. Research in aeronautical, now aerospace, engineering began with the Experimental Aerodynamics Laboratory founded by Milton J. Thompson in the Defense Research Laboratory in 1950 to carry out research on supersonic boundary layers at speeds up to five times that of sound. Out of this facility came some now classic measurements of surface friction drag upon which the subsequent design of supersonic missiles and aircraft was based. Since the early 1980s much of the original equipment has been replaced and the entire facility modernized under the direction of David S. Dolling.[10]

The Experimental Aerodynamics Laboratory (EAL) has expanded from the original supersonic wind tunnel to include two more testing complexes. One, the Rocket Exhaust Effects Facility, was built in the early 1970s by John J. Bertin to study flow problems which occur when the rocket exhaust gases interact with the launching apparatus, often causing destruction to both. Extensive work in this laboratory has been sponsored by the army and navy as

---

DIRECTORS OF ORGANIZED ENGINEERING RESEARCH UNITS

---

| | |
|---|---|
| Center for Aeronautical Research | J. Parker Lamb, Jr. |
| Texas Institute for Computational Mechanics | J. Tinsley Oden |
| Computer and Vision Research Center | J. K. Aggarwal |
| Construction Industry Institute | Richard L. Tucker |
| Center for Earth Sciences and Engineering | Kenneth E. Gray |
| Electrical Engineering Research Laboratory | Tatsuo Itoh |
| Center for Electromechanics | William F. Weldon |
| Electronics Research Center | Edward J. Powers, Jr. |
| Center for Fusion Engineering | Herbert H. Woodson |
| Geotechnical Engineering Center | Lymon C. Reese |
| Center for Materials Science and Engineering | Harris L. Marcus |
| Microelectronics Research Center | Ben G. Streetman |
| Center for Enhanced Oil and Gas Recovery Research | Larry W. Lake |
| Center for Polymer Research | Donald R. Paul |
| Center for Space Research and Applications | Byron D. Tapley |
| Phil M. Ferguson Structural Engineering Laboratory | James O. Jirsa |
| Center for Technology Development and Transfer | Stephen A. Szygenda |
| Center for Transportation Research | B. Franklin McCullough |
| Center for Research in Water Resources | Ernest T. Smerdon |

DIRECTORS OF UNIVERSITY RESEARCH UNITS CONDUCTING ENGINEERING-RELATED RESEARCH

---

| | |
|---|---|
| Applied Research Laboratories | Loyd D. Hampton |
| Center for Energy Studies | Herbert H. Woodson |

well as rocket manufacturers. For example, Bertin completed a decade–long project to develop the black glass and silica tiles which shielded the space shuttle from temperatures up to 2,800 degrees Farenheit during reentry. The second major expansion of the EAL has been the construction and operation of a large subsonic wind tunnel, designed by John J. Westkaemper, who, with a small amount of institutional funding and some student assistants, supervised its construction during the early 1970s. This tunnel, with a test section which measures five feet high, seven feet wide, and fifty feet long, can be adapted to test air flows at speeds up to 150 miles per hour over both air vehicles and buildings.[11]

The foregoing aerospace engineering test facilities are a part of the Center for Aeronautical Research (CAR), an outgrowth of the Thin Shell Structures Laboratory founded in 1967 by Ronald O. Stearman with support from the U.S. Air Force and NASA. Faculty have explored the dynamical behavior of aerospace structures exposed to extreme aerodynamic environments, devising structures and techniques for use in supersonic and hypersonic flight. Since 1980, the scope of work within the CAR has broadened to encompass the technology of structures, materials, and aerodynamics of vehicles for both atmospheric and space flight. The present CAR, under the direction of J. Parker Lamb, Jr., houses a Structures and Materials Group along with the Applied Aerodynamics Group led by Lamb, Bertin, and Westkaemper. The former includes Stearman, who is involved in aircraft accident investigations and product liability studies, Roy R. Craig, Jr., who leads the research in structural dynamics of aircraft and spacecraft, and a team of experimentalists including Ching–Hsie Yew and Stelios Kyriakides, who received a Presidential Young Investigator Award from the NSF in 1983.[12]

Development of the space program at the NASA Manned Spacecraft Center in Houston in the early 1960s attracted the attention of Byron D. Tapley, who initiated research in the computation of orbital trajectories. This early work led to the establishment of the Center for Space Research and Applications (CSRA) in 1981. The CSRA conducts research to expedite manned and unmanned space exploration activity and in the utility of artificial satellites for further exploration of the terrestrial environment. Current topics include technological support of the space shuttle program and manned orbiting space stations, oceanographic satellites such as SEASAT, TOPEX, GEOSAT, and N–ROSS, geodetic satellites such as LAGEOS, GEOS–3, BE–C, and Starlette, earth resources application satellites, primarily LANDSAT, navigational satellites such as GPS and TRANSIT, and experimental new interplanetary transfer and orbiting spacecraft.[13]

Current faculty involved with the CSRA include Roger A. Brouke, Bob A. Schutz, Wallace T. Fowler, Raynor L. Duncombe, and Victor G. Szebehely. Satellite laser–ranging technology has expedited studies on polar motion together with the international polar monitoring campaign (MERIT), as well as earth rotation, ocean tides, and plate tectonics as part of the NASA Crustal Dynamics Project. Efforts are underway with the National Oceanographic and Atmospheric Administration (NOAA) to develop the capability for the analysis of global remote sensing data from the NOAA Earth Satellite Program for agriculture and ocean surveillance. A final area of research concerns the stability of gravitational systems and theories of the motion of natural and artificial satellites which may lead to new knowledge about the evolution of the moon and planets in the solar system and aid in the deployment of more near–earth satellites.[14]

The Department of Aerospace Engineering and Engineering Mechanics also supports the Texas Institute for Computational Mechanics (TICOM), led by J. Tinsley Oden. TICOM was organized in 1973 as the focus for research leading to the development and application of computational methods to engineering problems. Topics include development of numerical simulators for two– and three–dimensional problems in fluid mechanics, analysis of elasto-meric structures, modeling of the interior ballistics of solid–propellant rocket engines, computational grid generation and numerical algorithms for supercom-puters, wave propagation in ocean sediments, stress and vibration analysis of buildings and bridges, metal forming and manufacturing processes, elasticity of rubbery materials, and chemical kinetics. TICOM provides services to Texas en-gineers who need software for design and analysis; much of the actual comput-ing is carried out in their laboratory, which contains a Harris 800 minicomputer. TICOM also is a regular host for many short courses and seminars to facilitate the introduction of new electronic technology to the engineering community. Associated faculty include Eric B. Becker, Graham F. Carey, Linda J. Hayes, and Morris Stern.[15]

Several additional research groups have served as adjuncts to the organized research centers. Faculty in the Engineering Mechanics Research Laboratory (EMRL) conduct studies in conjunction with the CAR, applying modern methods of measurement and analysis to problems in the offshore and petroleum industries as well as other nonaeronautical areas. Recent work has included a broad range of projects in solid and fluid mechanics, acoustics, and composite materials. In addition to Kyriakides, faculty associated with the EMRL include Anthony M. Bedford, Lawrence R. Mack, Lyle G. Clark, John W. Porter, and Eugene A. Ripperger, now retired, who founded the EMRL in 1949.[16]

The Celestial Mechanics Group, led by Szebehely, is an ancillary of the CSRA. Its research focus is on fundamental problems of dynamical astron-omy that have an impact on the development of space technology. Szebehely, a member of the National Academy of Engineers (NAE), has earned international recognition for his research in orbital mechanics. Other noted faculty in this group include Brouke, Duncombe, and Paul E. Nacozy. A recently emerging area of focused research is embodied in the Guidance and Control Group, directed by Jason L. Speyer together with David G. Hull. Projects involve both atmospheric and space flight, and encompass missile homing guidance, fault–tolerant digital flight control systems, guidance laws for aero–assisted orbital transfer vehicles, cyclic control optimization, and optimal trajectories for boost and maneuverable reentry vehicles.[17]

In addition to his work in TICOM, Carey directs the Computa-tional Fluid Dynamics Laboratory, organized in 1985 to promote teaching and research specialization in the computer simulation of flow problems. Work fo-cuses on the development and implementation of software and the construction of benchmark problems and test-case studies for instruction. In research, topics include predictive simulations of flow processes, new algorithms and computa-tional methods, and basic flow phenomena. Representative applications are as

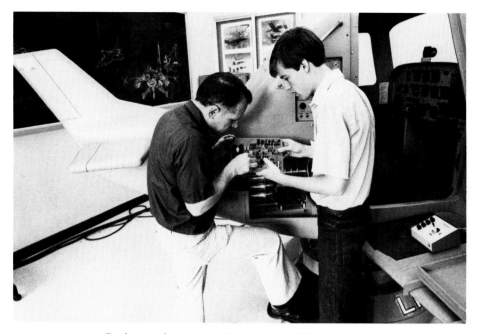

Professor of Aerospace Engineering Wallace T. Fowler and a student inspect the Link Trainer, used to simulate flight for the retrieval of valuable data. [College of Engineering, The University of Texas at Austin]

Associate Professor of Engineering Mechanics Linda J. Hayes is shown at the keyboard of the Harris 800 computer, located in the Texas Institute for Computational Mechanics. [College of Engineering, The University of Texas at Austin]

diverse as aerodynamics, reservoir simulation for the oil industry, and semi-conductor processing. The installation of the Cray supercomputer at the BRC in the spring of 1986 will expedite the development of even more innovative studies.[18]

Chemical engineering research has evolved into a broad range of activities and interests. After World War II, studies in the Department centered on the petroleum industry and the rapidly growing Texas chemical industry, thereby retaining the emphasis on helping the state to benefit more directly from its natural resources. Kenneth A. Kobe, Matthew Van Winkle, and former dean John J. McKetta, Jr., elected to the NAE in 1970, published data and correlations on thermodynamics and the phase behavior of hydrocarbons that were essential to the design and operation of petroleum refineries and chemical plants. These data are still widely used in the design and analysis of process operations. Van Winkle's pioneering work on distillation provided the procedures and data for accurate design analysis of complex distillation systems. John Griswold had earlier initiated work on extractive distillation that also proved to be valuable to the petrochemical industry. William A. Cunningham, a former student of Schoch, did much through his research to develop those industries which had a strong emphasis on industrial chemistry in Texas.[19]

Howard F. Rase brought the new field of applied kinetics and catalysis to the Department in the 1950s. His research, aided by his years of industrial experience, resulted in one of the first automatic microreactor systems, innovative catalysts, a better understanding of catalyst deactivation, and some of the first practical methods for modeling reactor systems. In the latter half of the fifties, David M. Himmelblau, Robert S. Schechter, and Eugene H. Wissler joined the faculty, bringing their strong mathematical and theoretical backgrounds to bear on a variety of problems in transport phenomena and modeling. All three used the rapidly developing, state–of–the–art computer facilities at The University. In more recent years, Schecter developed important programs in enhanced oil recovery and was elected to the NAE in 1976 in recognition of his achievements. Himmelblau specialized in developing modern methods for process optimization and fault detection, while Wissler has made significant contributions to mathematical simulation of human thermal systems with the goal of portraying biological behavior as it can be affected by various environmental conditions.[20]

In the 1960s, James R. Brock, Joel O. Hougen, Donald R. Paul, and Hugo Steinfink joined the Department with unique ideas and areas of specialization to further broaden the program. Brock applied his theoretical background to the study, by both experimental and mathematical modeling techniques, of the practical dynamics of particulate systems, including the role of aerosols in air pollution, which was becoming a major concern at that time. He has continued this work along with original research on particle–solid collisions and laser–particle interactions with an emphasis on new applications. Steinfink came to The University from Shell Development and has applied x–ray techniques to the study of transition–metal compounds and the development of semiconductor electrodes. Hougen came to the Department after a number of years in process control at Monsanto. His research focused on a key element of effective control: accurate measurements of process variables.[21]

Paul added a dynamic new dimension to the Department, bringing to it an academic and industrial background in polymer engineering. He initiated an important program in polymer research, initially related to gas solubility and diffusion in polymer membranes, that provided valuable data and concepts to aid in the industrial application of membranes as vehicles for the separation of gases from a mixture. As his work and interests expanded, Paul founded the Center for Polymer Research (CPR) in 1981 which has become internationally known for its contributions to membrane property relationships and polymer–blend technology. Associated faculty include Joel W. Barlow, William J. Koros, who in 1983 received a Presidential Young Investigator Award, and Isaac Trachtenberg, the first appointee under a Texas Instruments program to send senior technical staff to universities to teach and do research. Studies within the CPR expedited breakthroughs in the production of very thin yet efficient membranes for many vital applications. Faculty and graduate students from the Departments of Chemical and Civil Engineering, along with Chemistry and Pharmacy, have worked together in the CPR to devise uses for polymers, including controlled drug delivery, rubber toughening of brittle plastics, and components for microelectronic devices.[22]

The 1970s and the 1980s saw the most rapid growth in faculty size as the Department acted to maintain high standards for teaching and research in the face of large increases in both undergraduate and graduate enrollment. Thomas F. Edgar, with a strong modern theoretical background in process control, has built a vigorous program in this field and in the mathematical modeling of coal gasification and combustion systems. He became the first member of the Department to receive a national research award from the prestigious American Institute of Chemical Engineers. In 1979, the addition of John G. Eckerdt enhanced the area of catalysis research because of his thorough grounding in surface science. He has constructed an excellent laboratory facility to exploit these strengths in the investigation of molecular details of catalytic processes.[23]

Also in 1979, James R. Fair, elected to the NAE in 1974, joined the faculty following thirty–three years of advanced technology experience with Monsanto. In a short time, Fair established the Separations Research Program with support from thirty–eight firms with varying interests in separations. He has built bench–scale laboratories on campus and larger–scale facilities at the BRC. A number of more recent faculty additions are involved in this effort, such as Keith P. Johnston in supercritical extraction and Gary T. Rochelle in flue gas desulfurization and the removal of acid gas. Paul and Koros cooperate with Douglas R. Lloyd in a study of the separation of gases and liquids with membranes. Gas separation by synthetic membranes holds promise as a less energy–intensive competitor against current methods such as cryogenic distillation and solvent extraction and recovery. Such filters could economically yield greater quantities of oxygen, carbon dioxide, helium, hydrogen, and other gases for which the market is now limited because production costs are prohibitive.[24]

Research in civil engineering has traditionally been concerned with construction, transportation, sanitary engineering, and other projects closely associated with public works. Raymond F. Dawson continued studies of Texas soils and building materials throughout his career. He carefully monitored the settlement of the San Jacinto Monument beginning with its completion in 1936, and contributed to the studies of native clays for construction conducted by Robert L. Stone and E. Joseph Weiss of the Ceramics Kiln Laboratory from 1949 to 1954. Under the sponsorship of Acme Brick Company, six ceramic houses were built in Austin in 1953, a project combining Dawson's knowledge of soil mechanics, J. Neils Thompson's research in construction materials, Dean Wool-rich's efforts with cooling, and the work on Texas masonry resources done by Weiss and Stone. The group successfully demonstrated that high–rise masonry load–bearing walls could be constructed safely and economically. Their research was later expanded by Franklin B. Johnson and J. Neils Thompson with the sponsorship of the Clay Products Association of the Southwest and the Canadian Structural Clay Association.[25]

Dawson's work in soil mechanics was expanded into applications for offshore structures by Hudson Matlock and Lymon C. Reese. A study conducted by Matlock with Ripperger on piles under lateral loading in soft clay produced recommendations that were adopted by the American Petroleum Institute for the construction of oil platforms all over the world, as was Reese's research on pilings in sand. Reese, elected to the NAE in 1975, is now director of the Geotechnical Engineering Center (GEC), created in 1979 to coordinate research for better understanding of soil and rock in relation to foundations and earth and rock structures. Faculty involved in this effort include David E. Daniel,

The Polymer Processing Laboratory in the Chemical and Petroleum Engineering Building will expedite new research in polymers and their application. [College of Engineering, The University of Texas at Austin]

Jr., Roy E. Olson, Kenneth H. Stokoe II, Stephen G. Wright, Richard W. Miksad, and José M. Roesset.[26]

Research in the GEC includes studies of the utility of shallow land burial for low–level radioactive waste and the effects of landfill leachates on earth liners in hazardous waste storage and disposal sites. Inquiry on the application of surface geophysical methods in monitoring soil and rock mass changes in response to tunneling will facilitate mining deep deposits of coal, lignite, and other minerals. Efforts to improve the integrity of offshore platforms include developing better numerical models for coupled ocean–wave–sea–floor interaction to measure stress more exactly, which will expedite innovation in foundations and frameworks. This project also seeks to create a tool to take measurements in the sediments beneath the ocean bottom. Such a device would have

This state-of-the-art facility for separations research can be operated in several modes: distillation, gas adsorption, liquid stripping, and solvent extraction. [College of Engineering, The University of Texas at Austin]

many applications in the offshore oil industry as well as other enterprises that require the erection of structures on or under the sea. The GEC also actively sponsors short courses, lectures, seminars, and consulting work by faculty.[27]

J. Neils Thompson directed both the Materials Laboratory and the Structures Laboratory founded at the BRC in 1949. They merged in 1953 as the Civil Engineering Structures Research Laboratory under his continued direction. Research topics included a lengthy investigation of the use of prestressed reinforced concrete units by the navy in its construction program. Phil M. Ferguson won international acclaim for work in reinforced concrete structures and succeeded Thompson as director from 1963 to 1967, when John E. Breen took over. Both were later elected to the NAE, Ferguson in 1973, Breen three years later. Researchers under Ferguson conducted studies of the construction of long–span bridges using prestressed sections for the Texas Highway Department. Inquiries did not focus on concrete exclusively: Ferguson undertook studies to measure the combined moment, shear, and torsion in steel beams for the NSF; and Joseph A. Yura directed experiments to determine the behavior of steel beams in rigid building frames for the Iron and Steel Institute. A. Anthony Toprac analyzed the behavior of welded tubular joints, commonly used in building offshore oil platforms and other industrial structures.[28]

J. Neils Thompson also directed the Container Research Laboratory established in 1953 and renamed the Structural Mechanics Research Laboratory (SMRL) the next year. Ripperger and Matlock served as associate directors. They conducted air–drop research for the Quartermaster Research and Engineering Command, dropping parcels and heavy machinery from high altitudes in order to determine the best design for protective packaging. They were successful in devising shock–absorbing containers and received more funds from the Atomic Energy Commission to cooperate with the Engineering Mechanics Research Laboratory in high–velocity impact studies of plastics for the Sandia Corporation and from the Defense Atomic Support Agency to research methods to protect underground missile structures from damaging shock waves generated by nearby bomb blasts. Their techniques were later adopted in construction plans for civilian shelters.[29]

One of the SMRL's last research efforts in construction was the Austin Oaks Project, initiated on September 25, 1968, with funds from the Office of Housing and Urban Development for ten low–cost housing units. The foundations for the units were of several types, including concrete slabs and piers, and the construction methods ranged from conventional concrete block to stacked bags of concrete coated inside and out with mortar. On December 14, 1968, President Johnson declared at the dedication ceremony, "If we succeed here, then one day in this nation of so much wealth and abundance we can help every poor family to achieve its dream of homeownership." Some of the techniques demonstrated in Austin Oaks, such as prefabricated sections or even entire housing units delivered to the site complete, are now commonly used for homes and businesses in the United States.[30]

In the seventies, under Breen's direction, the Civil Engineering Structures Research Laboratory, renamed in honor of Ferguson, underwent its greatest period of expansion. James A. Jirsa, with NSF funding, supervised the construction at the BRC of the first testing slab in the United States designed for three–dimensional loading with extremely high forces. It has been used to simulate destructive internal forces such as high winds, earthquakes, and waves on man–made structures and materials. When engineers in 1980 needed to test the cables for the longest suspension bridge ever erected in this country, across the Mississippi River at Luling, Louisiana, the Phil M. Ferguson Structural Engineering Laboratory (PMFSEL) proved to be the only facility capable of conducting the vital stress evaluations on the mammoth lines. The Luling–Destrehan Bridge was the first designed to withstand the severe wind loads of Gulf Coast hurricanes and was selected by the venerable American Society of Civil Engineers as the outstanding achievement of 1984. Although a longer span exists in France, the Luling structure is wider and supports a much greater load.[31]

Currently directed by Jirsa, the PMFSEL is one of the largest facilities of its kind in the world, with research encompassing all areas of structural engineering. In addition to the massive three–dimensional testing platform, it also houses the slab laid by A. Anthony Toprac and Walter L. Moore in 1962 around which the Structures Fatigue Research Labratory was organized. The first such platform constructed at the BRC, it weighs almost a thousand tons and provides a virtually motionless base for a 300–ton capacity machine for vibration testing of concrete beams. David W. Fowler, who directs the Architectural Engineering Research Group, conducts research in structural mechanics along with Dan L. Wheat. Topics include evaluations of polymer aggregates for reinforced concrete. Polymers increase resistance to water and acid absorption to reduce weather damage and protect underlying steel supports. Ned H. Burns and Ramon L. Carrasquillo also conduct research in concrete aggregates along with Breen, while Joseph A. Yura continues studies of steel beams together with Karl H. Frank. C. Philip Johnson conducts structural analyses that complement the design research of Richard W. Furlong on composite structures incorporating steel and concrete as well as the studies of Jirsa and Richard E. Klingner on the response of structures to dynamic loads, such as earthquakes. Wheat also continues separate studies into the utility of wood.[32]

The initiative for aiding the building industry now lies with the Construction Industry Institute, founded in 1983 with Richard L. Tucker as director. Its creation marks an innovative step taken to counter the decline in productivity and the industry's share of the gross national product. A national forum, with over $1 million in research projects at sixteen state universities, it serves in Austin as a cooperative effort uniting construction company owners, contractors, and researchers in the College of Engineering to achieve the goal of increased cost–effectiveness. Fourteen task forces, with twenty–five funded research projects, address problems in project management, design, technology, data, contracts, cost and scheduling, and constructability. Nearly five hundred individuals and fifty companies have joined the project, which holds great promise for the rejuvenation of the faltering construction trades on the eve of a great period of growth and development for Texas as technological industry matures. Faculty associated with this effort include John D. Borcherding, James T. O'Connor, Calin M. Popescu, and David B. Ashley, selected as a Presidential Young Investigator in 1983.[33]

Highway research at The University was formally organized as the Center for Highway Research in 1965, directed initially by Clyde E. Lee. The

Geotechnical engineering faculty from The University of Texas aided in the reconstruction of the Sunshine Bridge across Tampa Bay in Florida after a ship carried away several spans in 1981. [College of Engineering, The University of Texas at Austin]

The high bay in the Phil M. Ferguson Structural Engineering Laboratory permits research in structures and materials that cannot be conducted anywhere else in the United States. [College of Engineering,
The University of Texas at Austin]

Council for Advanced Transportation Studies (CATS) began in 1972 as a campus-wide interdisciplinary research effort under the direction of Reese; within three years, through the leadership of new CATS Director Thomas W. Kennedy, The University ranked second only to MIT in grants received from the Department of Transportation. The two earlier highway research units were combined as the Center for Transportation Research (CTR) in 1981, under the direction of B. Franklin McCullough. The largest civil engineering research effort, the CTR throughout its history and that of its predecessors has performed studies primarily for the Texas Department of Highways, enabling the state to be a leader in the field of transportation research for over twenty years. Spinoffs include Fowler's work in the application of polymers in reinforced concrete and the research of Frank E. Masch in the flow of fluids through various types of culverts. Within the CTR, research continues by NAE member Robert Herman, C. Michael Walton, Randy B. Machemehl, Hani S. Mahmassani, and Alvin H. Meyer.[34]

Texas faces a crisis in the crumbling condition of its transport infrastructure; Kennedy, now director of the BER, said in 1985, "The southern and southeastern sections of the country, including Texas, are facing a virtual epidemic in the deterioration of their roads." The state is implementing a ten-year, $18.6 billion effort to restore its highway system to its former high standards for safety and service. Current studies in the CTR include the determination of guidelines in the use of high-strength concrete, experimentation with methods to repair slides in earth slopes, and establishment of procedures to identify and evaluate proposed toll roads in Texas. Kennedy is leading a research group that includes the former acting director of the CATS, William R. Hudson, in developing tests for paving material, with the eventual goal of reprocessing old pavement for reuse as a recycled surface.[35]

The most precious natural resource of Texas remains its water. Since the beginning, Taylor, Schoch, and others were involved in water supply and treatment problems. Organized research in water quality and management began in the Sanitary Engineering Research Laboratory (SERL) under Ernest W. Steel, Benjamin B. Ewing, and Earnest F. Gloyna in 1949. The hydraulics and hydrology program was developed at about the same time under the direction of Moore and Carl W. Morgan. The SERL became the Environmental Health Engineering Laboratory (EHEL) in 1953. Gloyna became director of the EHEL and also led the Center for Research in Water Resources (CRWR), founded in 1963 as the culmination of many years of water research by many University departments. The first comprehensive water and wastewater management studies on a river basin system led to the adoption of statewide water quality management plans. Other investigations led to the creation of the Gulf Coast Waste Disposal Authority. Too, the CRWR through Gloyna and his graduate students initiated interest in the United States in the storage of radioactive waste in underground salt formations.[36]

The CRWR worked together with the EHEL through the 1970s until they merged in 1984. Direction of the CRWR passed from Gloyna to Leo R. Beard in 1970, then Neal E. Armstrong in 1982, who in turn was succeeded by Ernest T. Smerdon after the consolidation. While supervising the CRWR, Armstrong also served as the last director of the EHEL, capping a tradition of leadership which passed from Gloyna to Joseph F. Malina, Jr., in 1970, then to

The Center for Research in Water Resources conducts studies for the enhancement of water quality and the conservation of Texas' most precious natural resource. [College of Engineering, The University of Texas at Austin]

Cullen M. Crain, left, and Harold W. Smith, right, of Electrical Engineering were pioneers in the development of the Electrical Engineering Research Laboratory. [College of Engineering, The University of Texas at Austin]

E. Gus Fruh in 1976 until his death in 1979. Under each director, researchers in both the CRWR and the EHEL have sought to increase the quality of the water supply in Texas. Grants from the National Institute of Health and other federal agencies facilitated development and brought national recognition for its graduate programs. Graduate students played a major role in devising innovative engineering solutions for the regulatory requirements established during the environmental movement of the 1970s.

Excellence in environmental research has been achieved through the efforts of an outstanding faculty. Gloyna, elected to the NAE in 1970, completed a twenty–year study on the transport and disposal of radioactive particles in 1973 for the Atomic Energy Commission. This research established the basis for evaluating the uptake and release of radioactivity as well as the ultimate storage of all levels of radioactive waste. The environmental team also included NAE member Gerard A. Rohlich, Davis L. Ford, and W. Wesley Eckenfelder. Led by Malina, Fruh, and Armstrong, this nationally recognized group developed new research in all aspects of water and wastewater treatment, publishing a series of critical reports for federal and state agencies. In 1985, NAE member Raymond C. Loehr, an expert in solid waste management, joined the faculty. Similarly, the hydraulics–hydrology group developed a broader research base. Beard, elected to the NAE in 1975, initiated methods for obtaining more reliable hydrologic data for small watersheds. Armstrong in his research contributed to a better understanding of Texas estuaries and the effect of urbanization on impounded water. Finally, the research effort in atmospheric pollution expanded through the efforts of Miksad, Joe O. Ledbetter, Norman K. Wagner, and E. Lothar Koschmeider.[37]

As Texas is now consuming its groundwater faster than it can be replenished, the CRWR under Smerdon, elected to the NAE in 1985, redoubled its efforts to improve methods for conservation as well as protection from hazardous pollutants. Research in the latter area is spearheaded by Edward R. Holley, whose interest is in experimental hydraulics, and by Randall J. Charbeneau, a noted authority on groundwater. Conservation has taken many forms due to the impact of initiatives from federal and state government. Smerdon is studying methods to improve the design of surge–flow irrigation, a more economical technique for watering crops. Larry W. Mays and David R. Maidment have begun development of computer models to more efficiently manage the seven dams and reservoirs of the Lower Colorado River Authority. Maidment has also devised a computerized forecasting tool that will aid cities to foresee periods when water consumption should be restricted. Other noted faculty include Howard M. Liljestrand and Desmond F. Lawler, who received a Presidential Young Investigator Award in 1984. During the last two decades, the CRWR has printed a continuing series of research reports and books on water quality and conservation that have found their way into the major technical libraries of the world.[38]

The Electrical Engineering Research Laboratory (EERL) became the first unit established at the BRC in 1946. Founded in 1945 by Archie W. Straiton, Edwin W. Hamlin, and Frederick E. Brooks of Electrical Engineering, the EERL expanded electronic propagation research begun by Ernest M. Siegel, a former professor at the Technical University in Prague, with Hamlin and Granberry in 1940 at The University of Texas. Hamlin departed in 1947, and Brooks, an alumnus of the College, resigned in 1956 to become director of research for Collins Radio Company, a leading Dallas manufacturer of electronics for aircraft. Straiton continued the development of a diverse research effort incorporating many elements of radio wave propagation. In 1965 the EERL reorganized into four groups: Millimeter Wave Sciences under Charles W. Tolbert, replaced by Straiton in 1967; Antennas and Propagation, directed by Alfred H. LaGrone; Geomagnetics, led by Harold W. Smith; and Atmospheric Science, which became an independent unit in 1966, directed by Kenneth H. Jehn.[39]

Research in meteorology had originated under Jehn as an important adjunct of the EERL shortly after its creation. The invention of an atmospheric refractometer by Cullen M. Crain to measure rapid change in atmospheric conditions, the first of its kind ever produced, brought widespread recognition. The device was adopted for use by the U.S. Navy and Air Force, which funded the project, and facilitated several major studies by the EERL of static and dynamic error in tracking and guidance equipment, which is caused by inhomogeneity in the atmosphere. Jehn and Straiton hosted an international conference on radio meteorology attended by several hundred representatives from a number of the most prestigious professional organizations in 1953, earning further praise.[40]

Straiton and Jehn later cooperated with the Air Force Cambridge Research Laboratories to conduct basic research into atmospheric turbulence, especially dangerous phenomena such as wind shears, during the 1960s. Following the separation of the Atmospheric Science Research Laboratory (ASRL) from the EERL in 1966, Jehn served as director of the ASRL until its demise in 1971. Research included studies of phenomena in the upper stratosphere under sponsorship of the Department of the Army, White Sands Missile Range; sea breeze investigation along the Texas upper coast with funds from the NSF, the National Center for Atmospheric Research (NCAR), and several private firms; a cloud census of selected West Texas stations for the Texas Water Development Board; a study of the information content of meteorological aircraft data completed for NCAR; and an experimental study on convective motions in fluids begun under NSF sponsorship.[41] Atmospheric studies since 1971 have been conducted by individual research centers as they related to the particular problems at hand.

Researchers in Millimeter Wave Sciences continued the studies of microwave communications initiated in 1945. Straiton and Tolbert built a radio telescope that was used in part to measure the radiation properties of the lunar surface. In conjunction with scientists in Malvern, England, in 1959, they received the first transmissions of microwaves from Europe by reflection from the moon's surface. Bob M. Fannin worked with Straiton to study the effect of atmospheric stratification on satellite communications systems in a joint project with the Goddard Space Flight Center. A radio telescope with a precise parabolic dish was transported to the Millimeter Wave Observatory (MWO) on Mount Locke near the McDonald Observatory in 1967 for use in astronomical observation. The MWO, now under Frank Bash, is administered in cooperation with the Department of Astronomy. Funded for about a half million dollars annually by the NSF, it is one of a few radio telescopes in the world capable of studying radiation from the clouds of molecular gas found among the stars of the Milky

Way. Studies of carbon monoxide, formaldehyde, and other molecules found in these clouds provide new insight into the chemistry of interstellar matter, the process of star formation, and the spiral structure of the galaxy. At the BRC, Wolfhard Vogel conducts research into the propagation of long–wavelength radiation under contract with the Jet Propulsion Laboratory in California in support of a system that will provide direct phone service by geosynchronous satellite to mobile telephones.[42]

The Antennae and Propagation Research Group conducted studies for the NSF on the effects of weather and clear–air turbulence on radio transmission and on radar anomalies and refraction. They also produced optical jamming techniques for radar with funds from the Department of the Army. Instrument landing devices for aircraft using high–frequency microwaves instead of unreliable ground–reflected waves for guidance, developed under LaGrone's supervision, greatly enhanced air–travel safety. Electromagnetic waves were used as remote sensors for weather, clear atmospheric phenomena, atmospheric pollution, migration of birds, vegetation, soil conditions, and mineral surveys. The Physical Electronics Group has now supplanted Antennae and Propagation, focusing its basic research on microwave, millimeter wave, and submillimeter wave systems. Theoretical and experimental studies are conducted in millimeter wave integrated circuits, quasi–optical devices, guided–wave structures, planar antennae, and millimeter wave imaging under contract for various private firms and federal agencies, including the Army Research Office and the Office of Naval Research. Faculty involved in this research include John R. Cogdell and John H. Davis.[43]

Geomagnetics researchers engaged in the measurement and analysis of ultralow–frequency electric and magnetic field variations resulting from the interaction of the solar wind with the earth's magnetic field. Applications included the detection of nuclear detonations high in the atmosphere or submarines deep below the suface of the ocean, exact determination of subsurface geologic formations and evaluation of subsurface communication systems, and extensive studies of the effects of solar disturbances on global communications. Straiton, who was elected to the NAE in 1976, retired in 1973 as director of the EERL and was succeeded by Smith, leader of the research effort in geomagnetics. Smith continued to work closely with Francis X. Bostick to pioneer electrical methods of probing the earth's interior, under the sponsorship of major petroleum companies, enhancing the search for hydrocarbon, geothermal, and mineral resources. The group recently formulated a new technique for mapping the electrical conductivity of subsurface structures more accurately than ever before.[44]

Research in the EERL, currently directed by Tatsuo Itoh, is now complemented by a host of other activities sponsored primarily by the Department of Defense Joint Services Electronics Program (JSEP). JSEP was established at The University of Texas in 1964, where it was initially administered within the Laboratories for Electronics and Related Science Research, renamed the Electronics Research Center (ERC) in 1968, with Arwin A. Dougal and Alfred H. LaGrone serving as director and associate director respectively. This program resulted from a contract on quantum electronics from the Air Force Office of Strategic Research, for which Dougal had served as the principle investigator.

Although research in the fields of microelectronics and communications expanded greatly with JSEP support, development continued in other areas as well. Herbert H. Woodson, William C. Duesterhoeft, Martin L. Baughman, and W. Mack Grady conduct research in power generation; Baxter F. Womack in cybernetics; Elmer L. Hixson in acoustics; Robert H. Flake in digital process control; and M. Ray Mercer, who won a Presidential Young Investigator Award in 1985, in computer–aided design.[45]

The JSEP operation at The University has been a dynamic one in that both the faculty involved and the focus of the research have continually evolved over the years. The initial program had work units dealing with biomedical electronics; information sciences; physical, quantum, and plasma electronics; and space, earth, and atmospheric radio sciences. During the early years of JSEP, some biomedical engineering activities were included, with the most significant studies focusing on the thermal response of tissue to laser irradiation. Dougal continued as director from 1964 to 1967, whereupon he accepted an assignment at the Pentagon as an Assistant Director of Defense Research and Engi-

A student readies the ion implanter, a unique research device operated by the Microelectronics Research Center. [College of Engineering, The University of Texas at Austin]

neering. Clarence L. Coates, a former chairman of Electrical Engineering, served as director from 1967 to 1971, when Dougal again resumed direction. In 1977, Edward J. Powers, Jr., became the director, a position he still holds. More than sixty faculty members have participated in the program, the vast majority from Electrical Engineering and Physics. For many of them, JSEP provided seminal support for programs that were ultimately spun off and supported by the Department of Defense or other federal agencies. JSEP provided over $600,000 in 1986 to The University, one of twelve schools in the country participating in this select program.[46]

Much of the solid–state research during the seventies focused on investigating the properties and applications of transition metal–oxide thin films fabricated by chemical vapor deposition. William H. Hartwig and K. J. Sladek conducted extensive research to define the basic process parameters for the deposition of titanium oxide thin films, to investigate and model the reaction mechanisms for chemical vapor deposition, to model the formation and structure of the amorphous oxides, and to develop electronic devices exploiting their unique characteristics.[47]

In 1978, Michael F. Becker and Rodger M. Walser reported their results from the first picosecond time–resolved phase transition in the solid state. Their work on processing and characterizing vanadium oxide was subsequently utilized by many Department of Defense contractors who employed these thin films for spacecraft thermal control and nuclear flash detection. Becker and Walser subsequently collaborated on studies of short–pulse laser damage in solids, especially semiconductors. They discovered the multiple–pulse damage accumulation effect and developed widely used methods for its systematic characterization. These methods are currently used to specify the expected lifetime of optical components in high–power short–pulse laser applications. In 1975, Robert W. Bené and Walser became interested in researching the interface reactions that occur at transition metal–silicide interfaces and lead to the formation of silicides. Their model of first–compound formation in interface reactions successfully predicts the first phase formed in all transition metal, silicon, and germanium diffusion couples and was the first compound selection rule developed for understanding phases selected by kinetics rather than equilibrium thermodynamics.[48]

The ERC now concentrates on four areas: solid–state electronics, as discussed above; quantum electronics; information electronics; and electromagnetics. Early work in quantum electronics included research on laser–induced breakdown of super–high–pressure gases and the first holograms of optically polarizable material through development of laser microholography by Dougal as well as studies in laser scattering from rough surfaces by Powers, to cite a few examples. Recent efforts focused on nonlinear optics, dynamical instabilities in optical systems, and nonlinear Raman scattering from molecular ions. Faculty involved in related topics include A. Bruce Buckman and Gary L. Wise.[49]

Researchers in information electronics have addressed a variety of problems in nonlinear estimation, digital signal and image processing, automata, optimal adaptive control, recognition of patterns, quasi–perfect codes, parallel–processing architecture, and natural languages. Eighteen previously unknown quasi–perfect double error–correcting codes, vital in defense communication and data retrieval, were discovered by Terry J. Wagner. Stephen I. Marcus studied the problem of deriving information about a system from noisy measurements by nonlinear state estimation, uncovering new finite dimensional recursive estimators for certain classes of problems.[50]

Organized research in electromagnetics research began in 1964 under Smith and Bostick, who have made important contributions in extremely low–frequency geomagnetics. Their results have been used to measure geomagnetic peturbations caused by solar wind interactions with the magnetosphere, to detect ship movement through measurement of man–made peturbations, and to characterize subsurface terrestial resistivities. Since 1979, Tatsuo Itoh, the present director of the EERL, has studied wave interaction with devices and circuits for application in millimeter–wave integrated circuits. Research by Dean P. Neikirk, who received a Presidential Young Investigator Award in 1985, complements this effort.[51]

The College of Engineering created the Microelectronics Research Center, an interdisciplinary program, in 1984 to enhance studies in microelectronics on campus, particularly in materials, device design, and fabrication. Under Director Ben G. Streetman, work focuses on developing the semiconductor materials and devices for the next generation of computer and communication systems. Topics include designing multilayer compound semiconductor structures, devising advanced fabrication methods for integrated structures, constructing optoelectronic devices, and determining the basic properties of semiconductor materials. Optoelectronics, one of the most innovative fields, studies the utility of semiconductor technology in solving problems for optical communications, such as providing sources and detectors for light fiber transmission of telephone transmissions. The future of electronics lies in further reduction of device dimensions, with resulting physical phenomena not found in larger models. Plans are to double the size of the program within the next few years, paralleling the anticipated growth in high–technology industry in Texas. This will require the addition of new faculty to supplement the work already underway by Charles H. Roth, Jr., and others.[52]

The Laboratory for Image and Signal Analysis, directed by J. K. Aggarwal, was reorganized in 1985 as the Computer and Vision Research Center to reflect its expanded research activities. The Center is devoted to the development of computational models and techniques for the analysis of one– and two–dimensional signals for application in the fields of bioengineering, image analysis, signal processing, and methods of integrating computer systems for high–performance parallel processing. As part of the BER, the Center is composed of faculty drawn from the Departments of Electrical and Computer Engineering, Computer Sciences, and Mechanical Engineering. Current research encompasses diverse fields: development of theoretical models for the construction of three–dimensional descriptions of objects from two–dimensional views and application of these to object recognition; derivation of techniques for improved analysis of thermal images of complex scenes, accompanied by the interpretation of these complex scenes through the integration of input from thermal and other

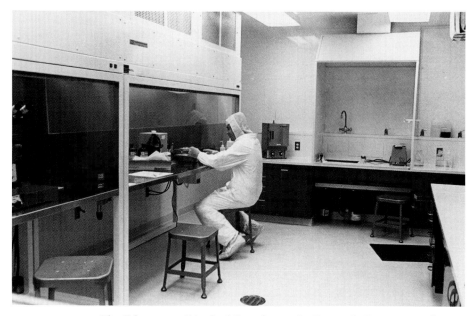

The "clean room" in the Microelectronics Research Center provides a proper environment for the testing and assembly of delicate micro-electronic devices. [College of Engineering, The University of Texas at Austin]

The Texas Reconfigurable Architecture Computer is a prototype for a fifth-generation supercomputer that will rely on high-speed communications to coordinate computations by as many as one hundred computers at once. [College of Engineering, The University of Texas at Austin]

This pit at the Center for Electromechanics is the world's largest source of pulsed electrical power: each one of the six homopolar generators can produce a pulse of ten million joules of electricity. [College of Engineering, The University of Texas at Austin]

Research in the Center for Materials Science and Engineering will lead to improved communication systems and protective packaging for microelectronic devices in the near future. [College of Engineering, The University of Texas at Austin]

sensors; and evaluation of a broad range of biomedical images relating to diagnostic assessment of diabetic retinopathy and burn wounds, as well as to the preservation of tissues through freezing.[53]

Gerald J. Lipovski is directing the design and construction of the Texas Reconfigurable Architecture Computer (TRAC), certainly the most ambitious program in computer architecture conducted at The University. TRAC is a prototype for a fifth–generation supercomputer which has been put in operation. Great advances have been made in semiconductor technology and magnetic physics, but future progress will be through application of the concept of parallel computing: two or more computers performing separate functions in a single process simultaneously. The great problem lies in communication and synchronization between the individual units, conceivably hundreds at a time, and revision of standard computer algorithms. The banyan, a dynamically reconfigurable interconnection switch that should foster synergism, is the key. If it works properly, the capacity of the system will be greater than the sum of its parts. The banyan has demonstrated the value of synergism, the first objective, but much more needs to be done in communications. The future depends on the development of optical connections for use in computer infrastructure in place of cumbersome pins and wires. Faculty associated with the TRAC program in addition to their other projects include NAE members Harvey G. Cragon, Willis A. Adcock, and Irwin W. Sandberg, as well as Miroslaw Malek and Chuan–Lin Wu, like Cragon a specialist in very large scale integrated devices.[54]

Woodson, elected to the NAE in 1975, focused on the production of electricity and heat from fusion reaction as a solution for long term energy needs. Engineers continue to work with The University of Texas Fusion Research Center (FRC) established in 1966. The FRC was supported initially by the Texas Atomic Energy Research Foundation, but a $20 million grant from the Department of Energy expedited the construction of the Texas Experimental Torus, the second TOKAMAK at The University, which brought greater national recognition to its work. The second major fusion research unit is the Institute for Fusion Studies (IFS), now one of the largest theoretical fusion research centers in the United States. Woodson directs the Center for Fusion Engineering, created in 1982 to provide the practical engineering component that complements the experimental thrust of the FRC and the theoretical activities of the IFS. Projects include development of a heavy ion beam probe to measure plasma space potential in the central cell of the TARA mirror fusion experiment at MIT; studies of the neutron multiplication properties of beryllium for use in fusion blanket designs; timely completion of a detailed computer model of the interaction between a fusion plasma and the wall of a TOKAMAK during severe plasma disruption; and analysis of the performance of a monolithic toroidal field coil for a TOKAMAK. The research led by Woodson is not expected to yield commercial benefits before the middle of the next century.[55]

The original research organization for mechanical engineering has changed its name and focus almost as often as it has gotten a new director. Venton L. Doughtie of Mechanical Engineering directed the Engines Test Laboratory at its creation in 1949. Rechristened the Engines Research Laboratory in 1951, it operated under the direction of Short from 1952 to 1959, except in 1953 when Myron L. Begeman served as the coordinator of activities. Studies were conducted in two areas: combustion of gases under steady flow conditions at pressures up to ninety pounds per square inch, and heating of sea water up to 330 degrees Fahrenheit, a project which received funding from the Texas Gulf Sulphur Company as part of its systematic effort to find methods to substitute salt water for fresh water in offshore sulphur mining.[56]

Kenneth C. Rathbun took command in 1959, changing both the name and emphasis to the Mechanical Engineering Propulsion Laboratory. After Rathbun's death in 1961, J. Parker Lamb, Jr., continued in this new direction. Wayne E. Long conducted studies on friction losses in high–velocity air–conditioning ducts, and the attendant noise generation of such systems, for various industrial sponsors and technical societies. Long's partner, John W. Heyt, became director in 1970 and elected to reorient the organization as the Mechanical Engineering Systems Laboratory; he and Long developed applications for high–velocity air flows in ducting for heating and air–conditioning systems in all varieties of buildings.[57]

The Mechanical Engineering Systems Laboratory altered its focus most drastically in its last decade. After a year under William F. Oberkampf, E. Linn Draper assumed direction in 1973, changing the title initially to the Mechanical Engineering Thermal Systems Laboratory, then to the Nuclear Radiation Laboratory (NRL) as research interests shifted. In conjunction with fusion research projects, Draper began investigations of fusion–reactor blanket materials and served as coordinator of nuclear studies for the CES, overseeing research in operational safety, atomic waste disposal, uranium mining, national policy analysis, and nuclear economics. Draper left The University for Gulf Coast Utilities, becoming the president of that organization by 1986.[58] The NRL no longer exists, but its research responsibilities have been assumed by faculty in other units within the BER.

The Center for Electromechanics (CEM), established in 1974 by H. Grady Rylander, Jr., and Herbert H. Woodson, is now directed by William F. Weldon. It represents a continuation of a traditional relationship in an increasingly technological world. The CEM primarily researches practical development and application of pulsed electrical power technology, recalling the turn of the century when the overriding concern of mechanical engineers was steam turbines for generating electricity. Most of the support for the CEM comes from sponsors interested in industrial and defense applications, a shift from the recent past when funds came mainly from sources interested in energy–related projects. Researchers have produced three devices important in fusion and alternative power studies: a homopolar generator, capable of discharging ten million joules of electric power in a pulse of less than a second, a compact six–megajoule version that weighs only 3,400 pounds and can be carried in a small vehicle, and the versatile compensated pulsed alternator or compulsator, the first fundamentally new rotating electrical machine to be invented in the twentieth century according to the U.S. Patent Office.[59]

The compulsator, which has won several prestigious awards for its innovative design, delivers multiple rather than single pulses of electric energy, providing a source of intense power for fusion devices such as the TOKAMAK. The homopolar generators deliver single instantaneous bursts of intense heat, useful for welding, sintering, and billet heating more rapidly than

Robotics has become one of the most rapidly expanding fields for engineering research in the College of Engineering. [College of Engineering, The University of Texas at Austin]

ever before. The compulsator is the heart of an entirely different enterprise: the Texas Railgun, a device capable of accelerating solid projectiles to velocities more than forty times greater than a bullet from a conventional gun. Applications being considered include space launches, well drilling, and alloy bonding. The most ambitious project is integration of the railgun into a satellite system as a weapon to intercept missiles in flight. Because it accelerates pellets so fast that they melt in the atmosphere, there would be no danger of an errant shot harming a neutral or friendly target on the Earth's surface. This system is one of those proposed for use by the Strategic Defense Initiative program, which provides much of the funding for continued research and development.[60]

Dale E. Klein from Mechanical Engineering directs the Nuclear Engineering Teaching Laboratory (NETL), conducting research in heat transfer and methods of reprocessing nuclear fuel for reuse instead of disposal as radioactive waste. The NETL houses the Mark I TRIGA thermal fission reactor originally licensed by the AEC to operate at 10 kw in 1963, then upgraded to a steady–state power level of 250 kw and pulsed power of 250 mw. Along with it in Taylor Hall are a subcritical assembly, a 2000 curie Cobalt–60 irradiator, and the electronic components used in specialized radiation detection and counting systems. A high–purity germanium detector with a microcomputer data acquisition and evaluation system facilitates measurements for neutron activation analysis techniques. A 14 MeV Texas Nuclear neutron generator in the basement of the Engineering Science Building permits examination of 14 MeV neutrons with various materials. Such equipment allows graduate students to study the

Pleasant Bayou Number One, a geopressured-geothermal test well in Brazoria County, Texas, constructed under the supervision of Myron H. Dorfman of Petroleum Engineering, was one of the most sophisticated onshore drilling rigs in the world when it was dedicated in 1978. [College of Engineering, The University of Texas at Austin]

operation of a fission reactor, presently the only device used for nuclear power generation, through its full cycle, from startup to shutdown, but Klein's current research is directed toward understanding neutrons in the fusion process, the method by which researchers hope electricity will be produced in the future. Billy V. Koen, in nuclear safety and reliability, and Nolan E. Hertel, in radiation shielding and protection, work with Klein in the NETL. A new research facility at the BRC, constructed in 1986, will provide both a new home for the TRIGA and more room for fusion research.[61]

Investigations by Gary C. Vliet and John R. Howell of Mechanical Engineering into economical solar heating and cooling systems for commercial and residential use complement nuclear research by providing a more immediate energy alternative. Vliet and Howell are also gathering data on wind and sunlight for the installation of a unique solar electrical plant in Austin and are evaluating sites and tracking systems for the production apparatus itself. When finished, it will be one of only nine photovoltaic plants in existence with a capacity of 300 kw, the largest in Texas and the first ever built without federal subsidy. Other researchers in the Conservation and Solar Energy Program sponsored by the Center for Energy Studies, including Jerold W. Jones, Ronald L. Panton, Ronald D. Matthews, Glenn Y. Masada, and Phillip S. Schmidt, are helping the city reduce energy costs through conservation and alternative methods of electric water heating such as passive solar units, the use of a heat pump to deliver warmth from the surrounding air, and a heat–recovery system which reclaims the waste heat from warm gases leaving the compressor of an air conditioner or heat pump. One design employs both evaporative and compressed vapor technology, updating a method explored by Woolrich as an alternative for modern application. Research by Vliet and Howell also focuses on radiation heat transfer for the CFE, expediting new studies in nuclear power generation.[62]

Researchers in the Center for Materials Science and Engineering (CMSE), organized in 1982 under Harris L. Marcus of Mechanical Engineering, contribute to electronics manufacture through study of catalysis; solid state transport theories and experiments; surface adsorption and chemical reactions; friction, wear, and corrosion; thin-film semiconductor materials; impurity effects in ceramics, metals, and semiconductors; and the rheological and engineering properties of polymers. The primary task, electronic packaging, involves two often contradictory goals: communication by the device with the outside world, and protection of delicate microelectronic circuitry from environmental impacts. Reductions in the size of electronic devices have spawned new problems in high packing density. Other efforts currently focus on reducing interface failure by eliminating mechanical instability between composite materials. Studies on the connection of a chip with the other system elements involve research in materials for bonds and wires, and even incorporate the light fibers being developed in the ERC. The CMSE also sponsors a project to devise better sealed casings from metal, ceramic, or polymers to protect the chip and systems from the elements. Faculty involved in the CMSE include Zwy Eliezer, Kurt M. Marshek, Kenneth M. Ralls, John P. Stark and David L. Bourell. Through their research, the CMSE will provide an environment for the next generation of computers that will not only protect them from hostile surroundings, but also enhance their ability to solve the problems of the future. This research should develop rapidly with the addition of four endowed chair appointments; the first, John B. Goodenough, a member of the NAE who specializes in ceramic materials, came to the College from Oxford University in 1986.[63]

The Department of Mechanical Engineering sponsors a number of research efforts that take place outside of the formal research centers. An active project is underway in manufacturing systems and processes; associated faculty include Eliezer, Charles S. Beightler, Paul A. Jensen, William G. Lesso and J. Wesley Barnes. In a related field, Delbert Tesar has initiated development of an innovative research program in robotics. Alfred E. Traver and Joseph J. Beaman, who received a Presidential Young Investigator Award in 1983, focus on dynamic systems. Computer–aided design studies are conducted by Davor Juricic, Margaret R. Baker, Ronald E. Barr, and Walter S. Reed. Additional topics include mechanical design analysis by Kurt M. Marshek and thermosciences by H. Alan Walls. The election of three more faculty as Presidential Young Investigators—Ilene Busch–Vishniac, Theodore L. Bergman, and Mark F. Hamilton—foreshadows the development to be made in the immediate future in mechanical engineering research.[64]

Texas engineering research has a continued focus on energy, the state's marketable natural resource. Many of the initial studies by the College at the BRC centered on the petroleum industry; of seventeen units in 1951, five years after its purchase, six were conducting investigations for the production or use of oil and natural gas. This work led in part to the creation of the Texas Petroleum Research Committee (TPRC). The TPRC was established through a joint resolution of chairman Ernest O. Thompson of the Texas Railroad Commission and the regents of The University of Texas and Texas A&M. George H. Fancher of the College in Austin became the first director in 1950 and appointed an associate director at each institution to initiate research by graduate students, who composed a majority of the staff. The emphasis was on enhanced secondary recovery from Texas fields. In 1954, the TPRC published the first comprehensive reconnaisance survey of the oil resources in the state. Most of the senior petroleum engineering faculty at The University have served as associate director of research for the TPRC; in 1986 the position was held by Irwin H. Silberberg.[65]

Although their share of the state's economic base is declining, Texas petroleum and natural gas producers still contributed the largest share among the domestic suppliers of energy in the United States in 1986. The CES is participating in the joint effort by the Gas Research Institute (GRI) and the Department of Energy (DOE) to facilitate recovery from played–out gas wells. Myron H. Dorfman directed a project with GRI and DOE sponsorship to explore sources of geothermal or geopressure energy along the Texas and Louisiana coast. While deep wells did not produce brine of the high temperature necessary for producing electrical power and did not recover fluids with enough dissolved methane to make it practical for commercial separation processes, the DOE and the GRI extended their support. Dorfman shifted the focus to the GRI's efforts in coproduction: pumping brine from watered–out wells to allow further recovery of natural gas. Estimates are that an additional fifty trillion cubic feet of natural gas may be recovered in this way. Faculty involved in this continuing effort include Kami Sepehrnoori and Ekwere J. Peters.[66]

Technician Charles Stephenson of the Center for Earth Sciences and Engineering prepares to test the characteristics of a rock sample. [College of Engineering, The University of Texas at Austin]

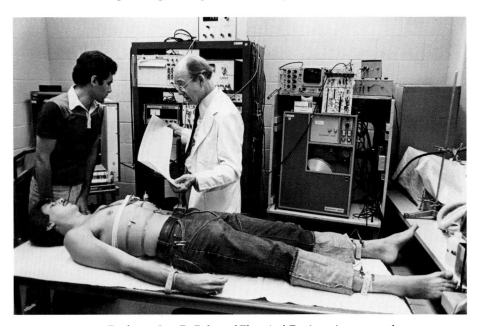

Professor Lee R. Baker of Electrical Engineering currently serves as the director of the biomedical engineering research program, an interdisciplinary effort which brings together engineering faculty with medical personnel. [College of Engineering, The University of Texas at Austin]

The Center for Enhanced Oil and Gas Recovery Research (CEOGRR), established by Gary A. Pope in 1982 and currently directed by Larry W. Lake, promotes interdisciplinary research projects to develop better technology for enhanced oil and gas recovery from known deposits. Studies by the faculty involved in the CEOGRR, including NAE members Robert S. Schechter and Claude R. Hocott, Augusto L. Podio, and Ben H. Caudle, focus on modeling improved reservoirs and development of tertiary recovery techniques to bring up oil from fields abandoned when existing methods proved unprofitable. Innovative methods for enhancing oil recovery include flooding with resilient materials such as polymers.[67]

The Center for Earth Sciences and Engineering (CESE), founded by Kenneth E. Gray in 1968, continued under his direction to take part in studies of the properties and behavior of rock formations under subsurface conditions. These studies are readily applicable in hydropressured and geopressured reservoir evaluation, drilling of deep wells, well logging, hole deviation, well bore stability, lost circulation, hydraulic fracturing, underground gasification of lignite and coal, and many additional industrial and academic applications. Studies by the CESE focusing on Texas lignite and overburden contributed to the research of Edgar and others in Chemical Engineering in methods to facilitate gasification for recovery and combustion of the soft mineral as a fuel.[68]

The Department of Petroleum Engineering has branched out into the study of the recovery of many other mineral resources in Texas, but its primary focus remains the production of petroleum and natural gas. In 1985, researchers initiated the Stimulation, Logging, and Formation Damage Research Program to aid in the development of improved methods for extracting oil and gas from reservoirs based on chemical and physical processes applied in the region surrounding a well. The program, directed by Assistant Professor A. Daniel Hill, is supported entirely by industry. In its first year of operation, twenty–two companies participated. Projects now being pursued include research in hydraulic and acid fracturing, origins and prevention of formation damage, emulsion blocking, wettability, production logging, matrix acidizing, geochemical modeling, and conformance profile treatments. In January 1986, the Drilling and Completion Fluids Research Program was formed to study the major problems associated with drilling fluids. This program is also funded by industry and is currently researching topics in oil muds, fluid rheology, mud filtration, and shale stability. Research facilities for petrophysics have been augmented with the development of specialized core analysis laboratories that place the Department at the forefront of petrophysics studies. It is hoped that these efforts will produce technology that will permit more economical exploration and subsequently increase drilling activity in Texas.[69]

Biomedical engineering research has become an interdisciplinary effort drawing on the talents of every department in the College. Robert M. Popovich from the Department of Chemical Engineering and Jack Moncrief, an Austin physician, developed a method for Continuous Ambulatory Peritoneal Dialysis, which uses a polymer membrane to filter blood. The technique, which is less than half as expensive as hemodialysis and has fewer debilitating side effects, is now used around the world. In Electrical Engineering, Ashley J. Welch with JSEP funding conducted lengthy studies of the thermal effect of laser irradiation on human tissue. Welch pioneered methods to repair stomach–wall lesions and halt retinal deterioration, which leads to glaucoma, with laser light. H. Grady Rylander III, an alumnus and part–time faculty member of the same department, won acclaim for his application of lasers in eye surgery. Thomas M. Runge of Electrical Engineering and his students constructed five electronic artificial hearts and conducted two successful trials of the devices at The University of Texas Medical Center in San Antonio.[70]

Researchers from departments other than Chemical Engineering and Electrical and Computer Engineering, which have traditionally dominated biomedical studies, also made important contributions. In Mechanical Engineering, Kenneth R. Diller researched methods for freezing, storing, and reviving human organs for transplant. George B. Thurston invented an instrument for monitoring the mechanical properties of blood during clotting that facilitated research on visco–elasticity, a previously unknown property of blood discovered at The University in 1970. Ripperger from Engineering Mechanics devised a thermocouple finer than a human hair that is capable of monitoring the temperature of a single human cell. A computer model devised by Royal E. Collins of Petroleum Engineering to predict the effect of acceleration on the circulatory system can help prevent the sometimes fatal side effects of blood loss to the brain and is being adapted to detect defects that impair the operation of the cardiovascular system. Under the direction of Lee R. Baker of Electrical and Computer Engineering, the members of the Biomedical Engineering Research Group continue their efforts to improve the quality of human life.[71]

Two University–directed centers conduct engineering research. The first government–sponsored research unit established at The University of Texas was the Applied Research Laboratory, which began as the War Research Laboratory (WRL) on campus in 1942 with Lucien J. B. Lacoste from the Department of Physics as its first director. The WRL conducted important studies on aerial gunnery, developing the Texas Tester, which was widely used to evaluate gunsights on the B–29 and other aircraft fire–control devices. It also initiated important studies of antimissile systems. In 1946, when it moved to the BRC, the WRL became the Military Physics Research Laboratory (MPRL). There it became one of the first University organizations to make extensive use of digital computers when it acquired three IBM systems. Later, the MPRL played an important role in the establishment of the Campus Computation Center.[72]

The MPRL merged with the Defense Research Laboratory (DRL) in 1964. The DRL had been established in 1945 to conduct research for the U.S. Navy on surface–to–air missiles, focusing on radar homing systems, fuels, and aerodynamics. Milton J. Thompson, of the Department of Aeronautical Engineering, directed research in the latter field until his retirement in 1971. Studies in the field of guidance technology began with the establishment of the Radar Division by C. Paul Boner of the Department of Physics in 1952, and has since branched out to include satellite navigation systems, high–resolution radar and radar countermeasures, and very–low–frequency propagation. Boner also initiated research in underwater acoustics which later focused on nonlinear acoustics, sonar systems, and submarine and torpedo masking and detection. The organization was renamed the Applied Research Laboratory (ARL) in 1968, but continued to perform classified research and development under Director

Professor Herbert H. Woodson of Electrical Engineering has served as director of the Center for Energy Studies since its organization in 1972. [College of Engineering, The University of Texas at Austin]

Chester M. McKinney of the Department of Physics, principally for the Department of Defense.[73]

The ARL, now directed by Loyd D. Hampton, remains one of the most important research organizations at the BRC. It is the only laboratory within The University of Texas System conducting classified research, on which it expended nearly $26 million in 1984–1985, primarily for the Department of the Navy. Without such access, research in Texas could not remain at the cutting edge of technology. Many of the projects conducted with government funds are far too expensive and time–consuming to be supported by private industry. At the same time, the knowledge gained has both military and civilian applications; indeed, the dividing line is often indistinguishable.[74]

The faculty and students from Electrical Engineering constitute the second largest contingent, behind Physics, on the staff of the ARL, but members from all engineering fields are present. More engineers than students from any other discipline earn advance degrees through the ARL, and they have led the way in founding new commercial ventures in the private sector using the technology developed in the ARL and its predecessors. Frank W. McBee, for example, who earned his bachelor and master of science degrees in mechanical engineering from The University and joined the faculty, founded Tracor, Inc., with several co–workers from the DRL in 1962 and developed it into a mainstay of the Texas electronics industry. Tracor, Inc., was the only Austin–based Fortune 500 company in 1986. McBee also served as chairman of the Texas Aerospace and National Defense Technology Development Council, and was recognized as a Distinguished Graduate by the College of Engineering of The University of Texas in 1978.[75]

Woodson of Electrical and Computer Engineering directs the Center for Energy Studies (CES), founded as a University research unit independent of the BER in 1972 to facilitate the exploration of alternative energy sources by faculty in almost every discipline represented on campus. The CES coordinates the research efforts in enhanced oil recovery and geothermal power by members of the Department of Petroleum Engineering, solar and electromechanical energy by faculty from Mechanical Engineering, and more reliable methods for generating electric power with coal and fissionable materials by chemical and electrical engineers. The CES received a large proportion of its funding during its initial period of development from the Engineering Foundation, indicating its active interest in alternative energy sources to be found in Texas. This concern for energy continued through the oil boom in the United States in the latter half of the 1970s, and has now accelerated noticeably with the decline of new oil exploration in West Texas since 1982.[76]

Engineering research would be of little use if new knowledge were not disseminated in a timely fashion to the business community for further development. The Center for Technology Development and Transfer (CTDT) was created by the College in 1985 to promote the expansion of technology in Texas. Its activities facilitate commercial application of ongoing research within the College and centers conducting engineering–related studies. New materials, devices, techniques, and theoretical advances are first assessed for technical feasibility and marketability, then targeted for development. The CTDT also provides legal and financial guidance. John J. Locy served as acting director until the appointment of Stephen A. Szygenda as director in 1986, and remains as associate director of the facility.[77]

Research conducted by the College of Engineering has been crucial for maintaining a high level of academic excellence. As a direct result, engineering graduates from The University have given much to aid in the development of both the state and the nation. Texas changed dramatically during the past century. Perhaps the most significant evolution was the shift from an economy dominated by agriculture, timber, and oil to a diverse economic base grounded in new enterprises such as the electronics industry. Engineering research at The University initially developed in response to the needs of the state. With the accelerated pace of technological development, however, the College assumed a leadership role. The key factor remained teamwork between faculty and students, as graduate students took an active role in solving the engineering problems of today, and between the College and those supporters of technological enterprise who recognized the importance of academic centers of excellence in education and research. Through both its graduates and its research, the College has maintained the high standards expected of a "university of the first class."

Joe Moore, Harry Fritz, and Glenn Vaughn pose with the original Alec, which they rescued from his law student captors at a farm near Pflugerville, Texas. [Barker Texas History Center, The University of Texas at Austin]

# THE CHILDREN OF ALEC:

*Student Life and Tradition in the College of Engineering*

The traditions of the College of Engineering anchor a strong bond of loyalty between students, faculty, alumni, and the College. Dean Taylor actively fostered many rough-and-tumble customs in order to create school spirit within the engineering program, and carefully extended that into an unbreakable tie of devotion to The University. Dean Woolrich retained the emphasis on forging a separate identity for the engineers, but also began efforts to provide academic services through student organizations for both the College of Engineering and the campus at large. This ideal continued to develop under his successors until institutionalized by Dean Gloyna. Today the many engineering student societies remain proudly aware of their traditions, but also play an active role in the development of a more professional College in the quest for excellence.

Dean Taylor began soon after his arrival to foster engineering unity through tradition. On March 23, 1892, he held a banquet for his students, then twenty–four in all, instituting a custom that would endure for more than forty years. The greatest ever celebrated Dean Taylor's quarter centennial at The University. Invitations were sent to alumni working all over the globe, and a solid contingent was on hand for the festivities. As had become customary, the revelers convened at the Driskill Hotel, and the night was filled with long–winded speeches and boisterous toasts to the "Old Man," as Dean Taylor had become known. The next day, on February 22, 1913, alumnus "Alf" Toombs led the Fililula Band in a parade from the Engineering Building to the Capitol and back, followed by the entire engineering student body. They secured the cannon on the Capitol grounds and dragged it back to campus, but it was too wet to be fired. The day was not a total loss; Dean Taylor regaled his audience with a typically loud and long recounting of his tenure in Austin. Six years later the occasion was more solemn as the engineers dedicated the banquet to the fourteen alumni killed in World War I. Dean Taylor gave a eulogy for all those "gone West," and a moment of silence ended the meeting. The last great official gathering of alumni that Dean Taylor presided over was the dedication of the Engineering Building in 1933. Adjourning to his new office, they fired a twenty–one–gun salute from a Brazilian hydraulic gun someone had dragged along, shattering many of the windows and causing general consternation on campus.[1]

The Engineer's Banquet was just one of the activities sponsored by the great number of student organizations begun in the early period of the College's history. An Engineering Association appeared in the *Cactus* of 1897 for the first time. It had official colors—gamboge, brindle, black, and blue—and an engineering yell for football games and other occasions:

> Moments, stresses, strains, and shears
> Viaducts, aqueducts, canals, dams, weirs
> Cantilever, trusses, girders, and piers
> Texas, Texas, Engineers!

The engineers adopted the belligerent motto "pinch in everything, pinch pretty rough, stick it to everyone, been stuck enough," and adhered to it strictly in the periodic battles between students on campus.[2]

Dean Taylor joined the American Society of Civil Engineers in 1900, initiating a rush of new engineering student clubs. The Engineers' Club began at the turn of the century, including alumni, faculty, and students among its members. Its prime purpose was to "encourage and promote a spirit of original study and research in engineering lines," but the members seem to have also spent a lot of time finding new ways of socializing. They hosted a party, first held in 1900, which developed into the Engineers' Reception in 1910, a formal open house and dance to which the entire University student body was invited. Other notable groups included the T–Square Club, which took over the tradition of passing the symbolic t–square, signed by all the seniors, to the junior class at commencement each year. Senior engineering students also formed the Kwehees, an elite club that became the unofficial focus of engineering social life after its formation in 1907. The University of Texas Society of Civil Engineers, a professional organization under the direction of Dean Taylor, Bantel, Finch, and Wagner, tried to organize in 1909, but the small engineering student body could not support yet another group, and so it lasted less than a year.[3]

Engineers even established a fraternity. Dean Taylor opposed fraternities, although he himself had joined Kappa Sigma at the University of Virginia. He declared, "The only way to cure fraternities is like curing a dog from barking—cut off its tail right behind the ears." Nevertheless, many engineering faculty served as sponsors of fraternities at The University of Texas, having joined while in school, and engineering students became active in their leadership. Theta Xi, originally established at Rensselaer Polytechnic Institute in 1864, began at The University on the occasion of Taylor's twenty–fifth anniversary banquet, and was formed primarily for engineers. In 1936, the editors of the *Cactus* remonstrated, "It must be recalled that the founders of the local chapter had been ousted from the band and forcefully ejected from a meeting of the Rusticusses before it dawned on them that they would make perfect Theta Xi's." The members of Theta Xi continued to "infest" the band after their formation, but their true origin appears well–known to the rest of the campus. Their chapter house at 2506 Whitis was described in 1922 as " a boarding house for engineers hiding behind Greek letters in the fond hope of deluding the rest of the colony. But these exponents of the slip–stick have had very little luck in getting away with the scheme." Their herald contained the familiar images of Alec, the T–square, and a transit.[4]

Engineering students also developed a spirit of unity through common experience. They were generally quite poor and rural in background, as were most of the students at The University of Texas in its first fifty years of operation. To provide a home for those who did not join the fraternities, regent George Y. Brackenridge donated the funds to build a dormitory for men on campus. Named in his honor, the hall opened in December 1890, with engineering student Harry Y. Benedict drawing the first lot for a room. The dormitory, the only one for men on campus for almost three decades, became the domain of the Barbarians, or nonfraternity students, whose own clubs bore such names as the Rusticusses, Gory Goo Roos, and Skull and Bones. Engineers dominated these activities, winning a reputation as hellions in an era remarkable for its rough manners and violent hazing. A faculty member who lived in B Hall while he was a student later recalled, "Barely a week passed that some freakish cuss did not spring something entirely original, and not half of it ever got into the magazines or newspapers." Governor James E. Ferguson, the demagogic opponent of The University, admitted, "The laws of Texas stop at the doors of B Hall." The Barbarians flew their own flag, a red pirate banner with "B Hall" emblazoned in black, which they defiantly carried down Congress Avenue in 1917 to spearhead the student protest against Ferguson. The dormitory was converted into offices after a 1925 student skirmish that caused several thousand dollars in damage. Dean Taylor and engineering alumni opposed the conversion, but to no avail. In 1952, it was torn down, and the Computation Center now occupies the site.[5]

One of the most treasured stunts ever pulled by the engineering students in those early days was one they pulled on Dean Taylor himself. On October 16, 1902, Taylor was in his office in the Main Building when two engineering students brought a "motherly looking old lady" to visit him. They introduced her as Carry Nation, and quickly vanished. Nation had already won a national reputation as the hatchet–wielding, saloon–wrecking champion of prohibition. Dean Taylor recalled, "There being only one door to the office and the window about sixteen feet from the ground, I immediately got up, and asked Mrs. Nation to have a chair." He made polite conversation, but could not help asking if she had a hatchet with her. Brandishing a small Bible, she replied, "This is my hatchet—the sword of the spirit; I always carry it with me. Are you a prohibitionist?" Dean Taylor assured her that he and his entire family were stalwart champions of temperance. Meanwhile a crowd of several hundred students had gathered at the steps of the Main Building, called by the denizens of B Hall. The engineering students returned and escorted Nation outside, where she regaled the audience with fire and brimstone. President Prather tried to stop her, but retreated before the force of her invective. She returned two days before Thanksgiving in 1904 and accepted an invitation to have dinner with the Barbarians in B Hall. They convinced her that Dean Taylor was a reprobate, but he deftly turned her verbal assault when cornered in front of the Main Building and slipped away in time to make the kickoff of the Thanksgiving Day football game.[6]

When the Engineering Building was constructed in 1904, its design included a water tank to ensure adequate pressure in times of drought. Although never filled, it offered an inviting space for students to paint "cabalistic signs, numerals, and insignia," and served as the focus of fierce combat until finally torn down in 1918. Junior law students became the first to decorate the tank, which was seventy–five feet above the ground and accessible only by a single narrow ladder. The Engineers took their feat as a direct challenge, and after supper the next night overwhelmed the "Laws" around the base of the water tank and clambered up. They spent an entire night painting their own designs, including their names and graduation dates, a skull and crossbones, and a picture of a jackass branded with the mark of the Junior Laws. The campus feud up to that time had raged between the Junior Laws and the freshman academic students; "Alf" Toombs and his fellow Engineers instigated a new rivalry that overshadowed the old and endured for almost four decades. The base of the water tank became the scene of annual combats between engineering and law students that were always violent but rarely harmful. The ladder to reach the platform around the base of the tank was removed, but this did not deter those who were determined to leave their mark. The battles continued annually until forbidden after an especially bloody clash between freshmen and sophomores in 1912.[7]

Dean Taylor took the competition with the Laws seriously, but did not let it get out of hand. A young lady "dear to the heart of a football hero" who happened to be an engineering student sewed a banner to be auctioned for charity in some forgotten cause. The Engineers outbid the Laws in a spirited exchange, then proudly bore their prize back to the Engineering Building. Dean Taylor joined the celebrants, saying, "Boys, if you had let the Lawyers take that banner, I would have been ashamed to look you in the face." On the other hand, when engineering students in drawing class in 1907 spied the Laws dragging one of their compatriots into the "gloomy recesses of Lawdom" for a paddling and stormed downstairs ready for a fight, Dean Taylor intervened to prevent a possibly ugly conflict.[8]

By 1910 the traditional feud between the Engineers and the Laws had settled into an amiable but fiercely contested rivalry. On March 2, Texas Independence Day, which was customarily reserved for celebration and contests involving the entire campus, the Engineers carried out a hair–raising scheme to deliver a harsh blow to their rivals. A group of Engineers taunted the Laws in B Hall and their comrades who soon gathered. A scuffle ensued, as it always did, and Charles Evans Townes, dean of the Law School, was called by the law students to help stop the battle before serious casualties resulted. Just as Judge Townes arrived, the Engineers dragged what appeared to be a Law into the Engineering Building, only to reappear with their hapless prisoner at the window of the drawing room on the third floor. Other Engineers holding a blanket on the ground almost four stories below called to their companions to throw the Law down: they would catch him in the blanket. All the Engineers took up the cry to "throw him down." The Engineers had previously prepared a dummy, and as the Laws and Judge Townes watched in horror, the dummy was hurled to the ground, where it rolled limply down the slope to the basement of the Engineering Building. Before Dean Townes could come up, the prisoner, actually an engineering freshman in a white shirt smeared with red ink, was substituted for the dummy. Dean Townes, seeing a boy writhing in agony on an old quilt on the sidewalk, with Engineers rubbing his hands and calling for a doctor, was certain they had killed his student. Dean Taylor said the stunt had gone far enough, ordered the "prisoner" to get up, and a moment or so later the engineering freshman was brought out and presented to the dazed Laws.[9]

The Laws did try unsuccessfully to top this trick. April 1, 1913, was a scheduled dinner date of the University Faculty Club, and the program was to be presented by the law faculty. They devised a kangaroo court, with Dean Taylor as the intended culprit. The charges were not important, but the penalty to be assessed was a dinner for them at the defendant's expense. The program committee appointed as bailiff a husky young professor to guarantee Dean Taylor's cooperation. Dean Taylor somehow learned ahead of time of the plot against him and enlisted a group of nine engineering students, later known as Taylor's Bandits, to rescue him from the Laws. Shortly after the kangaroo court convened, perhaps just as the law faculty were beginning to enjoy themselves, a signal brought Taylor's Bandits rampaging into the banquet room from the kitchen. The courtroom was filled with gunsmoke and shouts, and in the confusion Dean Taylor slipped away. The Bandits hurried him to the railway station where he boarded a train bound for San Antonio. The big bailiff tangled with one of the engineering students, but came away from the fracas much the worse for wear. A few days later Taylor hosted a dinner, but it was for his Bandits, not the Laws.[10]

The focus of rivalry between the Engineers and the Laws became their respective mascots. Peregrinus, a caricature adopted by the Laws as a symbol of the changing and even contradictory nature of their profession, originally was an image on a banner. The Freshman Academics cut up the first one in December 1901. A more elaborate rendering of "Perry" was cut into pieces by the Engineers in the spring of 1912, but that fall both a new banner and a papier-mache figure of Peregrinus were constructed. This statue was taken on the eve of commencement in June 1921 by engineering students as it was being transported in an automobile from his place of safekeeping to the ceremony where it was traditionally handed from the senior to the junior law class. The *Cactus* for 1922 memorialized the event: "As Perry was taking the capital turn, he was ambuscaded by six carloads of Slide Rule Eaters, hated enemy to the genus Law." In April 1925 they returned him unharmed to the Laws. A wooden Perry was constructed, which the Engineers captured on December 6, 1930, between the American National Bank and the Driskill Hotel, then destroyed, two years after the annual combats between Engineers and Laws had been "virtually stopped" by The University of Texas administration. Two engineering students were tried for contempt in the affair, but were exonerated on December 8, 1930. In 1931 an Engineer disguised as a waiter smashed the original Peregrinus in the banquet room of the Driskill Hotel before the stunned Laws and escaped before they could recover. Each event in the tumultous life of the Peregrinus came as a direct result of the spirited rivalry between the Engineers and the Laws, usually after some heinous crime committed by the latter against Alexander Frederic Claire, patron saint of the College of Engineering.[11]

"Alec" was first introduced to the College in a song, written to the tune of "Frau Diavilo," taught by engineering student Edward Coward Connor to Lee William Forsgard, a member of the Hickey Quartet. This group, originally formed in 1895, sometimes numbered as many as a dozen singers, including their most noted leader, Orland Lecompte Sims, or "Sunny Jim," and was credited with introducing organized yelling at The University. They would assemble at the Engineering Building and, after a few preliminary yells, would lead a procession two abreast to the game, singing "Hi Ho Balls." The Engineers changed the words from the original to suit their purpose:

Oh, Alexander Frederic Claire,
Known at every county faire
As the bold and dashing enginaire,
The man who could throw the balls.

Chorus:

Hi ho balls, balls as heavy as lead;
He gives them a twist
With a turn of his wrist
And the balls fly over his head

A co-ed was walking down a side street
With a little pet hound right at her feet;
She thought she'd stop and see the treat.
The man who could throw the balls.

Chorus

But while he was twisting and turning around
One of the balls fell on the hound
And crushed him bleeding to the ground—
One of the great big balls.
(Poor little hound—poor little dog—poor little pup)

Chorus

The co-ed screamed and swore a swear
She stamped her foot and tore her hair
And called ole Alec a grizzly bear
Because he dropped that ball.

Chorus
Alternate Final Verse:

The Co-ed gladly said thru her tears,
I will forgive all Engineers,
For I have known them many years
And I love 'em one and all.

Alterate Chorus:

Hi Ho Balls, Balls as heavy as lead
He flips them loose
At the Peregrinoos
And the balls fly over his head.

Saint Patrick serves as the patron of all engineers, but the engineering students at
The University wanted a more personal guardian. They found one in Alec.[12]

During the winter of 1907–1908 about fifteen sophomore engineers formed the TECEM Club, whose purpose was to promote "practically
everything but learning and scholarly entertainments." They met regularly, and
on the night of March 31, 1908, determined that classes should not meet the
following morning, April Fool's Day. Their plan depended on finding some dogs,
tying tin cans filled with rocks to their tails, and releasing them down the stair-
case of the Main Building during the first class hour, expecting that the noise
would accomplish their purpose. They sallied forth, but their search uncovered
only "one poor old dog that did not respond to the incentive of a tin can." Five of
the scouting party retired, sorely disappointed, to Jacoby's Beer Garden, which
then stood at the corner of Guadalupe and 24th Street. Upon leaving the garden
at a little past midnight, they spied a wooden statue under a porch shed near the
exit. The statue was of a little fat-bellied Dutchman holding aloft a stein of beer,
an advertisement for Falstaff beer. William S. Carruthers, Joe S. Gill, O. K.
Greene, Murray Gill, Banks L. McLaurin, and Cy Jones spirited the image away
to B Hall. Later some would insist they only borrowed the statue, but borrowed
or stolen, Alec never returned to Jacoby's Beer Garden.[13]

The purloined image of Alec was brought to B Hall at two o'clock
in the morning, April 1, 1908. At nine o'clock that morning the Engineers cut
classes and formed a parade in front of the Engineering Building, with Alec at
the head. They marched around the campus and back to the Main Building,
where some three hundred students gathered, mostly engineers. Gill, as one of
the captors, presented Alec to the junior class with an elaborate speech that gave
the saint credit for building the Hanging Gardens of Babylon, the Pyramids, and
the aqueducts of Rome. A veil, actually a dirty handkerchief thumbtacked to the
statue's forehead, was removed to reveal his features for the first time to a properly appreciative audience. Alf Toombs broke a small vial of "red water" over the
image to officially christen him Alexander Frederic Claire, patron saint of The
University of Texas Engineers. Toombs finished the job the next year, topping Gill
by tracing Alec's lineage to Genesis: "In the beginning was the word, and the
word was 'Alec'." The celebration became an annual ritual; Dean Taylor surrendered and began predicting every year before the first of April that the weather
would be too bad to call the roll.[14]

The Laws stole Alec for the first time on March 3, 1910, from the
foot of the stairs in the Engineering Building. Dean Townes ordered him returned, which they did on March 31, but Alec's odyssey, and the most colorful
period of the rivalry between the Engineers and the Laws, had just begun. Dean
Taylor quickly took personal charge of Alec, storing him first in an instrument
closet, then placing him again at the foot of the stairs in a wire cage. On February
21, 1913, before the quarter–centennial celebration, the Laws took Alec again.

Acting on a tip from the unhappy girl friend of a Law, engineering students Glenn Vaughn, Harry Fritz, and Joe Moore, all members of the Kweehee Club, which had assumed the heavy responsibility of protecting Alec, obtained a warrant and rescued their patron with the aid of a constable from a Pflugerville farm on November 30, 1913. The event was particularly humiliating for the Engineers because their car broke down, and they had to complete their odyssey in a mule-drawn cart. The 1914 *Cactus* added insult to injury by printing pictures of Alec in a pigpen and being "tortured" by the Laws. For safekeeping, Alec was then stored in a vault at the American National Bank, just across the alley from the Driskill Hotel where the engineering banquet took place. A new guardian organization, the A.F.C. Club, organized in 1915 to defend the Engineer's patron saint. Alec was not always the focus for conflict, however; the Knights of A.F.C., begun in 1911, required only that its members dance the two–step or "make a violent assault with intent to execute the same."[15]

The Laws carried out a much more successful plan to obtain Alec in 1916. They purchased the statue from Jacoby's widow and had Alec removed from the bank vault and handed over to them. While in their custody, Alec was tried and convicted for vagrancy by a bemused Law alumnus. Outraged, the Engineers rescued their patron and persuaded Governor Ferguson to issue a full pardon, but the bill of sale remained. Dean Taylor would have to place the statue beyond the reach of the Laws. As president of the engineering student body in 1917, Joe E. Ward boasted of having been the last student to see the old Alec and the first to see the new. He was called to Dean Taylor's office and told that Alec was in an attic in San Antonio. Dean Taylor wanted the image shipped to his farm near St. Joseph, Virginia. With three confederates, including the omnipresent Alf Toombs, Ward did as he was told, packing Alec in a coffin box and leaving it on the station agent's porch to be shipped. That was the last time he saw the original Alec intact. About a year later, Ward lifted Dean Taylor's briefcase in order to sit in a chair. Intrigued by a clanking noise, he opened the bag and found little pieces of Alec, each stamped CELAFOTRAP, or "PART OF ALEC" spelled backwards. Later that year, Ward and two others were told by Dean Taylor to pick up Alec at his home. Ward recalled, "It was a poor reproduction of Alec. Just as large but not as fine a piece of art." The slivers of wood were shipped to the Texas Engineers overseas in the American Expeditionary Force, but outsiders on campus could only speculate as to whether Alec remained in Austin, in reach of the Laws and their bill of sale, or if a dummy had been substituted.[16]

On February 21, 1927, the eve of the Engineer's Banquet, the Laws took Alec once more. They bribed a bellhop to let them into the room where he was being guarded by Dean Taylor, and sixteen of them carried the statue down the fire escape onto Brazos Street where a car waited. They dismembered the image, sending the head to Governor Daniel Moody and parceling out the remaining pieces to various Law alumni. The torso was hung in a tree on campus as their stunt for March 2, but was removed before daylight. Dean Taylor received the head from Moody, and perhaps recovered other parts from different sources, and commissioned Peter Mansbendel to build a new Alec from the pieces, which also may have included portions of the old Alec. The Austin wood-carver completed his task quickly, and in May 1927 the Engineers were able to

Dean Taylor stands with the Alec reconstructed in 1928, which resides now in the Richard W. McKinney Engineering Library. [College of Engineering, The University of Texas at Austin]

parade triumphantly with their restored saint. Because the Laws had sworn they had destroyed the original, Alec was safe from their bill of sale.[17]

As retirement approached, Dean Taylor became very secretive about Alec. Banks L. McLaurin later recalled keeping the statue many times in his barn near Webberville, Texas, and, while a student, Leonardt F. Kreisle once kept Alec at his home outside Austin. Engineering alumnus William C. Darter stored the image under some cases in his Coca–Cola bottling plant in Giddings, Texas, for some months. Bouldin Crofton also kept Alec for a time, and Major W. J. Powell, a friend of Dean Taylor, stowed the statue in his cellar in Dallas. Dean Taylor also sent him at least once to the farm in Virginia. While Alec traveled he was kept in a box about the size and shape of a small coffin, clearly labeled "Surveying Instruments." For his last public appearance in Austin in 1936, he was so shipped to Austin, where McLaurin and John A. Focht helped to uncrate Alec and secret him in a closet in the new Engineering Building. President Benedict, responding to rumors that Dean Taylor had armed a bodyguard for Alec with clubs, rescinded his permission to parade with the image. Later that night, Taylor had others remove Alec once more. No one knows how many times he again moved the statue to ensure its safety from the Laws before his death in 1941.[18]

During Dean Woolrich's tenure, Alec remained in hiding, stored by the Texas Memorial Museum in a house on Archway. Some journalism students uncovered him there in 1952, following a report that someone had spotted a coffin in the basement of the empty house. Alec was restored but made only a quiet appearance at the revived Engineer's Ball, held by the Student Engineering Council in 1953. The statue was kept in safekeeping by Carl J. Eckhardt, Jr., director of the Physical Plant, engineering professor and loyal alumnus, until 1972. Alec did make infrequent public appearances, as in 1964, when he returned to the campus on the occasion of the publication of Dean Woolrich's history of the College and the dedication of the new Engineering Science Building.[19]

Alec resurfaced once more to preside over the crowning of the 1972 engineering sweetheart. He was placed in a position of honor within a glass case in the Engineering Library after his stay in the Dean's office proved too much of a temptation for practical jokesters. In the library he has generally enjoyed a peaceful existence, although occasionally the memories of old times take charge. In 1979 Alec disappeared from his protective case; his kidnappers left a note that declared, "The spirit of 1909 lives on." He was found outside the Lyndon Baines Johnson Auditorium during the convocation awards ceremony months later, with a note around his neck that confessed, "It was one hell of a party." Alec had previously attended some of the picnics and gatherings of the engineering students, but a decision was made to keep the image in the case for its own good. The hand of the Alec cut up by the Laws in 1927 was recovered from a Brownsville attorney in 1934 by an enterprising engineering student, and now is also displayed in Ernest Cockrell, Jr., Hall.[20]

The College of Engineering during its history has harbored other mythical figures. Megathemollipod was the evil nemesis of the sophomore engineers at the turn of the century. He was a beast who preyed on those who had poor grades, but "only those who had met him knew his visage, and even those lacked power to convey by word or sketch the real terrors of his awful aspect!"

Architects had Ptah, a similarly mysterious but much less terrible image. A sculptor or engraver, Ptah was a chief handicraftsman in metal or stone and had constructed the universe. Represented as a bearded man with a bald head, often dressed in almost skin–tight clothes and wearing a pendant and bearing a scepter, Ptah enjoyed a quiet and benevolent reign. The University of Texas students declined to design any representative or image of Ptah, perhaps prudently, but his spirit attended all occasions.[21]

Dean Taylor also served as custodian of other beloved traditions of the campus and one treasured mascot. Pig Bellmont, a bulldog, was adopted by The University, where he lived from 1914 to 1923. In January of the latter year, he was hit by a car, and died of his injuries. Dean Taylor delivered his eulogy, concluding, "In that haven to which he has gone there is a rainbow spanning the sky, reaching almost to zenith, composed not of the prismatic colors but of two colors—Orange and White—and on that rainbow are the words, 'Always loyal to the team, and win or lose, the team.'" Some alumni insisted it was the best speech Dean Taylor ever made. Dean Taylor was also the force for the establishment of the honor system, which he first learned at the University of Virginia, at The University of Texas. All engineering students, and many in other departments, were required to sign a pledge each time they were tested, declaring, "I have neither given nor received aid on this examination, nor have I seen anyone giving or receiving aid." The student council of The University, on which five Engineers were serving, adopted the oath for use campuswide in 1914, but it was dropped in 1929 due to rising opposition from many quarters. The University was growing up, and the students, believing themselves to be more cosmopolitan, abolished an outdated system which they thought properly belonged to the Victorian era.[22]

More substantially, Dean Taylor founded the Engineers' Loan Fund with the excess proceeds from the annual engineers' ball in 1910. He gave this money to needy students from every discipline, but provided even more generously for his Engineers by establishing the T. U. Taylor Foundation following his retirement. The first awards from the Foundation were given in the spring of 1938, and continued under the direction of Focht, John D. Miller, and Charles E. Rowe. In 1972, the Foundation, then directed by Focht, Miller, and Ned H. Burns, was dissolved and its assets given to the Engineering Foundation. Meanwhile, the Engineers' Loan Fund had continued to grow; directed initially by McLaurin, James D. McFarland, and Venton L. Doughtie, a bequest of $100,000 from engineering alumnus Louis C. Wagner in 1951 placed it on a solid footing. As these faculty retired, the Loan Fund remained active under the direction of a series of mentors, including Kreisle, William C. Duesterhoeft, H. Grady Rylander, Jr., and Carl W. Morgan. At present, both funds are administered by the Office of Engineering Scholarships. Dean Taylor could not turn down an opportunity to help students; he took part in every Christmas dinner given for those who had to stay on campus from his arrival until the late 1930s when the banquets were discontinued, often serving as host after the original sponsor, James S. Clark, died in 1908.[23]

One of the most enduring legacies of Dean Taylor has become the ramshorn. When he arrived at the University of Virginia in 1881, he found "corks" and "curls" as part of the student vocabulary. The former meant bustees, or failures, and the latter indicated an honor student. Dean Taylor, after coming to The University of Texas, marked perfect papers with the word "curl," but soon began making a check mark with a long flourishing tail. About 1905, he over-heard some students in the hall discussing papers he had just handed back to them, when he heard one exclaim that he had earned a "ramshorn." The label stuck, becoming over time "an emblem of faith, a watchword for engineers."[24] The mark is well-known to all students of the College, no matter when they matriculated, and proudly adorns official correspondence as a distinguishing symbol of The University of Texas Engineers.

It became Dean Taylor's habit to give to all engineering seniors a watch fob engraved on its obverse with the ramshorn. On the reverse was the "Engineer's Yell," composed by Harry Y. Benedict and first heard from the street in front of Dean Taylor's house after the 1892 Engineers' Banquet:

T. U. Taylor, T—Y—Ty
X square, Y square, two X Y.

In the spring of 1937 an energetic group of seniors established the Ramshorn Society on a formal basis. Its constitution divided membership into associate members, those who would soon finish their degrees, and members, alumni who still wished to take part in and contribute to the College. Dean Taylor handed out signed certificates to each graduate in a separate ceremony before each commencement; the practice continued after his death until 1959, when the Ramshorn Association, overshadowed by many professional student organiza-tions and the Engineering Foundation, had ceased to operate as an effective auxiliary.[25]

James D. McFarland served as chairman of the faculty coordinat-ing committee for the entire life of the organization. The members included alumni, who supported College activities through advice and donations before the creation of the Engineering Foundation, which developed from the activity of a separate organization with the College emblem, the Ramshorn Club. When Dean Woolrich acted to revive engineering customs suspended during World War II, the Ramshorn Association sponsored an awards convocation and dance in Gregory Gym beginning in 1947. In 1956 the Ramshorn Association revised its constitution to exclude students in order to expedite the establishment of a stu-dent chapter of the Texas Society of Professional Engineers in the College. The Ramshorn Association as an alumni service assembly was superseded by the creation of the Engineering Foundation in 1957, and it was formally disbanded and its remaining funds given to the Student Engineering Council in 1961.[26]

The members of the Ramshorn Association sponsored one of the most popular events staged by the College, the Engineering Power Show. An annual exposition, the first was held in 1909. Every student organization and department worked for months to outdo each other in displays of ingenuity and even showmanship. The projects had to be professional in theme, demonstrating knowledge the students gained in their studies. The entire campus attended, and soon the small affair developed into a social gathering with many of the aspects of a carnival. The Student Engineering Council inherited responsibility for the Power Show and streamlined it at the order of Dean Hagerty. The emphasis on professional spirit again came to the fore. The quality of the workmanship had always remained, but many faculty thought that the objective of the Power Show had been subsumed to the festive spirit. With renewed purpose, the exposition continued into the present. As the Centennial of The University of Texas approached, the engineering open house became one of many elements in the campus "Showcase." Student projects still delight the crowds who attend the annual event, and it has proven almost impossible to completely stifle the exhibitionist zeal of the Engineers.[27]

Dean Woolrich fostered engineering tradition in a completely different style than his predecessor. Much of the change came from within the student body. The rural Texas population that had dominated the College, as well as The University, had begun to give way to students from all over the United States and many foreign countries. This transition accelerated after World War II, complemented by a shift in Texas demography as the state became increasingly urban. The change had been reflected in a rejection of many traditions by the students of The University as early as the 1920s, when the honor system and the passing of class symbols—the T–square for the Engineers, Peregrinus for the Laws, and the blue–back speller for the Academics—had been discontinued with scarcely a murmur. In 1938 the "Cactus Thorn" section of the yearbook, a section customarily reserved for rough humor, was abolished outright by the Board of Publications of The University, indicating the passing of a distinct era in student tastes. Dean Woolrich did not encourage the traditions of the past which he believed embodied the spirit of hooliganism, such as much of the activity which surrounded Alec. He did continue to push for engineering unity with a new stress on professional decorum. The Engineering Student's Association formalized the organization of the student body in 1937, sponsoring projects such as the Power Show to absorb their energy.[28]

The Engineering Students' Association became a casualty of World War II: because the College population was preoccupied with more serious matters, the organization was discontinued in 1945. The Ramshorn Association, with its strong cadre of older alumni, took over direction of the Power Show and sponsored events such as the awards convocation and dance. It provided a forum for the preservation of engineering tradition but, more important, also served as an auxiliary to the College. Through their advice and financial support, the engineering program at The University developed strongly in the postwar decade. These alumni, however, did not have the organization necessary to effect substantial progress in many areas. They aided Dean Woolrich and the faculty in the campaign to establish the Engineering Foundation, and many later served on the Advisory Council.[29]

During the early fall of 1952, Charles D. Anderson, Richard E. Bailey, Thomas E. Fairey, Jerry Garrett, W. Charles Mills, and other engineering students began to seriously discuss what could be done to improve the student *esprit de corps* and at the same time strengthen their loyalty to the College. To accomplish this, in the tradition that students who work together stay together, they considered the possibility of having engineering students build a recreation and study lounge for the engineers so that they would not have to walk across the campus to the distant Texas Union. This, along with the absence of an organization to serve as the governing and representative body of the engineering students, led directly to the creation of the Student Engineering Council (SEC). The SEC was incorporated December 6, 1952, by the state of Texas to correlate the student professional and honor societies of the College of Engineering, to promote construction of new student and faculty recreational and lounge facilities in the Engineering Building, and to further the good will, spirit, and traditions of the College. As an independent corporation, the SEC coordinated the activities of all student organizations, with two representatives of each sitting in common council.[30]

The students, with the encouragement of faculty advisors Leonardt F. Kreisle and Carl J. Eckhardt, Jr., decided to build a basement beneath the Engineering Building. To do so, they would remove over 2,000 cubic yards of dirt and rock to create a space approximately 160 feet by 50 feet, to a depth of 8 feet. On December 4, 1952, twenty–one students and two faculty members, A. Anthony Toprac and Kreisle, began the laborious process of digging the area out by hand. The first official shovel of dirt was removed and preserved for posterity at an official opening ceremony one week later, at which former Assistant Dean Edward C. H. Bantel related many of the historical traditions of the College. The assembly dedicated the project, in the words of Dean Taylor, "To all Alecs and other choice spirits who are square as 90 degrees, who are as straight as a bee line, who are as upright as a plumb line, who love God, who hate the devil, who revere the honor system, and who keep their word." The student lounge was named in the late Dean's honor, and became known as the Taylor T Room. The diggers themselves christened their effort Operation Gopher and adopted a groundhog as their mascot. They initially named the creature Patrick "Digger" O'Dell, but changed that to Christine when they discovered their mistake.[31]

With the leadership of numerous student officers and the aid of Kreisle and Eckhardt, the project was completed in four years. Three thousand students moved 2,300 cubic yards of rock and dirt using equipment donated by the Rolfe–Crutcher–Cummings Company. Alumni contributed $27,000 for necessary finishing touches, such as floors, walls, ceilings, and furniture. Eckhardt and his crew did much of the wiring and plumbing free of charge, thus sparing the SEC from a great expense. Moore Construction Company finished the T Room in time for its dedication on May 13, 1957, at which Governor Price Daniel, Dean Woolrich, and others spoke before a crowd of 350 spectators. The area provided vending machines for hot and cold food vending, study space, and offices for student organizations, all nominally supervised and maintained by the SEC. The T Room remains the only permanent construction on The University of Texas campus built by students. The College has moved from Taylor Hall, which has become the home of the Computation Center, but a new lounge in Engineering Teaching Center II bears Dean Taylor's name.[32]

The SEC continues to coordinate a broad spectrum of student activities and organizations. Its goal is to promote a greater ethos of professionalism to aid in The University's quest to be an institution of the first class, but it retains a lighter side. The SEC revived the Engineer's Ball in 1953, now said to be the last remaining campuswide dance at The University. The Order of Alec was founded by SEC members in 1982 to keep the traditions of the College alive. The SEC prints the *Vector*, the official student newsletter. It hosts both the Engi-

Participants in Operation Gopher, the construction of the Taylor T Room, celebrate the official ground-breaking with their mascot, Christine "Digger" O'Dell. [College of Engineering, The University of Texas at Austin]

Former student leaders reunite at the College of Engineering. [College of Engineering, The University of Texas at Austin]

STUDENT ENGINEERING COUNCIL ENGINEERING LEADERSHIP SERVICE AWARD, 1970–1986

| | | | |
|---|---|---|---|
| 1970 | Alan T. Derby<br>Thomas W. Rioux<br>John R. Stratton<br>Gary W. Watt | 1979 | William C. Barron<br>Jamin L. Patrick<br>Kyle M. Schultz<br>Steven L. Thomson |
| 1971 | R. Bruce Anderson<br>Bobby L. Boldt<br>Mark E. Goode<br>Jack B. McWilliams<br>Sherry S. Zwiebel | 1980 | David Dean<br>Sylvia Escobar<br>Daniel Neal<br>Larry Seitzman<br>Jeanmarie Nolley Strohmayer |
| 1972 | Thomas G. Arthur<br>Robert C. Olsen | 1981 | Diana Carranza<br>David D. Kennedy<br>Linda A. Kubena<br>Mark C. Sherman<br>Daniel W. Wettig |
| 1973 | Philip C. Crouse<br>John B. Gordon<br>William M. Kazmann<br>Kenneth E. Martin | 1982 | Mark Blair<br>Catherine French<br>Jacquelin D. McKinney<br>Christy L. Parsons<br>John R. Waggoner |
| 1974 | Richard G. Dargatz<br>David F. Gloyna<br>Patrick D. Kelly<br>Larry L. Lehman<br>Max O. Reinbach, Jr. | 1983 | Park W. Burrets<br>Karen S. Irion<br>Julia A. Johnson<br>Sandra D. Vaughn |
| 1975 | Victoria L. Blashke<br>Sue Cash Gloyna<br>Brennan P. Hatley<br>Kennedy K. McElroy, Jr.<br>Randall W. Williams<br>Gary J. Wolff | 1984 | Joan F. Brennecke<br>Rolla Lee Derr<br>Ronald Albert Kubena<br>Robert Mechler<br>Sotiris Pagdadis<br>Connie Vaughn |
| 1976 | Mark P. Evans<br>Marsha L. Hamby<br>Chester Malins<br>Patricia D. McKay<br>Horace P. Seale<br>Brian R. Sullivan | 1985 | David R. DeKraker<br>Robbin Hereford<br>Larry Hilgert<br>Philip A. Karpos<br>George O. Wilkinson, Jr. |
| 1977 | Alex M. Cranberg<br>Teresa Sipes Hurley<br>Loren T. Lancaster<br>David S. Mothersole<br>Donald F. Schorr II | 1986 | Leon Carayannopoulos<br>David Chen<br>Robert Combs<br>Donald S. Glover<br>John Hicks |
| 1978 | K. Alan Keisner<br>Candice E. Koederitz<br>Jack E. Marvin<br>Larry R. Phillips<br>Charles L. Sharrai<br>David K. Stenssy | | |

neering Exposition, a two–day event in which students meet with company representatives to discuss career objectives, and a spring picnic, noted for its five–man chariot races and other inspired competitions. The SEC coordinates awards and endowments, student services, and faculty meetings with students. The College of Engineering Awards Day Convocation originated with the SEC in 1969; held in conjunction with National Engineers' Week, the day falls near the Engineers' Banquet date in February of each year. These efforts of the SEC are supplemented by the Graduate Engineering Council, organized by Dean Gloyna to extend representation into that section of the student population and increase their involvement.[33]

Dean Gloyna also instituted a seminar for all student leaders of engineering organizations in which they take part in the College administration, learning about the requirements and opportunity for individual and institutional growth as well as the importance of teamwork to future development. The institutionalization of *esprit de corps* among the engineering students took place in an atmosphere of increasing professionalism. Students assumed an important role in the development of the engineering program, of which they had always been a part but were rarely allowed to influence directly. Much of their activity centered on the many professional and honor associations within the College. In order to recognize the achievements of outstanding individuals, the SEC initiated the Engineering Leadership Service Award for those who had been most influential in the development of the College. Both men and women from all departments have earned this honor. After they leave the College, such student leaders remain loyal alumni. Alec and the ramshorn have become symbolic images of the drive for greater professionalism in the development of engineering research and education both within the College and through its supporters outside of The University.

The SEC depends on a vast array of honorary, professional, and minority organizations for effective representation. The College has hosted a number of assemblies that no longer exist. The old Engineers' Graduate Club, established in 1929, lasted only a few years. The Sons of Alec organized on February 2, 1937 but were quickly overshadowed by the Ramshorn Association. Professional assemblies such as the student chapters of the American Institute of Military Engineers and the Institute of the Aeronautical Sciences, both begun in the late 1950s, were too specialized to attract many students, and enjoyed only a brief life. Engineering honor societies were the first to succeed at The University of Texas, preceding by several years the establishment of durable professional organizations. Minority assemblies came about under Dean Gloyna as efforts to recruit and retain students from the nontraditional sectors increased. Each club contributes in some measure to the overall goal of the College, forging lasting ties between alumni and their alma mater for professional development and camaraderie.[34]

The first engineering honor society in Texas, Tau Beta Pi, was chartered at The University of Texas on June 10, 1916. It hosted the first national convention of the parent organization held in the Southwest in October 1937. With members in attendance from all over the United States, that event marked a milestone for the developing recognition of the College. Eta Kappa Nu, the honor society for electrical engineers, followed in April 1928. Pi Tau Sigma, a

Members of the student chapter of the Society of Women Engineers at The University of Texas at Austin pose proudly during The University's centennial in 1983. [College of Engineering, The University of Texas at Austin]

Calvin Moree, president of Pi Sigma Pi in 1985–1986, stands with Richard Rosales of Dow Chemical Corporation, a loyal supporter of the Equal Opportunity in Engineering program, Associate Dean for Academic Affairs Charles A. Sorber, and Tom Backus, coordinator of the minority education effort in the College of Engineering. [College of Engineering, The University of Texas at Austin]

Two of the fifty-six maces designed and constructed by Professor Emeritus Carl J. Eckhardt, Jr., of Mechanical Engineering flank the podium while John E. Kasch, Chairman of the Engineering Foundation Advisory Council, addresses the engineers at their commencement in 1983. [College of Engineering, The University of Texas at Austin]

mechanical engineering honor society, established its Kappa Chapter at The University on March 1, 1925; after a false start, it was rechartered on April 18, 1931. Chi Epsilon, the honorary civil engineering fraternity, started in May 1934. Pi Epsilon, for petroleum engineers, began November 26, 1935, and was reorganized as the Kappa Chapter of Pi Epsilon Tau in 1961. Iota Sigma Pi, a chemical honor society for women, was chartered in 1931, eleven years after the founding of Phi Lambda Upsilon, an honorary fraternity in chemistry. Both societies welcomed chemical engineers, and Schoch served as a faculty director for the latter. Omega Chi Epsilon, a national honor society for chemical engineers only, organized October 7, 1941. The Gamma Chapter of Alpha Alpha Gamma, for women architectural students, began only a few months after the founding of the national organization at Washington University in 1923. The Sphinx Club, for male honor students in architecture, organized on October 30, 1930. The Mu Chapter of Tau Sigma Delta, an honor society open to all architecture students, formed at The University in 1931. The last was Sigma Gamma Tau, formed in 1953 for honor students in aerospace engineering. Delta Nu Alpha, an honor society for transportation majors, began in 1949 but expired in the late 1960s.[35]

Professional associations in the College got a slower start. The engineering literary association, the Ramshorn Society, became the Ramshorn Chapter of the American Association of Engineers (AAE) in 1920. The student chapter of the Texas Society of Professional Engineers adopted a Ramshorn symbol in 1956 as the AAE had faded. A student chapter of the American Society of Mechanical Engineers was established at The University in January 1920. It expanded the Power Show with its first in 1936. The student chapter of the American Society of Civil Engineers was begun on February 4, 1920. The American Institute of Electrical Engineers, after a small start in 1909, finally got established on campus in 1928. The Petroleum Club was founded on February 3, 1929 but was later supplanted by the American Institute of Mining Engineers chapter at The University, begun in 1928, now the Society of Petroleum Engineers of the American Institute of Mining, Metallurgical, and Petroleum Engineers. The American Institute of Aeronautics was originally chartered as the Institute of Aeronautical Sciences in 1941, then rechartered as the American Institute of Aeronautics and Astronautics in February 1963. The American Institute of Chemical Engineers formed on September 19, 1941; it remains active, along with another organization for chemical engineering students, Alpha Chi Sigma. Alpha Rho Chi, a social fraternity for architectural students, founded the Dinocrates Chapter at The University on April 19, 1924, with architectural engineers Werner W. Dornberger and Raymond Everett as members. The Association of Student Architects, open to all students in related disciplines, was organized in 1931. The American Association of Architectural Engineers formed in 1952 after the separation of the School of Architecture from the College of Engineering; it changed its name in 1983 to the National Association of Architectural Engineers. The Society of Engineering Science formed on February 25, 1964, but endured only a few semesters. The Engineering Management Society organized in the fall of 1982 and remains active.[36]

Minority organizations have largely been a recent innovation. Women joined engineering organizations since their inception at The University, and the Society of Women Student Architects and Engineers, begun in 1946, proved to be short–lived. The Society of Women Engineers at The University was established on June 24, 1970. Although it does accept men into its membership as auxiliaries, its primary purpose is to provide professional ties for female engineering students. Pi Sigma Pi was established on April 4, 1973. A service organization formed to aid minorities, it provides services such as tutoring, social contacts, and professional development. It conducts an aggressive recruiting program, including the World of Engineering exhibit each year to expose high school students to the opportunities afforded by an engineering education. Pi Sigma Pi also constitutes a forum by which minority students can make their voices heard in the administration of the College. The impact of such organizations on student assemblies is becoming more obvious as people from all backgrounds come together to conduct projects. A good example is the Society of Automotive Engineers. Begun as a student club in February 1980, the Texas organization initiated the Formula SAE National Intercollegiate Student Engineering Design Competition in 1981, which it hosted until 1984 and won in 1982. Promoted to student branch status in 1984, it was voted the most outstanding in North America for 1984–1985.[37]

The other professional societies have regularly garnered similar honors, bringing more distinction to the College of Engineering. The active student chapter of the Texas Society of Professional Engineers plays a key role in maintaining The University's preeminence in education. Dean Gloyna carried out the wishes of alumnus Lowber D. Snow, a loyal supporter of student activities, by establishing three $10,000 endowments in 1978 for the student chapters of the Texas Society of Professional Engineers and the American Society of Civil Engineers, along with the Student Engineering Council. The Bettie Margaret Smith estate provided a similar endowment for the Graduate Student Council in 1984.

Engineers have also excelled in sports for The University. Dean Taylor was an avid sports fan and pressed the Engineers to excel in intramurals as well as varsity competition. The great rivalry was with the Laws; when the Engineers' baseball team defeated the Laws for the first time in 1902, the *Cactus* crowed, "No longer is the Engineering Department to be a worthless factor in University athletic contests." Engineers consistently dominated departmental events until their abolition in 1932: basketball, wrestling, boxing, track, swimming, tennis, football, baseball, cross–country, and handball. They won the D. A. Frank trophy, established in 1917 to honor the former engineering student who coined the term "Longhorns," by winning the overall intramural championship for three consecutive years: 1919–1920, 1920–1921, and 1921–1922. Permanent possession was given to the Engineers; the cup now resides in the dean's office. The *Cactus* in 1924 declared, "The Engineers have shown more spirit and achieved more results than any other group." In 1924, at the end of another successful year, the editors added, "School spirit exists in this College perhaps to a higher degree than any other part of the University." Since the reorganization of intramural sports in 1933, engineering students have continued to take an active part in sporting events. The student chapter of the American Society of Civil Engineers in 1975 initiated a concrete canoe competition with rival clubs at other schools, combining engineering skill with muscle power. The University crews have consistently placed in the top ranks, more often than not coming home first.[38]

COLLEGE OF
ENGINEERING GRADUATES
WHO ARE DISTINGUISHED ALUMNI
OF THE UNIVERSITY OF TEXAS
AT AUSTIN

1965
C. W. (Tex) Cook
Retired Chairman and
Chief Executive Officer,
General Foods
Corporation
BS EE 1930

1968
Bob R. Dorsey
Retired Chairman and
Chief Executive Officer,
Gulf Oil Corporation,
Pittsburgh
BS ChE 1940

1969
Fernando Belaunde-
Terry
Former President of
Peru
BS Arch 1935

1970
Alan L. Bean
Retired Captain, USN
BS AsE 1955

1970
Luis Flores-Arias
Retired President,
Concreto, S.A.
BS CE 1923

1972
Jack S. Josey
Chairman, Josey Oil
Company
BS PE 1939

Engineers have won distinction in varsity sports as well. As a student body, they provided most of the labor for raising the grandstand at Clark Field, the first athletic facility, and were active in raising enough money to build Memorial Stadium, funded almost entirely by students, alumni, and faculty and dedicated at the Thanksgiving game on November 27, 1924. Its flagpole was named in honor of Louis Jordan, captain of the undefeated 1914 football team, the first Southern athlete ever named to Walter Camp's All–America team and the first University alumnus to die in World War I, on March 5, 1918. The scoreboard in Memorial Stadium bears the name of another engineer, Freddie Steinmark, a great strong safety who lost a courageous battle against cancer shortly after his last season in 1982.[39]

Jordan was the first inductee into the Longhorn Hall of Fame when it was created in 1957 to honor great University athletes. Other members include Ed Bluestein, an outstanding football player for The University and a professional engineer widely recognized for his achievements, and J. Neils Thompson, a professor of civil engineering, director of Balcones Research Center, and longtime member of the board of directors for the Southwest Confer-

1975
Maurice F. Granville
Retired Chairman and
Chief Executive Officer,
Texaco, Inc.
BS ChE 1937

1979
Robert L. Parker
Chairman and Chief
Executive Officer,
Parker Drilling
Company
BS PE 1944

1980
Dan M. Krausse
President, Krausse
Company
BS ChE 1947

1982
Dr. Thomas D.
Barrow
Vice-Chairman,
Standard Oil of Ohio
BS PE 1945

1983
Joe J. King
Retired Vice-Chairman,
Tenneco Chemicals, Inc.
BS ME 1925

1984
Robert L. Crippen
Captain, USN
BS AsE 1960

1985
Joe C. Walter, Jr.
President, Walter Oil
and Gas Corporation
BS PE 1949

1986
William A.
Cunningham
Professor Emeritus,
College of Engineering,
The University of Texas
at Austin
BS ChE 1927,
MS ChE 1929,
PhD ChE 1941

ence. More engineers are premier candidates for later election, such as Doug Dawson, an All–American offensive lineman and petroleum engineering graduate in 1983 who now plays professional football for the St. Louis Cardinals. The Marvin Wright Engineering Athlete Award, established in honor of Wright, who was a track letterman and a 1909 graduate of the College, has been annually presented since 1966 to an engineering student to recognize significant achievement both on the field and in the classroom. The Zapalac twins, one of whom, William F. Zapalac, Jr., was an architectural engineer, left their mark as scholars and as professional football players; William won the Wright award in 1973.[40]

        Engineering faculty have been active in creating and maintaining tradition at The University of Texas. Eugene P. Schoch, as a student, played first violin and managed the University Glee Club. When he returned as a professor, he founded the Longhorn Band. He purchased the instruments from a pawnshop in time for the group to make its marching debut at the football game between Texas and Kansas City in 1900. The following year, University administrators bought new equipment and at Schoch's insistence employed a professional musician as director, although Schoch served as manager until

1910. Eckhardt designed and supervised construction of the maces carried in the commencement procession. The College of Engineering mace, for example, bears the ramshorn and is topped with a brass miniature of Alec. Much of the wood from which they are made came from campus buildings and landmarks that have been demolished. Eckhardt also oversaw installation of bronze plaques in each building on campus recording their history and the contribution of their namesake. With Walter P. Webb, he erected the original Santa Rita oil rig on the campus in Austin, where it was dedicated in a ceremony before the kickoff of the game with Texas A&M on Thanksgiving Day, 1958. Later Eckhardt was active in the installation of the Burleson Bells on campus. The mechanical engineering laboratories produced Smokey, the cannon fired when Texas scores in its football games. If The University wins, the triumph is memorialized by a "victory light" display devised by Eckhardt using the tower of the Main Building. The official color rendition of the seal of The University was designed by Kreisle in 1949; until that time the school had not adopted an official emblem in color. Kreisle established the hue as a bright orange, and his design was accepted by The University on May 4, 1957, although it had been in constant use for eight years.[41]

The College of Engineering at The University of Texas rests on a solid foundation of tradition. Through its customs and recorded folk history, it has forged strong bonds of loyalty with alumni and its present student body. As the institution has developed, these traditions have become the basis for organizations that teach professionalism at its highest level. Engineering student societies, at the same time, have not squelched the zeal for fun that is the source of future tall tales and folkways. A lively fringe exists outside the established framework. One example is the DUNGS, or Dinosaur Underground Natural Gas Source hunters, who insist that the plentiful Texas natural gas deposits result from the waste of a giant armadillo who haunted the tunnels under The University and the hills nearby. Jacoby's Beer Garden has long since been torn down, but the group met at Uncle Nasty's to discuss their lack of success in tracking down this elusive creature. Similarly, the imaginative spirit lives on within the professional organizations in events such as the five–man chariot races and the egg–drop contest, in which contestants must devise a vehicle to prevent the cargo inside from bursting when dropped from the top of Memorial Stadium.[42] As long as the desire for innovation and the zest for fun remain coupled with the drive for greater achievement through professionalism, the College will continue to enjoy the support of its students in its quest for excellence.

The bond of tradition complements the high level of academic excellence maintained by the College during its one–hundred–year history. Engineering graduates from The University of Texas have contributed greatly to the development of both the state and the nation. The roster of Distinguished Graduates of the College, initiated in 1957, contains the names of many who reached the highest pinnacle in their chosen field, whether business, government, or academia. Many of these have also been selected as Distinguished Alumni of The University in recognition of their accomplishments. Through their research, entrepreneurship and public service, this dedicated cadre have brought distinction to all of the "children of Alec," and have demonstrated the role of the College of Engineering in building a "university of the first class."

# EDUCATION FOR TECHNOLOGICAL LEADERSHIP:

*A Look to the Future*

Thef greatest wealth of a society originates in the classrooms and research laboratories of the university. In the final analysis, a better quality of life ultimately depends on the ability of institutions of higher education to develop the native intellect, on the capability of states to establish appropriate educational priorities, and on the capacity of free–enterprise systems to provide for the development of recognized pinnacles of academic excellence. Universities of the first class and, specifically, outstanding engineering programs can contribute materially to the long–term economic well–being of society.

When all accounts are added up, there is a price that must be paid. The development of a world–class technological base is certainly a most arduous and costly undertaking. The scientific discoveries and engineering developments that lead to the great technological advancements of any era have growth characteristics similar to the building of a coral atoll. The total body of knowledge increases through a lengthy layering process. Initially each layer seems singularly fragile but ultimately, after having passed the test of time, it becomes increasingly more substantial than the previously deposited work of nature. Sporadic disruption in the process will result in atrophy and possibly catastrophic dissolution.

Fortunately, the educational base in Texas permits the building of academic atolls for engineering excellence. The University of Texas at Austin, on the occasion of its centennial in 1983, renewed efforts to fulfill its mission as a "university of the first class." The College of Engineering, within this mandate, established goals and undertook the development of an academic base having global perspectives. The mission of the College is clear, for the innovative concepts developed in the environs of The University will fuel the societal needs of tomorrow and thereby contribute to a better economic foundation for Texas.

The task of developing technological leadership in the students will not be easy. Faculty must be alert to needed changes in traditional educational concepts. Because the human element dominates all social phenomena, the engineers of tomorrow must be capable of communicating more effectively, of applying the principles of management more judiciously, of exercising the concepts of organization more effectively, and of adapting the total body of scientific and technological knowledge into the design process more expertly.

## The Plan: A Commitment to Excellence

In order to facilitate development, any institution must have a goal and clearly defined objectives. There must be direction, all clearly communicated to faculty, students, administrators, alumni, and employers of graduates. During the last decade the College of Engineering at The University of Texas has developed a planning methodology that has resulted in an annually updated six–year plan. This effort has contributed to a resolution of many foreseeable objectives and has helped to provide longer–range direction of faculty recruitment for emerging programs.

The University of Texas at Austin organized a commission on the occasion of its centennial to evaluate its role. Beginning with their report in 1983, a strategic plan evolved that embodies The University's mission to become an institution of the first class. For the next decade, the administration committed itself to an effort to recruit faculty whose accomplishments and promise of continued intellectual development place them in the forefront of academia, to develop a student body whose performance reflects constant progress, to increase support for research and teaching from outside sources, and to satisfy vital needs for facilities and equipment through a program of new construction, remodeling, and acquisition. Maintenance of a standard of excellence required "ever–escalating" activities to "respond with flexibility to the challenges ahead, many of which can only be imagined, and most of which cannot now be anticipated." These renewed vows to expedite the development of education in Texas came within the context of a changing economic future which lent urgency to the mission.

Development of a nationally recognized, first–class engineering education and research university became a major goal of The University. Preeminent engineering research universities have been shown to have a positive impact on the economy of a state, region, or country. Mutually beneficial relationships between research universities, high–technology industry, and the economy have occurred in several areas of the United States. Notable and widely recognized examples include Silicon Valley in California, which developed near the campus of Stanford University; the large federally funded research complexes located at the University of California at Berkeley; the concentration of industrial research and development facilities near Harvard and MIT; and the growing high–technology environment of the Research Triangle in North Carolina. In each of these areas, the development of an academic center of excellence in engineering research resulted in greater high–technology investment, lower unemployment, and a stronger economy.

The Centennial Commission defined the role of The University as, in part, "to promote the development of the human resources of Texas and the nation to their highest potential of intellectual achievement and personal growth." Within this context, the goal of the College of Engineering has become to expand its function as a major center of academic excellence. Eight objectives have been delineated to fulfill this task. Projected over a six–year period, they are based on the premise that teaching, including research, can best be achieved by developing a distinguished faculty who enjoy interacting with highly motivated students and modern facilities. The areas for improvement include faculty, facilities and equipment, students, academic programs, research, academic support, the budget, and external support. Through an ongoing effort in each of these broad categories, the College will maintain the standards necessary for academic leadership and regenerate the vital initiative for industrial diversification in Texas.

## Faculty

To facilitate a return to smaller classes on the undergraduate level and provide for the expected increase in graduate students, the College will continue aggressive faculty development. Plans include an ongoing emphasis on improving teaching effectiveness and expanding the professional stature of the teaching staff. Of major importance in the cultivation of academic excellence will be the recruitment of additional young and experienced professors and more effective utilization of their time through the use of teaching assistants, qualified technicians, and staff. To fulfill the goals of the College, the full–time–equivalent faculty must expand by 40 percent before the fall of 1991, along with a small increase of 4 percent in the total number of graduate students who serve as assistant instructors and teaching assistants. Since academia claims only about a fourth of the new engineering doctorates each year, the College must conduct an active campaign to attract good faculty and overcome the national shortage of engineering teaching staff.

## Facilities and Equipment

Modern laboratory and teaching facilities are required to achieve and maintain academic excellence, attract outstanding students, recruit prominent faculty, and develop premier graduate research programs. The first priority is the construction of buildings or additions to existing facilities at the Balcones Research Center (BRC) to house the major research projects of the College. The centers for materials science and engineering, manufacturing systems engineering, and microelectronics will occupy Building I, while those for transportation, construction, and geotechnical engineering will fill Building II; presently, both facilities are still on the drawing board. The Phil M. Ferguson Structural Engineering Research Laboratory will be enlarged to accomodate greater effort in structures research, and the Center for Research in Water Resources will expand in order to expedite broader studies in fluid dynamics.

On campus, a new building is needed to relieve many overflowing classrooms and laboratories in the Departments of Aerospace, Civil, and Electrical and Computer Engineering. The latter now teaches some laboratory courses in temporary trailers, and the graduate research program in satellite applications in Aerospace Engineering and Engineering Mechanics is housed in off–campus rental space. With the removal of all research centers to the BRC, the completion of a building on campus, and an ongoing renovation of the existing quarters, including expansion of the RWM Engineering Library by one–third, the College will be able to alleviate these conditions and provide for future growth.

Coupled with the need for space is the increasing requirement for state–of–the–art equipment in teaching and research. In 1982 the Texas Society of Professional Engineers surveyed the institutions of higher education in engineering in the state and reported a "crisis" of technological obsolescence in existing facilities, in proportion to the reported lack of modern equipment in academic engineering laboratories across the United States. The total need of The University of Texas at Austin, recognized as the flagship of the engineering education system in Texas, was estimated to be over $28.7 million, with a critical need of nearly $7.7 million for laboratory equipment involved in technological instruction directly related to the economic needs of the state. In 1985, the College estimated its critical need had nearly doubled, while the cost of refurbishing all obsolescent facilities stood at $40 million.

Much of the cost lies in computational equipment. A CRAY X–MP/24 supercomputer, the first at any educational institution in Texas, was installed at the BRC during the spring of 1986 as part of the Center for High–Performance Computing. Accessible from campus through a microwave link, this machine, with four million words of memory and two processors, will perform many applications beyond the capability of existing facilities. Nevertheless, there is a growing need for more direct support by smaller computers for data analysis, word processing, and communication, requiring a forecasted expenditure by the College of $11.7 million, in 1985 dollars, over the next six years.

## Students

Continued enrollment management should stabilize the number of engineering undergraduates at about five thousand. This will facilitate a return to smaller student–teacher ratios, with a commensurate increase in the quality of individual educational experiences. Concurrently, graduate enrollment should increase to approximately two thousand by 1992, divided into twelve hundred master's and eight hundred doctoral candidates. Engineering educators across the United States have remarked on the growing proportion of foreign students in graduate programs. Americans holding baccalaureates have gone into industry, attracted by high salaries. An objective of the College is to increase the number of graduate students from institutions in the United States. If the current trend continues, the nation could experience a severe shortage of engineers educated for employment at the management level and in advanced research and development.

A continued effort to increase the participation of minority students on all academic levels will accompany the focus on enrollment management. The Equal Opportunity in Engineering program is committed to the recruitment and retention of highly qualified minority students. A variety of activities including scholarships, counseling, tutoring, and orientation sessions for prospective students encourage qualified candidates to seek admission and provide support for admitted students. Since the program is operated entirely through private support, increased efforts are underway to expand its financial base.

## Academic Programs

Within the context of the College goals, the six departments will be strengthened, selected programs will be given special emphasis, and research centers will be given an opportunity to contribute. Special endowed positions have been given to four areas for the purpose of developing them into preeminent status. These are microelectronics, manufacturing systems engineering, materials science and engineering, and computer engineering. Each of these will remain interdisciplinary areas that draw on the resources of The University, integrating faculty from the Colleges of Engineering, Natural Sciences, and Business. Other high–priority areas of study that have been singled out for special attention include those that impact on the infrastructure of the country: energy, transportation, water resources, and construction. At the same time, undergraduate curricula in established fields will be expanded to incorporate greater emphasis on communication skills and computer competency while retaining both a common core and liberal arts requirements for all degree programs. Graduate students will enjoy access to ongoing studies in nationally recognized centers of research excellence.

## Research

The expanded faculty and increased complexity of the research effort will require additional professional staff. By developing its graduate student research in both quantity and quality, the College can significantly aid the Texas economy by attracting new industry and industrial research facilities, acquiring external funds from the federal government and industry, initiating more entrepreneurial enterprise, and providing superior engineering graduates. Through modernization of the research facilities available to the College and reorganization of the necessary administrative and technical support services, a major objective will be accomplished in the strengthening of the Bureau of Engineering Research (BER). To increase the annual research budget to $60 million by 1991 will require great coordination and more professional direction. This has been accomplished by adding an associate dean for development and planning and a director for the Center for Technology Development and Transfer.

The Center for Technology Development and Transfer will provide a liaison between The University, venture capital, and industry, which will help to identify, develop, and commercialize new products, technology, and scientific information generated by engineering research. Funding ultimately will be obtained from private sources, but support during the Center's first two years will be required from The University. The program will focus on the identification and development of high–technology innovations and the improvement of areas critical to the state's industrial expansion.

## Academic Support

An objective of the College is to enhance teaching effectiveness and administration by increasing services, which are directed toward students and faculty. The Office of Student Affairs will place additional emphasis on preventive counseling, remedial summer courses for underprepared students, improved communication of changes in academic regulations, and the use of computers in handling student records. A computerized scheduling system will be used by the Engineering Career Assistance Center to aid degree candidates in obtaining interviews. The RWM Engineering Library will require an annual budget of nearly $100,000 to keep its collections up to date. Within the mission of providing better–qualified engineers, a primary objective of the College is to maintain the high level of activity achieved by the Cooperative Engineering Education Program, with an emphasis on sustaining the high quality of co–op students and job experiences. The Bureau of Engineering Teaching continues to foster the development and implementation of improved teaching techniques. Providing a superior continuing education program for practicing engineers remains an important objective in the College. Through the development of more night courses and classes offered through live television and delayed videotape, the faculty will be able to meet the growing demand of this constituency.

## Financial Support

Continued development of the College into a recognized center of excellence in engineering education and research will require a greatly expanded budget. Financial support requirements for undergraduate students are expected to increase 30 percent in the next six years, and an even greater increase will be required for minority and graduate students. The total annual cost of faculty salaries during the same period, in order to remain competitive, will nearly double by 1991, rising to over $18 million. At the same time, requirements for faculty salary supplements will increase threefold. Projected construction and renovation needs will require an outlay of $47 million, in addition to the expense already outlined for more modern equipment. The development of academic support on both the department and College level will require a funding increase of over $8 million. The BER is expected to more than double the amount of funded research that it coordinates, from $24.8 million in fiscal year 1985 to $60 million in 1991. All of these figures are in 1985 dollars, and do not take monetary inflation into consideration.

## *External Support*

In order to meet its projected financial needs, the College must increasingly rely on sources of fiscal support apart from state–appropriated funds. The Engineering Foundation will remain one of the most important adjuncts of the College, providing funds for student assistance, faculty development, and programs for research excellence through contributions from alumni, industry, and other private sources. The Foundation must also continue its role in the management of the College, providing advice and direction in curricula and research. The departmental visiting committees will perform a similar function. These advisors are usually even more directly associated with the engineering and research activities of industry than the Engineering Foundation Advisory Council members. The endowment objective of both the Foundation and the visiting committees is to increase the number of endowed positions in the College by a total of ninety–three, including nineteen chairs endowed for $500,000 and twenty–three for $1 million. Together with an enhanced effort in providing for the improvement of teaching and research facilities and student aid, the Engineering Foundation and the visiting committees will expedite progress toward the goal of academic excellence.

## *Conclusion*

Technological progress is the key to the future economic security of Texas. Development can only come through a lengthy process of research and application. This will require an unprecedented investment in higher education, especially engineering, and the establishment of recognized centers of academic excellence within the state. The College of Engineering at The University of Texas at Austin has demonstrated its commitment to the goal of a better quality of life and has set forth a plan for sustained growth in the immediate future. With the continued support of loyal alumni and friends of the College, the engineering program will continue to develop in the context of a "university of the first class."

# EPILOGUE:

## *A Challenge for the Future*

The first century of the College of Engineering provided a price-less heritage: one to reflect upon, to uphold, and to nurture. This rich heritage is a tribute to the shining academic qualities of the past, which were a reflection of the societal needs of the era. Change is inevitable but educational excellence cannot be maintained or expanded without ceaseless development of faculty, of teaching effectiveness, of research, of continuing professional education, and of technology transfer. Clearly a world–class engineering college can make the difference between creditable technological contributions and a lesser standard of livelihood. To achieve these levels of expectation, substantial funds must be dedicated toward the development and maintenance of a pre-scribed center of teaching excellence; but, more important, objectivity and dedication of purpose are of primary concern.

When at the crossroads of development, it is time to ponder the future and develop strategies. The College must commit itself to integrating the necessary disciplines to expedite technological leadership. Faculty must look beyond parochial issues and promote leadership by adopting changes in curric-ula appropriate to the evolution of society and the mission of the College. Engineering curricula, in this age of technology, must also systematically consider the dignity of mankind through the inclusion of liberal arts courses. Increasing the breadth of traditional curricula at the expense of disciplinary programs will not be easy, but the bottom line is academic leadership.

Faculty must assume the responsibility to move beyond specific disciplines and provide an educational process that will instill leadership capa-bilities in students. Faculty have the primary opportunity for exploring new ways of developing technological leadership in the student. This is an important concept for the future, because engineers will be asked to be more sensitive to the problems about which they have the capability of doing some good. Surely, the faculty must continue to develop analytical capacities in their pupils. Excessive specialization within a traditional four–year undergraduate time frame is probably the most immediate problem faculty must address in the next decade.

Much has been written about teaching effectiveness, but what about "teaching" during the coming decades? The leadership of the faculty will most likely be exhibited through the lecture and conventional professor–student contact. Greater effort must be put forth to improve the teaching skills of the faculty. To accomplish this goal, the College must overcome some great myths. The most persistent is that every person who holds a doctorate is a learned individual and therefore can teach without help and guidance in teaching effectiveness. A second myth is that educational productivity is dependent on the time students are kept in the program. Knowledge is accumulating at a rapid rate, and increased productivity by the student and professor is paramount. This task will be no less difficult in the future, because faculty have shown resistance to technological change.

Today, and even more so in the future within a multifaceted and complex society, technologically oriented programs will develop through the organized efforts of many. This means that technology development and transfer will require reevaluation. In contrast to ancient times, when new knowledge and its appreciation was generally thought to be the product of individual genius and required a long time to develop, special effort is now underway to bring the combined talents of many to productive use as quickly as possible. Professional associations will most likely become more necessary, for the modern engineering community relies on organization to share information.

As the engineer has been the heir of the ages, sound instinct has worked to keep technology open to new and developing talents. The profession historically has not allowed itself to ossify into a learned caste. It is reasonable to believe that as long as the engineering educators work cooperatively with the practitioners, future graduates from The University of Texas at Austin will be proud to list "engineer" as their profession.

# NOTES

## NOTES TO INTRODUCTION

1. Benjamin R. Teare, Jr., "Graduate Programs and Research in Engineering Colleges in the United States of America," *Journal of Engineering Education* 51 (January 1961): 354–355; James K. Finch, *The Story of Engineering*, 3d ed. (New York: Doubleday, 1960), p. 257; Richard S. Kirby et al., *Engineering in History* (New York: McGraw–Hill, 1956), p. 495.

2. Finch, *The Story of Engineering*, pp. 137, 163; W. H. G. Armytage, *A Social History of Engineering* (London: Faber and Faber, 1961), pp. 77–78, 95–96; Richard S. Kirby and Philip G. Laurson, *The Early Years of Modern Civil Engineering* (New Haven: Yale University Press, 1932), pp. 136, 298; F. O. Macmillan, "Our Heritage From Engineering Education," *Electrical Engineering* 71 (June 1952): 487; Frederic T. Mavis, "History of Engineering Education," in *Centennial of Engineering, 1852–1952: History and Proceedings of Symposia*, ed. Lenox R. Lohr (Chicago: Centennial of Engineering, 1952, Incorporated, 1953), p. 191.

3. James K. Finch, *A History of the School of Engineering at Columbia University* (New York: Columbia University Press, 1954), pp. 3–6; Armytage, *A Social History*, p. 96; Kirby and Laurson, *The Early Years*, pp. xvi, 14–15, 18n, 24–25; Finch, *The Story of Engineering*, p. 185.

4. Armytage, *A Social History*, pp. 84–91, 100; Kirby and Laurson, *The Early Years*, p. xvi; John E. Watkins, "The Beginnings of Engineering," in *The Civil Engineer: His Origins*, ed. Clifford A. Betts et al. (New York: American Society of Civil Engineers, 1970), p. 33.

5. Armytage, *A Social History*, pp. 100–105; James K. Finch, "The Evolution of the Engineering Profession: An Historical Outline," in Lohr, ed., *Centennial of Engineering*, p. 128; Willis R. Woolrich, *Men of Ingenuity from Beneath the Orange Tower 1884–1964* (Austin: Engineering Foundation of the College of Engineering, The University of Texas at Austin, 1964), pp. 7–8; R. D. Henson, "The Development of Engineering as a Profession," *Electrical Engineering* 70 (March 1951): 215; Willis R. Woolrich, "The Recognition of the Engineering Profession and the Engineering Council for Professional Development," *Texas Engineer* 8 (February 1938): 8–12.

6. Finch, *Columbia University*, pp. 5, 8–9; Armytage, *A Social History*, pp. 149–150, 328; Woolrich, *Men of Ingenuity*, pp. 10–11; Macmillan, "Our Heritage," p. 488; E. G. Sterland, "The Teaching of Engineering in Cambridge University," *Engineering*, June 19, 1953, 796–797; Watkins, "The Beginnings of Engineering," p. 31.

7. Armytage, *A Social History*, p. 188; Finch, *Engineering and Western Civilization* (New York: McGraw–Hill, 1951), pp. 308–310; J. Ford Johnston, "Technical Education in Germany and the United States," *Journal of Architecture, Engineering, and Industry* 1 (December 1938): 4; Mavis, "History of Engineering Education," p. 191; Finch, *Columbia University*, p. 3.

8. Armytage, *A Social History*, pp. 177–178; Lawrence P. Grayson, "The American Revolution and the Want of Engineers," *Engineering Education* 75 (February 1985): 268–274.

9. Henry C. Dethloff, *A Centennial History of Texas A&M University 1876–1976*, vol. 2 (College

Station: Texas A&M University Press, 1975), p. 245; Woolrich, *Men of Ingenuity*, pp. 7–8, 10–11; Armytage, *A Social History*, pp. 177–178; MacMillan, "Our Heritage," pp. 488–489; H. P. Hammond, "Engineering Education—The Past," *Journal of Engineering Education* 34 (September 1943): 29; H. G. Good, *A History of American Education*, 2d ed. (New York: Macmillan, 1962), pp. 288–289; Mavis, "History of Engineering Education," p. 191; Grayson, "The American Revolution and the Want of Engineers," pp. 274–275; Watkins, "The Beginnings of Engineering," p. 39.

10. Armytage, *A Social History*, pp. 160, 177–178; Woolrich, *Men of Ingenuity*, pp. 10–11; Kirby et al., *Engineering in History*, p. 495; Kirby and Laurson, *The Early Years of Modern Civil Engineering*, p. 133; Dethloff, *Centennial History*, vol. 2, p. 245; Henson, "Development of Engineering," p. 215; George A. Stetson, "100 Years of Engineering," *Mechanical Engineering* 74 (November 1952): 867–876; Mavis, "History of Engineering Education," p. 191; Watkins, "The Beginnings of Engineering," pp. 76–78; Willis R. Woolrich, "The Rise and Development of Engineering Education in the United States," *Texas Professional Engineer* 13 (March 1954): 10–11, 20–23.

11. Finch, *The Story of Engineering*, p. 258.

12. Armytage, *A Social History*, pp. 168, 178; Thorndike Saville, "Achievements in Engineering Education," in Lohr, ed., *Centennial of Engineering*, p. 332; Teare, "Graduate Programs and Research," pp. 355, 358; Woolrich, *Men of Ingenuity*, pp. 17–18; Hammond, "Engineering Education," p. 29; Willis R. Woolrich, "50 Years of Progress in Engineering Education," *National Engineer* 51 (August 1947): 598; Mavis, "History of Engineering Education," p. 191.

13. Armytage, *A Social History*, pp. 168–170; Mavis, "History of Engineering Education," p. 191; Kirby and Laurson, *Early Years*, pp. 41, 104.

14. Blake R. Van Leer, "Discussion of 'History of Engineering Education, by Frederic T. Mavis,'" in Lohr, ed., *Centennial of Engineering*, p. 200; Woolrich, *Men of Ingenuity*, pp. 10–11, 18; Thomas U. Taylor and Richard Denny Parker, "Engineering," *University Record* 2 (June 1900): 144–145; C. W. Crawford, *One Hundred Years of Engineering at Texas A&M 1876–1976* (College Station: Privately Printed, 1976), pp. 18–20.

15. Harry Yandell Benedict, *A Source Book for the University of Texas* (Austin: Privately Printed, 1917), p. 2; Thomas U. Taylor, "Fifty Years on Forty Acres", vol. 3, p. 6, TSS, n.d., Thomas Ulvan Taylor Papers, Barker Texas History Center, The University of Texas at Austin, henceforth cited as BTHC.

16. Benedict, *Source Book*, pp. 15–16.

17. Benedict, *Source Book*, p. 17; John J. Lane, *History of the University of Texas* (Austin: Privately Printed, 1891), p. 3.

18. Benedict, *Source Book*, pp. 61–64, 86–87, 170–171.

19. Benedict, *Source Book*, p. 161.

20. Benedict, *Source Book*, pp. 233–234.

21. Taylor, "Fifty Years," vol. 3, pp. 4–5, Taylor Papers, BTHC; Benedict, *Source Book*, pp. 260–263.

22. Benedict, *Source Book*, pp. 260–263; Joe B. Frantz, *Forty Acres Follies* (Austin: Texas Monthly Press, 1982), pp. 1–5.

23. Ellen H. Marquis, "The Acequias of San Antonio during the Spanish Mission Period, 1680–1793," *Texas Civil Engineer* 50 (May 1980): 19–21; William J. Powell, "A Century of Engineering in Texas," *Texas Engineer* 23 (January 1953): 7–11; "Historical Landmark Dedicated Last Year in San Antonio," *Texas Civil Engineer* 49 (November 1979): 4.

24. Benedict, *Source Book*, pp. 89–90; Lane, *History of the University of Texas*, p. 192.

25. Benedict, *Source Book*, p. 109.

26. Benedict, *Source Book*, p. 271; Woolrich, *Men of Ingenuity*, pp. 17–18.

27. Benedict, *Source Book*, p. 288.

28. *Catalog of the University of Texas, 1883–1884* (Austin: The University of Texas, 1884–1985), pp. 55–56, 62.

29. Carl J. Eckhardt, *The Promise of Greatness: Early Experiences at The University of Texas* (Austin: Privately Published, 1978), p. 18; Frantz, *Forty Acres Follies*, p. 3; Thomas U. Taylor, *Fifty Years on Forty Acres* (Kingsport, TN: Kingsport Press, 1938), p. 83; Woolrich, *Men of Ingenuity*, pp. 20–21.

30. Woolrich, *Men of Ingenuity*, pp. 17–18, 21; *Catalog, 1883–1884*, p. 20; *Report of the President and Faculty, The University of Texas, 1898–1899* (Austin: The University of Texas, 1899), pp. 294–295.

31. *Report of the President and Faculty, 1898–1899*, p. 20; "John William Mallet, A.B., Ph.D., M.D., LL.D., F.R.S., F.R.C.," *Alcalde* 1 (April–August, 1913): 17; Taylor, "Fifty Years," vol. 3, p. 46, Taylor Papers, BTHC.

32. "John William Mallet," p. 17; Woolrich, *Men of Ingenuity*, p. 21; *Texas Siftings* 3 (September 22, 1883): 5.

33. Woolrich, *Men of Ingenuity*, p. 21; *Catalog, 1884–1885*, p. 5.

34. John A. Focht, "Civil Engineering at the University of Texas at Austin, 1883–1917," *Texas Civil Engineer* 53 (June–July 1983): 18–19; *Catalog, 1883–1884*, pp. 5, 10, 12, 14, 18, 31; "Report of the Board of Regents, 1883–1884," in *Catalog, 1883–1884*, p. 6; "Supplement," in *Catalog, 1883–1884*,

p. 8; Frederick C. Morse, *The Ex–Students History of The University of Texas in Pictures* (Austin: Ex–Students Association, The University of Texas at Austin, 1970), p. 6.

35. *Catalog, 1885–1886*, pp. 15, 20–21, 54; *Faculty Report of The University of Texas, 1887–1888* (Austin: The University of Texas, 1888–1902), p. 17.

36. Woolrich, *Men of Ingenuity*, p. 21; *Catalog, 1886–1887*, pp. 10–12; *Faculty Report, 1887–1888*, pp. 5, 17; *Catalog, 1887–1888*, pp. 9–16.

37. William H. P. Hunnicutt to Dean Thomas U. Taylor, February 13, 1913, speech of James C. Nagle, February 21, 1913, in "Thomas Ulvan Taylor's Quarter–Centennial Book," pp. 110–112, 319–324, TSS, 1913, Taylor Papers, BTHC.

## NOTES TO FIFTY YEARS ON FORTY ACRES

1. *Catalog, 1887–1888*, p. 5; Taylor, *Fifty Years*, pp. 92–93, 186–187; J. Neils Thompson, "The Paradox We Face," *Alcalde* 45 (October 1952): 20–21, 36; Scrapbook, 1898, Taylor Papers, BTHC; Eckhardt, *Fifty Stars in the University Firmament* (Austin: Privately Printed, 1977), pp. 94–95; Dean Taylor to William M. W. Splawn, President of The University of Texas, May 8, 1926, in President's Office Files, BTHC; *Dallas Morning News*, May 29, 1941; *New York Times*, January 18, 1940; *Austin American Statesman*, January 14, 1940; John A. Focht, "Memoir: Thomas Ulvan Taylor, Honorary Member of the American Society of Civil Engineers," in Faculty File: Thomas U. Taylor, Office of the Dean of Engineering, henceforth cited as ODE; interview with Professor Leonardt F. Kreisle, February 8, 1985.

2. Taylor, *Fifty Years*, p. 81; Morse, *Ex–Students' History*, pp. 1–6; *Daily Texan*, November 25, 1926; speech of James C. Nagle in "Taylor's Quarter–Centennial Book," pp. 319–324, Taylor Papers, BTHC.

3. Taylor, *Fifty Years*, pp. 82–85; Eckhardt, *Promise of Greatness*, pp. 37–38; Thomas U. Taylor, "Dr. Leslie Waggener as I Knew Him," *Alcalde* 5 (March 1917): 213–214; *Daily Texan*, November 24, 1912.

4. *Catalog, 1888–1889*, pp. 5, 57–58; *Faculty Report, 1888–1889*, pp. 11–12.

5. Benedict, *Source Book*, pp. 177–182, 186, 206; Lane, *History of The University of Texas*, p. 197.

6. Morse, *Ex–Students' History*, p. 4; Lane, *History of The University of Texas*, pp. 7–10; Benedict, *Source Book*, pp. 353–354, 207–208.

7. Taylor, "Fifty Years," vol. 3, pp. 89–90, Taylor Papers, BTHC; Frantz, *Forty Acres Follies*, p. 1; Lane, *History of The University of Texas*, pp. 7–10, 78–80, 84–85; Benedict, *Source Book*, pp. 233–234, 239–240, 265, 315, 355, 394–395; *Catalog, 1883–1884*, p. 8; David F. Prindle, "Oil and the Permanent University Fund," *Southwestern Historical Quarterly* 86 (October 1982): 277–278.

8. Lane, *History of The University of Texas*, pp. 69, 75, 143–149; *Daily Texan*, November 29, 1924; Harry Y. Benedict, President of The University of Texas, to Dean Taylor, January 20, 1934, and Scrapbook, 1898, Taylor Papers, BTHC; Woolrich, *Men of Ingenuity*, pp. 58–59.

9. Focht, "Civil Engineering," p. 18; *Faculty Report, 1888–1889*, p. 11; Woolrich, *Men of Ingenuity*, p. 46; *Catalog, 1889–1890*, pp. 54–55.

10. Eckhardt, *Promise of Greatness*, pp. 37–39; *Catalog, 1892–1893*, pp. 56, 59; *Catalog, 1894–1895*, pp. 111–114; James D. McFarland, "The Development of the College of Engineering at The University of Texas," pp. 1–2, TSS, n.d., History File, ODE.

11. *Catalog, 1890–1891*, p. 7; *Catalog, 1891–1892*, p. 5; *Catalog, 1892–1893*, pp. 6, 29, 32; *University Record* 2 (December 1901): 394–395.

12. Benedict, *Source Book*, pp. 371, 388, 395; Taylor, *Fifty Years*, pp. 100–101; Scrapbook, 1894, Taylor Papers, BTHC.

13. Woolrich, *Men of Ingenuity*, pp. 21–22; *Catalog, 1894–1895*, pp. 123–125; *Cactus, 1895* (Austin: The University of Texas, 1895–1986), pp. 89–90.

14. *Faculty Report, 1895–1896*, pp. 24–25; *Faculty Report, 1897–1898*, p. 3; *Catalog, 1896–1897*, p. 114; *Catalog, 1897–1898*, p. 105; *Catalog, 1898–1899*, p. 7, 112–124; *Cactus, 1897*, pp. 7, 50; speech of Dean Taylor, February 21, 1913, in "Taylor's Quarter–Centennial Book," pp. 378–383, Taylor Papers, BTHC; interview with Professor Kreisle, February 8, 1985; Taylor, *Fifty Years*, p. 107.

15. Woolrich, *Men of Ingenuity*, pp. 47–48; *Cactus, 1896*, p. 26; *University Record* 6 (February 1905): 59; *The Department of Engineering, 1904*, Bulletin of The University of Texas, no. 110 (1904), henceforth cited as UT Bulletin; "Engineering Faculty Minutes," vol. 1: January 1906 to May 1927, minutes of meetings on April 20, 1912, May 21, 1925, MSS and TSS, ODE; L. L. Click, "Summer School Opens," *Alcalde* 15 (January 1927): 187; John A. Focht, *An Engineer Remembers* (Austin: Privately Printed, 1978), p. 119.

16. *Faculty Report, 1898–1899*, p. 3; *Catalog, 1901–1902*, p. 139; *Cactus, 1899*, p. 16; *Cactus, 1901*, p. 48; *Cactus, 1902*, pp. 17, 63, 66; Carl J. Eckhardt, Jr., *Fifty Stars*, pp. 10–11; Woolrich, *Men of Ingenuity*, p. 48; "Edward Christian Henry Bantel," *Journal of Architecture, Engineering, and Industry* 6 (November 1944): 2–3, 29.

17. Woolrich, *Men of Ingenuity*, p. 48; Thomas U. Taylor, "The Engineering Department," *Uni-*

versity Record 4 (July 1902): 378–380; Catalog, 1902–1903, p. 8; Catalog, 1905–1906, p. 171; Catalog, 1909–1910, pp. 232–233; Faculty Report, 1901–1902, p. 76; William J. Battle, "A Concise History of The University of Texas 1883–1950," Southwestern Historical Quarterly 54 (April 1951): 411.

18. Taylor, "Engineering Department," University Record 4 (July 1902): 378–380; Faculty Report, 1898–1899, p. 295; Catalog, 1903–1904, p. 174; Woolrich, Men of Ingenuity, pp. 48, 130–132; Catalog, 1911–1912, pp. 204–205; C. W. Crawford, One Hundred Years, p. 36.

19. Faculty Report, 1900–1901, p. 30; Faculty Report, 1901–1902, pp. 76–77; Thomas U. Taylor, "The Department of Engineering," The University Record 5 (August 1903): 189; Daily Texan, November 23, 1912; Cactus, 1899, p. 52; N. T. Blackburn to Dean Taylor, January 30, 1913, in "Taylor's Quarter–Centennial Book," p. 189, Taylor Papers, BTHC; Cactus, 1900, p. 8; Cactus, 1904, pp. 56–57; Walter M. W. Splawn, "The University of Texas—Its Origin and Growth to 1928," vol. 1, p. 84, TSS, n.d., Walter Marshall William Splawn Papers, BTHC.

20. San Antonio Daily Express, September 3, 1905; Report of the Board of Regents, December 1899 (Austin: The University of Texas, 1885–1919), p. 10; Regents' Report, October 1902, p. 30; Benedict, Source Book, pp. 435–436; Thomas U. Taylor, "The Department of Engineering," University Record 7 (February 1905): 57–58; Margaret C. Berry, The University of Texas: A Pictorial Account of Its First Century (Austin: The University of Texas Press, 1980), p. 66.

21. San Antonio Daily Express, September 3, 1905; Taylor, "Engineering," University Record 7 (February 1905): 55–57; Taylor, "The Engineering Department," University Record 7 (August 1905): 164–165; Catalog, 1906–1907, pp. 176–179; Catalog, 1911–1912, p. 209; The University of Texas, The Engineering Department, UT Bulletin, no. 40 (1905), pp. 11–20.

22. Taylor, "Engineering," University Record 7 (February 1905): 53–55; Taylor, "Engineering," University Record 8 (October 1906): 143–145; Cactus, 1905, p. 27; Cactus, 1906, p. 315; Crawford, One Hundred Years, p. 31; Taylor, Fifty Years, p. 104.

23. "Engineering Faculty Minutes," vol. 1, December 8, 1907, October 18, 1910, ODE; Woolrich, Men of Ingenuity, p. 169; Frantz, Forty Acres Follies, p. 34; Scrapbook, 1907, Taylor Papers, BTHC; Catalog, 1911–1912, pp. 212, 217, 220.

24. Woolrich, Men of Ingenuity, pp. 83, 91–93, 126–127; Cactus, 1906, p. 315; Catalog, 1910–1911, p. 196–200; Crawford, One Hundred Years, p. 37.

25. Focht, An Engineer Remembers, p. 127; "Report of the Department of Drawing for 1936," TSS, n.d., Records of the College of Engineering, BTHC.

26. "Engineering Faculty Minutes," vol. 1, January 23, 1906, October 21, 1913, ODE; Focht, "Civil Engineering," p. 20; Catalog, 1910–1911, p. 194; Catalog, 1912–1913, p. 227; Catalog, 1913–1914, p. 256.

27. Taylor, Fifty Years, p. 105.

28. Cactus, 1919, p. 32.

29. Focht, "Civil Engineering," p. 21; Texas Engineering Notes 1 (February 1917): 1; Eckhardt, Fifty Stars, pp. 30–31; Woolrich, Men of Ingenuity, p. 118.

30. "Engineering Faculty Minutes," vol. 1, November 19 and 25, 1913, January 20, 1914, November 28, 1916, December 19, 1916, ODE; E. J. Amey, "The Texas Highway Department," Journal of Architecture, Engineering, and Industry 1 (March 1939): 5–6, 16–17.

31. Woolrich, Men of Ingenuity, pp. 148–150; Catalog, 1916–1917, p. 218; "Engineering Faculty Minutes," vol. 1, December 19, 1916, ODE; Catalog, 1920–1921, p. 216; Splawn, "The University of Texas," vol. 1, p. 53, Splawn Papers, BTHC; McFarland, "Development," p. 5, History File, ODE.

32. Woolrich, Men of Ingenuity, pp. 27, 131–132; "Engineering Faculty Minutes," vol. 1, December 19, 1916, ODE.

33. Catalog, 1917–1918, p. 212; Berry, Pictorial Account, p. 152; Eckhardt, Fifty Stars, pp. 80–81.

34. Woolrich, Men of Ingenuity, pp. 108–109; "Engineering Faculty Minutes," vol. 1, May 23, October 18, 1917, ODE.

35. Woolrich, Men of Ingenuity, pp. 108–109; Catalog, 1920–1921, p. 214; The Department of Engineering, UT Bulletin, no. 1715 (March 10, 1917), pp. 18–19.

36. Woolrich, Men of Ingenuity, pp. 108–110; Catalog, 1927–1928, p. 257.

37. Berry, Pictorial Account, pp. 158–159; Dethloff, Centennial History of Texas A&M, vol. 2, p. 250.

38. Woolrich, Men of Ingenuity, pp. 83–84; "Engineering Faculty Minutes," vol. 1, December 4, 1917, March 5, 1918, ODE; Crawford, One Hundred Years, pp. 24, 32.

39. Woolrich, Men of Ingenuity, p. 50; Taylor, Fifty Years, pp. 245–246, 251–252.

40. Taylor, Fifty Years, p. 251; Morse, Ex–Students' History, pp. 68–69.

41. Splawn, "The University of Texas," vol. 1, p. 54, Splawn Papers, BTHC; "Engineering Faculty Minutes," vol. 1, March 5, 1918, ODE.

42. Berry, Pictorial Account, p. 39; Taylor, Fifty Years, pp. 106–107; Focht, An Engineer Remembers, p. 70; "Engineering Faculty Minutes," vol. 1, January 18, 1919, ODE; Woolrich, Men of Ingenuity, pp. 28, 51.

43. Woolrich, *Men of Ingenuity*, pp. 50–51; "Engineering Faculty Minutes," vol. 1, March 5, 1918, ODE.

44. Woolrich, *Men Of Ingenuity*, pp. 28–29; Berry, *Pictorial Account*, p. 212; Benedict, *Source Book*, p. 569.

45. Steven Land Tillotson, *Remnant of an Era: The History of the Little Campus Site 1859–1977* (Austin: The University of Texas at Austin, 1978), p. 167.

46. Tillotson, *Remnant*, p. 167.

47. Tillotson, *Remnant*, p. 168; Woolrich, *Men of Ingenuity*, p. 72.

48. Tillotson, *Remnant*, p. 168; Woolrich, *Men of Ingenuity*, pp. 28–29.

49. Tillotson, *Remnant*, pp. 171, 180, 183–184.

50. Tillotson, *Remnant*, p. 171; Benedict, *Source Book*, p. 536.

51. Tillotson, *Remnant*, pp. 182–183, 185, 187–188; Morse, *Ex–Students' History*, pp. 68–69; *Cactus, 1919*, p. 145.

52. Berry, *Pictorial Account*, p. 213; Taylor, *Fifty Years*, pp. 250–252; *Cactus, 1919*, p. 207.

53. Woolrich, *Men of Ingenuity*, pp. 29, 50–51, 152; "Engineering Faculty Minutes," vol. 1, January 18, 1919, ODE; Edward C. H. Bantel to Robert E. Vinson, President of The University of Texas, January 20, 1919, President's Office Files, BTHC; Morse, *Ex–Students' History*, p. 70; Saville, "Achievements in Engineering Education," p. 218.

54. Woolrich, *Men of Ingenuity*, pp. 11, 29–30.

55. Dean Taylor to President Vinson, July 10, 1917, July 18, 1919, October 19, 1921, Dean Taylor to President Splawn, June 10, 1926, President's Office Files, BTHC.

56. Woolrich, *Men of Ingenuity*, p. 85; Dethloff, *Centennial History*, vol. 2, p. 250; "Engineering Faculty Minutes," vol. 1, November 26, 1923, March 18, 1926, May 20, 1927, ODE; Splawn, "The University of Texas," vol. 2, pp. 480–481, Splawn Papers, BTHC.

57. Woolrich, *Men of Ingenuity*, pp. 85–87; *Catalog, 1930–1931*, p. 95.

58. "Engineering Faculty Minutes," vol. 1, March 18, 1920, ODE; *Dallas News*, January 11, 1925; Berry, *Pictorial Account*, pp. 158–160.

59. Carl J. Eckhardt, Jr., *Fifty Who Loved and Served The University* (Austin: Privately Printed, 1978), p. 102; Woolrich, *Men of Ingenuity*, pp. 118–120, 152–153; *Catalog, 1928–1929*, p. 279; *Texas Engineering Notes* 1 (February 1917): 1; Dean Taylor to President Splawn, February 7, July 13 and 23, 1925, President's Office Files, BTHC; interview with Professor Focht, February 11, 1985; Focht, *An Engineer Remembers*, pp. 116–117, 123.

60. "Report of a Small Preliminary Conference of Inquiry on the Subject of Commercial Engineering . . . ," Dean Taylor to President Vinson, May 1, 1919, President's Office Files, BTHC; "Engineering Faculty Minutes," vol. 1, May 20, 1927, ODE; *Catalog, 1928–1929*, p. 251; "Minutes of the Civil Engineering Faculty Meeting, October 3, 1935," TSS, Records of the College of Engineering, BTHC.

61. Taylor, *Fifty Years*, p. 108; Splawn, "The University of Texas," vol. 2, p. 436, Splawn Papers, BTHC; *Daily Texan*, September 19, 1926.

62. Woolrich, *Men of Ingenuity*, pp. 150–151; "Engineering Faculty Minutes," vol. 1, January 16, 1923, April 19, 1923, ODE; Splawn, "The University of Texas," vol. 2, p. 455–457, Splawn Papers, BTHC; *Daily Texan*, March 3 and September 19, 1926.

63. Taylor, *Fifty Years*, p. 108; Splawn, "The University of Texas," vol. 2, p. 468, Splawn Papers, BTHC; *Daily Texan*, September 19, 1926; "Engineering Faculty Minutes," vol. 1, April 27, 1925, ODE.

64. Woolrich, *Men of Ingenuity*, pp. 72–73; *Catalog, 1927–1928*, p. 236; "University Aeronautical Society," *University of Texas Engineer* 1 (January 1931): 36; John M. Bryant to President Splawn, August 4, 1926, President's Office Files, BTHC.

65. Woolrich, *Men of Ingenuity*, pp. 72–73; *Catalog, 1927–1928*, pp. 270–271; Bryant to Dean Taylor, June 9, 1927, President's Office Files, BTHC.

66. Woolrich, *Men of Ingenuity*, p. 161; *Catalog, 1927–1928*, pp. 236, 271; McFarland, "Development," p. 5, History File, ODE; "A Memorial to the Advisory Board of the Department of Petroleum Engineering of The University of Texas," p. 2, TSS, 1956, photocopy in History File, ODE; W. Keene Ferguson, *History of the Bureau of Economic Geology, 1909–1960* (Austin: Bureau of Economic Geology, The University of Texas at Austin, 1981), pp. 290–292.

67. Dean Taylor to President Vinson, September 25, 1916, President's Office Files, BTHC; Bantel to President Vinson, in "Engineering Faculty Minutes," vol. 1, January 20, 1919, ODE.

68. "Memorial of Governor William P. Hobby, January 12, 1921," TSS, Splawn Papers, BTHC; Berry, *Pictorial Account*, p. 214; Margaret Berry, *UT Austin: Traditions and Nostalgia* (Austin: Shoal Creek Publishers, 1975), p. 51; "Engineering Faculty Minutes," vol. 1, February 12, 1923, ODE.

69. Prindle, "Oil and the Permanent University Fund," p. 278; Benedict, *Source Book*, pp. 461–462, 472, 564–565.

70. Benedict, *Source Book*, pp. 475–476, 478, 504; Morse, *Ex–Students' History*, p. 68.

71. Frantz, *Forty Acres Follies*, p. 123; Splawn, "The University of Texas," vol. 1, p. 257, Splawn

Papers, BTHC; Prindle, "Oil and the Permanent University Fund," p. 280; Eckhardt, *Fifty Stars*, pp. 98–99.

72. Frantz, *Forty Acres Follies*, p. 123; Prindle, "Oil and the Permanent University Fund," pp. 282, 286–287, 290.

73. Splawn, "The University of Texas," vol. 2, pp. 328–332, 345–346, 356, Splawn Papers, BTHC; *The University of Texas*, UT Bulletin, no. 2716 (April 22, 1927), p. 11.

74. Berry, *Pictorial Account*, p. 69; Morse, *Ex–Students' History*, p. 92; Woolrich, *Men of Ingenuity*, pp. 54–55; "Report of the Building Committee of the Engineering Faculty, March 18, 1926," TSS, President's Office Files, BTHC; "Engineering Faculty Minutes," vol. 1, March 18, 1926, May 11, 18, 1926, ODE.

75. Woolrich, *Men of Ingenuity*, pp. 54–55, 85, 152; *Cactus, 1927*, p. 104; E. J. Mathews, "Campus and Curriculum," *Alcalde* 15 (November 1926): 35.

76. Woolrich, *Men of Ingenuity*, p. 152; *Catalog, 1927–1928*, p. 236; Berry, *Pictorial Account*, pp. 71, 344; Robert L. White to Splawn, February 21, 1956, Splawn Papers, BTHC; Eckhardt, *Fifty Who Loved and Served The University*, p. 102; "Building Program Begins to Take Shape," *Alcalde* 16 (February 1928): 227.

77. "Building Begins, Contracts Let," *Alcalde* 20 (February 1932): 105; "Hydraulic Gun Dedication," *Alcalde* 22 (October 1933): 8; "The Engineering Building," *Alcalde* 22 (December 1933): 57–58; "Engineering Faculty Minutes," vol. 1, May 18, 1926, ODE; Splawn, "The University of Texas," vol. 2, Appendix C, Splawn Papers, BTHC; Berry, *Pictorial Account*, pp. 57–58.

78. Woolrich, *Men of Ingenuity*, pp. 54–55; "Ten Months of Building: A Survey of the Plans for Texas," *Alcalde* 21 (November 1932): 33–34; "The Engineering Building," pp. 57–58; McFarland, "Development," p. 6, History File, ODE.

79. Splawn, "The University of Texas," vol. 2, Appendix C, Splawn Papers, BTHC; Berry, *Pictorial Account*, 57–58; Walter L. Rolfe, "The Architecture Building," *Alcalde* 22 (December 1933): 55–56.

80. Morse, *Ex–Students' History*, pp. 95–96; Woolrich, *Men of Ingenuity*, pp. 34–35; "Budget of the College of Engineering, 1930–1931, 1931–1932, and 1932–1933," TSS, Dean Taylor to President Benedict, July 5, 1933, Taylor Papers, BTHC; interview with Professor Focht, February 11, 1985; Focht, *An Engineer Remembers*, p. 127; Splawn, "The University of Texas," vol. 2, p. 379e, Splawn Papers, BTHC.

81. Woolrich, *Men of Ingenuity*, pp. 43, 251–252; Taylor, *Fifty Years*, p. 264.

82. Woolrich, *Men of Ingenuity*, pp. 264–265; *Faculty Report, 1901–1902*, p. 77; Splawn, "The University of Texas," vol. 2, p. 356, Splawn Papers, BTHC; *Daily Texan*, October 29, 1926; Edwin L. Caldwell, "Highlights of the Development of Manufacturing in Texas 1900–1960," *Southwestern Historical Quarterly* 68 (April 1965): 407; Ernest O. Thompson, "The Function of Geological and Engineering Science in the Conservation Movement: A Statistical Supplement," pp. 3–6, 9–12, TSS, n.d., BTHC; Walter P. Webb and H. Bailey Carroll, *The Handbook of Texas*, vol. 2 (Austin: Texas State Historical Association, 1952), p. 305; Gibb Gilchrist, "The History of Highway Development in Texas," *Texas Engineer* 6 (December 1936): 107; Colonel F. G. Jonah, "The Development of Railways in Texas," *Texas Engineer* 6 (December 1936): 57; Julian Montgomery, "The Development of Municipal Engineering in Texas," *Texas Engineer* 6 (December 1936): 82–93.

## NOTES TO MEN OF INGENUITY

1. *Engineering–Science News* 6 (July–August 1958).

2. Dean Taylor to Dean Willis R. Woolrich, August 21, 29, 1936, Records of the College of Engineering, BTHC; interview with Professor Kreisle, February 22, 1985; conversation with Professor Carl J. Eckhardt, Jr., April 14, 1985; Woolrich, *Men of Ingenuity*, pp. 55, 89.

3. Willis R. Woolrich, *Odyssey of a Professional Engineer* (San Antonio: Privately Printed, 1971), pp. 35–55; interviews with Professor Kreisle, February 22 and April 10, 1985; conversation with Professor Eckhardt, April 14, 1985.

4. Interview with Professor William A. Cunningham, May 8, 1985; interview with Professor Kreisle, February 22, 1985.

5. "Engineering Faculty Minutes," vol. 3: September 1937 to August 1944, minutes of meeting on January 19, 1940, ODE; interview with Professor Cunningham, May 8, 1985; interview with Professor Kreisle, April 10, 1985; interview with Dean John J. McKetta, Jr., May 10, 1985; interview with Professor Archie W. Straiton, May 8, 1985; Woolrich, *Men of Ingenuity*, pp. 33–34.

6. Israel W. Santry, Jr., *The First Fifty Years: A History of the Texas Section, American Society of Civil Engineers* (Dallas: Texas Section, American Society of Civil Engineers, 1964), pp. 1–29; J. M. Howe, "Foundation of Texas Section of American Society of Civil Engineers," *Texas Engineer* 3 (November 1933): 3–4; "The Birth of Texas Section, American Society of Civil Engineers," *Texas Civil Engineer* 53 (May 1983): 14; "Historical Sketch of the Texas Society of Professional Engineers," *Texas Professional Engineer* 10 (August 1951): 8; Uel Stephens, "The Texas State Board of Registration for Professional

Engineers," *Texas Professional Engineer* 22 (October 1964): 14–16; "NSPE: Fifty Years of Professionalism," *Professional Engineer* 54 (Summer 1984): 6–8.

7. "Engineering Faculty Minutes," vol. 2: October 1927 to November 1937, minutes of meeting on November 3, 1936, ODE; Dean Taylor to Dean Woolrich, August 21, 1936, Records of the College of Engineering, BTHC.

8. H. P. Hammond, "Engineering Education—The Past," *Journal of Engineering Education* 34 (September 1943): 29–30; F. O. MacMillan, "Our Heritage from Engineering Education," pp. 489–491; Woolrich, *Men of Ingenuity*, pp. 10–12, 43–44, 57.

9. Woolrich, *Men of Ingenuity*, pp. 10–12, 43–44, 57; "Woolrich Honored with ASEE Presidency," *Texas Professional Engineer* 11 (August 1952): 17.

10. *Catalog, 1958–1960*, Part IV, pp. 14–15; "Engineering Faculty Minutes," vol. 2, November 3, 1937, ODE; Woolrich, *Men of Ingenuity*, pp. 38–39, 57.

11. "Engineering Faculty Minutes," vol. 2, November 3, 1937, vol. 3, May 11, 1937, May 15, 1940, ODE; Woolrich, *Men of Ingenuity*, p. 57.

12. "Engineering Faculty Minutes," vol. 2, December 14, 1927, March 6 and May 28, 1928, February 11, 1931, May 10, 1934, November 5, 1935, November 3, 1937, vol. 3, November 1, 1938, April 8, 1941, ODE; *Catalog, 1936–1937*, IV, pp. 16–29; *Catalog, 1938–1939*, IV, pp. 18–33; *Catalog, 1941–1942*, IV, pp. 18–34; Quinton B. Graves, "The Growth of the College of Engineering," *Journal of Architecture, Engineering, and Industry* 7 (February 1946): 15.

13. "Engineering Faculty Minutes," vol. 2, March 25, 1937, vol. 3, September 16, 1940, ODE; *Catalog, 1936–1937*, VII, pp. 22–23; *Catalog, 1938–1939*, VII, p. 30; *Catalog, 1940–1941*, VII, p. 32; W. W. McLean, "Impressions of the New Chemical Engineering Practice Course," *Journal of Architecture, Engineering, and Industry* 3 (September 1940): 14; Woolrich, *Men of Ingenuity*, pp. 120–121.

14. *Catalog, 1936–1937*, VII, p. 9;"Engineering Faculty Minutes," vol. 2, November 17, 1933, ODE; Woolrich, *Men of Ingenuity*, pp. 44, 53, 55.

15. Woolrich, *Men of Ingenuity*, pp. 153, 170–171; "Report of the Committee on the Doctorate Degree with Major Work in Engineering," TSS, n.d., Records of the College of Engineering, BTHC; "Engineering Faculty Minutes," vol. 3, May 15, 1940, ODE; *Catalog, 1940–1941*, VII, p. 14.

16. William A. Felsing, Chairman of the Department of Chemistry at The University of Texas, to Homer P. Rainey, President of The University of Texas, December 22, 1939, Dean Woolrich to Harry L. Kent, Jr., Administrative Assistant, Texas Technical College, February 20, 1940, "Report of Committee," TSS, May 3, 1940, Records of the College of Engineering, BTHC; "Engineering Faculty Minutes," vol. 3, April 13, 1938, ODE; John Griswold, "The University of Texas Engineering Building," *Journal of Architecture, Engineering, and Industry* 3 (September 1940): 12; John Griswold, "The Present Status of the College of Engineering," *Journal of Architecture, Engineering, and Industry* 7 (February 1946): 17; Woolrich, *Men of Ingenuity*, pp. 38–39, 109, 111; Woolrich, *Odyssey*, p. 57; "Report of the Department of Petroleum Engineering," appended to "Annual Report of the College of Engineering, 1957–1958," TSS, History File, ODE.

17. Griswold, "University of Texas Chemical Engineering Building," p. 12; Edwin B. Dow, "Chemical Engineering at the University of Texas," *Journal of Architecture, Engineering, and Industry* 7 (February 1946): 33; Eugene P. Schoch to Dean Woolrich, December 20, 1939, Schoch to President Rainey, January 17, 1940, Records of the College of Engineering, BTHC; Woolrich, *Men of Ingenuity*, pp. 110–111, 162.

18. "Engineering Graduate School Report, 1936," TSS, Dean Woolrich to Donald Coney, Librarian of The University of Texas, June 26, 1939, Dean Woolrich to Alexander Moffit, Librarian of the College of Engineering, August 7, 1946, Raymond F. Dawson to Dean Woolrich, May 20, 1947, Records of the College of Engineering, BTHC.

19. "Engineering Faculty Minutes," vol. 1, December 13, 1907, January 28, May 20, and October 21, 1913, ODE; Dean Taylor to Edwin W. Winkler, Librarian of The University of Texas, May 26, 1933, Taylor Papers, BTHC; Woolrich, *Men of Ingenuity*, p. 210.

20. Dean Taylor to President Vinson, July 8, 1920, President's Office File, BTHC; Dean Taylor to the Members of the Administrative Council of The University of Texas, June 21, 1933, Taylor Papers, BTHC; Dean Taylor to Dean Woolrich, August 29, 1936, Records of the College of Engineering, BTHC; "Engineering Faculty Minutes," vol. 2, October 16, 1928, ODE; *Librarian's Report, 1934–1935, 1935–1936*, UT Bulletin, no. 3707 (February 15, 1937), pp. 5, 10.

21. "Engineering Faculty Minutes," vol. 2, February 2, 1936, vol. 3, November 3, 1942, ODE; Ethel G. Swafford, Librarian of the College of Engineering, to Dean Woolrich, September 1, 1940, November 1, 1941, Records of the College of Engineering, BTHC; Marian Seiders, "Your Engineering Library," *Journal of Architecture, Engineering, and Industry* 1 (December 1938): 22; Woolrich, *Men of Ingenuity*, p. 211.

22. *Catalog, 1934–1935*, IV, p. 8; *Catalog, 1940–1941*, IV, p. 9; *Catalog, 1949–1950*, IV, p. 18; "University Science and Engineering Libraries," *Journal of Engineering and Industrial Research* 11 (Spring 1952): 26; Woolrich, *Men of Ingenuity*, pp. 212–213.

23. John A. Focht, "The Engineering Students' Association," *Journal of Architecture, Engineer-*

*ing, and Industry* 1 (December 1938): 22; "Engineering Faculty Minutes," vol. 2, February 2, 1937, vol. 3, September 15, 1939, ODE; interview with Professor Straiton, May 8, 1985; Walter Rolfe, "Advising Students in the College," *Journal of Architecture, Engineering, and Industry* 1 (December 1938): 11; interview with Dean McKetta, May 10, 1985; Woolrich, *Men of Ingenuity*, pp. 56, 60–61.

24. "Engineering Faculty Minutes," vol. 2, April 7, 1937, vol. 7: September 1950 to April 1957, minutes of meetings on February 21 and November 25, 1952; Walter H. McNeill, "Getting Suitable Jobs for our Engineering Graduates," *Journal of Architecture, Engineering, and Industry* 1 (March 1939), 5–6: Woolrich, *Men of Ingenuity*, pp. 57, 60–61.

25. Woolrich, *Men of Ingenuity*, pp. 32–33.

26. "Engineering Faculty Minutes," vol. 2, April 7, 1937, ODE; Woolrich, *Men of Ingenuity*, pp. 58, 220–221; *Engineering Digest*, July–October 1979.

27. Woolrich, "Progress in the Mechanical Processing of Cottonseed," *Journal of Architecture, Engineering, and Industry* 2 (September 1939): 2, 34; L. W. Wallace, "There Are Frontiers," *Journal of Architecture, Engineering, and Industry* 2 (June 1940): 5; Alvin H. Willis, "Air Conditioning Research at the University," *Journal of Architecture, Engineering, and Industry* 1 (September 1938): 27–29; Byron E. Short, "Heat Transfer and Pressure Drop," *Journal of Architecture, Engineering, and Industry* 1 (September 1938): 5–6; interview with Professor Kreisle, April 10, 1985.

28. *Dr. E. P. Schoch, 1871–1961*, pamphlet, n.d., History File, ODE; interview with Professor Cunningham, May 8, 1985; Woolrich, *Men of Ingenuity*, pp. 225–229.

29. News Release, May 21, 1938, Records of the College of Engineering, BTHC; "Engineering Faculty Minutes," vol. 3, May 20, 1938, ODE.

30. "Engineering Faculty Minutes," vol. 2, November 4 and December 16, 1930, vol. 3, May 20, 1938, vol. 7, November 22, 1951, ODE; Woolrich, *Men of Ingenuity*, p. 58; *University of Texas Engineer* 1 (January 1931); *Engineering–Science News*, 1 (January–February 1953).

31. Quinton B. Graves, "The Growth of the College of Engineering," *Journal of Architecture, Engineering, and Industry* 7 (February 1946): 14–16; D. B. Prentice, "College Antecedents of Successful Engineers," *Mechanical Engineering* 71 (May 1949): 397–398.

32. Frantz, *Forty Acres Follies*, pp. 81–84; "Engineering Faculty Minutes," vol. 3, November 5, 1940, ODE; Woolrich, "The Dean's Letter," *Journal of Architecture, Engineering, and Industry* 3 (December 1940): 3; "The National Defense Program in the College of Engineering," TSS, n.d., Records of the College of Engineering, BTHC.

33. Leland L. Antes, "War Training Activities of the College of Engineering," *Journal of Architecture, Engineering, and Industry*, 7 (February 1946): 19; "Engineering Faculty Minutes," vol. 3, November 5, 1940, ODE; "The National Defense Program in the College of Engineering," Records of the College of Engineering, BTHC; Woolrich, *Men of Ingenuity*, pp. 35–36; Woolrich, *Odyssey*, p. 61.

34. Antes, "War Training Activities," pp. 19–20; "Engineering Faculty Minutes," vol. 4: April 1941 to July 1946, "The University of Texas Engineer in the War Effort," n.d., vol. 3, December 13, 1941, ODE; Woolrich, *Men of Ingenuity*, pp. 35–36, 111, 121, 153; interview with Professor Cunningham, May 8, 1985; interview with Professor Straiton, May 8, 1985; interview with Professor Kreisle, April 10, 1985.

35. Homer P. Rainey, "Your University Goes to War," TSS, February 20, 1942, Records of the College of Engineering, BTHC; "Engineering Faculty Minutes," vol. 3, February 23, 1943, ODE; Woolrich, *Men of Ingenuity*, pp. 35–36, 153, 111; Woolrich, *Odyssey*, pp. 60–61; Graves, "Growth of the College of Engineering," p. 14.

36. "The National Defense Program in the College of Engineering," Records of the College of Engineering, BTHC; "Engineering Faculty Minutes," vol. 3, September 15, 1941, July 25, 1942, ODE; *Catalog, 1943–1944*, IV, p. 20; Marilyn Broom, "The History of the Aeronautical Engineering Department," *Journal of Architecture, Engineering, and Industry* 7 (February 1946): 30; Woolrich, *Men of Ingenuity*, pp. 72–75, 155; "Origin and Development of Aero–Space Engineering at The University of Texas," mimeograph, n.d. [1963], pp. 5–6, History File, ODE.

37. "Origin and Development of Aero-Space Engineering," pp. 5–6, History File, ODE; Oran M. Roberts, "A History of the Establishment of the University of the State of Texas," *Quarterly of the Texas State Historical Association* 1 (April 1898): 244–247; "Sixteen Girls in Engineering at UT," *Texas Professional Engineer* 16 (May 1957): 13; Grace M. Kunkel, "Leah Moncure: P. E. No. 2250," photocopy, n.d., in History File, ODE.

38. Rainey, "Your University Goes to War," Records of the College of Engineering, BTHC; interview with Professor Straiton, May 8, 1985; interview with Professor Cunningham, May 8, 1985; Woolrich, *Men of Ingenuity*, pp. 111, 222–223; Graves, "Growth of the College of Engineering," p. 16.

39. "Engineering Faculty Minutes," vol. 3, October 28, 1936, ODE; Archie W. Straiton, "Electrical Engineering Advanced Degrees Conferred 1949–1961," TSS, n.d., in possession of Archie W. Straiton; Norman N. Barish, *Engineering Enrollment in the United States* (New York: New York University Press, 1957), pp. 11, 21; Frantz, *Forty Acres Follies*, pp. 200–201; Woolrich, *Men of Ingenuity*, pp. 36–37; Woolrich, *Odyssey*, pp. 62–63.

40. Teare, "Graduate Programs and Research," p. 355; L. E. Grinter, "A Survey of Current Changes That are Modernizing Engineering Education," *Journal of Engineering Education* 49 (March 1959): 559, 564; A. A. Potter, "Engineering Education—The Present," *Journal of Engineering Education* 34 (September 1943): 37; Robert M. Lockwood, "The Last Hundred Years," *Texas Business Review* 50 (January 1976): 5; Ross E. McKinney, "Ph.D. and P.E. in Civil Engineering Education," *Civil Engineering* 35 (March 1965): 48–49; Phil Simpson, "The Electronics Industry and Texas," *Texas Business Review* 34 (August 1960): 6–8; Phil Simpson, "The Electronics Industry and Texas," *Texas Business Review* 34 (September 1960): 13–16.

41. "Our First Woman Engineering Professor," *Journal of Architecture, Engineering, and Industry* 8 (August 1947): 11; James E. Brittain, "From Computor to Electrical Engineer: The Remarkable Career of Edith Clarke," *IEEE Transactions on Engineering Education* E-28 (November 1985): 184–189; interview with Professor Kreisle, April 10, 1985; interview with Professor Straiton, May 8, 1985; interview with Professor Cunningham, May 8, 1985; interview with Dean McKetta, May 10, 1985; Woolrich, *Men of Ingenuity*, pp. 60, 66, 122–123, 134–135, 165; *Phil M. Ferguson*, pamphlet, n.d., History File, ODE.

42. Interview with Professor Cunningham, May 8, 1985; interview with Dean McKetta, May 10, 1985; Woolrich, *Men of Ingenuity*, pp. 78–79, 154; "Engineering Research Projects," *Journal of Architecture, Engineering, and Industry* 7 (July 1946): 21–25.

43. "Engineering Research Projects," pp. 21–25; interview with Professor Straiton, May 8, 1985; interview with Dean McKetta, May 10, 1985; Woolrich, *Men of Ingenuity*, pp. 75–76, 134–136; conversation with Professors Harold W. Smith and William C. Duesterhoeft, September 12, 1985.

44. "Engineering Research Projects," pp. 21–25; Teare, "Graduate Programs and Research," p. 360; conversation with Dean Earnest F. Gloyna, April 14, 1985.

45. Woolrich, *Men of Ingenuity*, pp. 77–78, 121; *Engineering-Science News* 1 (May–June 1953); J. Neils Thompson, Director of the Balcones Research Center, to Norman Hackerman, President of The University of Texas at Austin, May 1, 1970, in *The University of Texas at Austin, Balcones Research Center, Twentieth Anniversary Report, December 20, 1979* (Austin: Balcones Research Center, The University of Texas at Austin, 1970), p. 1; James J. Kelly, *31 Years of Research: Balcones Research Center, The University of Texas at Austin* (Austin: Balcones Research Center, The University of Texas at Austin, 1978), p. 3; interview with Professor J. Neils Thompson, June 26, 1985.

46. F. D. Thompson, "University Research Aids Oil Industry," *Journal of Engineering and Industrial Research* 11 (Summer 1951): 10–12; *Catalog, 1958–1960*, IV, p. 10; Woolrich, *Men of Ingenuity*, p. 165; Harry H. Power to Dean Woolrich, August 26, 1957, in "Annual Report of the College of Engineering, 1955–1956," TSS. History File, ODE; *Annual Report of the Department of Petroleum Engineering, 1984–1985* (Austin: College of Engineering, The University of Texas at Austin, 1985), pp. 56–57; George H. Fancher, Robert L. Whiting, and James H. Cretsinger, *The Oil Resources of Texas: A Reconnaisance Survey of Primary and Secondary Reserves of Oil* (Austin: Texas Petroleum Research Council, 1954); conversation with Professor George H. Fancher, April 29, 1986.

47. "Engineering Faculty Minutes," vol. 4: April 1941 to July 1948, minutes of meeting on June 21, 1945, ODE; interview with Professor Cunningham, May 8, 1985; *Catalog, 1945–1946*, IV, p. 36; Woolrich, *Men of Ingenuity*, pp. 146–147.

48. "Engineering Faculty Minutes," vol. 4, June 24, 1948, vol. 5: September 1944 to August 1947, minutes of meetings on January 10 and August 30, 1945, September 17, 1946, ODE; *Catalog, 1946–1947*, IV, p. 41; *Catalog, 1951–1952*, VII, p. 52; Woolrich, *Men of Ingenuity*, pp. 39, 104–107.

49. "Engineering Faculty Minutes," vol. 4, April 4, 1946, April 13 and May 30, 1950, vol. 5, April 4, 1946, vol. 6: September 1947 to August 1950, minutes of meetings on April 13 and May 30, 1950, ODE; *Catalog, 1949–1950*, IV, pp. 50–51; Woolrich, *Men of Ingenuity*, pp. 100–103; *Engineering-Science News* 1 (November–December 1953); Milton J. Thompson to Dean Woolrich, July 5, 1956, in "Annual Report, 1955–1956," "Annual Report, 1957–1958," p. 7, History File, ODE.

50. "Engineering Faculty Minutes," vol. 4, February 14, 1946, ODE; *Catalog, 1947–1948*, VII, 7, 30; Woolrich, *Men of Ingenuity*, pp. 119, 138–143; *Engineering-Science News* 1 (January–February 1953).

51. "Engineering Faculty Minutes," vol. 7: September 1950 to April 1957, minutes of meeting on February 7, 1957, ODE; *Catalog, 1951–1952*, VII, pp. 28, 52; *Catalog, 1955–1956*, VII, p. 33; Woolrich, *Men of Ingenuity*, pp. 125, 127–128, 170–171; "Annual Report, 1956–1957," p. 4, History File, ODE.

52. "Engineering Faculty Minutes," vol. 3, May 12 and October 14, 1943, vol. 4, April 17, 1947, May 17, 1951, vol. 5, May 17, 1951, ODE; *Catalog, 1943–1944*, IV, p. 24; *Catalog, 1949–1950*, IV, pp. 30, 38; Berry, *Pictorial Account*, pp. 158–160; Woolrich, *Men of Ingenuity*, pp. 91–98; Werner W. Dornberger to Dean Woolrich, n.d., in "Annual Report, 1956–1957," History File, ODE.

53. "Engineering Faculty Minutes," vol. 7, September 16 and November 12, 1953, ODE; Woolrich, *Men of Ingenuity*, pp. 39–40.

54. Engineering Faculty Minutes," vol. 7, February 12, 1953, March 12, 1955, ODE; Woolrich,

*Odyssey,* pp. 62–63; interview with Professor Cunningham, May 8, 1985; interview with Dean McKetta, May 10, 1985; Woolrich, *Men of Ingenuity,* pp. 198–201; "Annual Report, 1956–1957," p. 2, "Annual Report, 1957–1958," p. 2, History File, ODE.

55. Joe J. King to Richard B. McCaslin, January 16, 1986, William B. Franklin to McCaslin, January 16, 1986, "Annual Report, 1956–1957," p. 2, "Annual Report, 1957–1958," p. 2, History File, ODE.

56. "University of Texas Engineers Aid Thailand," *Alcalde* 44 (October 1955): 4–5; "New Engineer's World," *Alcalde* 45 (December 1956): 6–8; "Engineering Faculty Minutes," vol. 7, November 8, 1956, ODE; Woolrich, *Men of Ingenuity,* pp. 124–125; "Annual Report, 1955–1956," pp. 2–3, "Annual Report, 1956–1957," p. 3, "Annual Report, 1957–1958," p. 2, History File, ODE.

57. *Engineering–Science News* 6 (July–August 1958); Straiton, "Electrical Engineering Advanced Degrees Conferred," in possession of Professor Straiton; "Annual Report, 1955–1956," p. 1 "Annual Report, 1956–1957," p. 1, "Annual Report, 1957–1958," p. 5, History File, ODE.

## NOTES TO AN EXPERIMENT WITH ENGINEERING SCIENCE

1. Grinter, "Survey of Current Changes," p. 559; Teare, "Graduate Programs and Research," p. 355; Simpson, "Electronics Industry and Texas," pp. 6–8; Simpson, "Electronics Industry and Texas," pp. 13–16.

2. Grinter, "Survey of Current Changes," p. 564; Teare, "Graduate Programs and Research," pp. 355, 358.

3. Lockwood, "The Last Hundred Years," p. 5.

4. "New Dean Named," *Alcalde* 47 (June 1958): 22; Woolrich, *Men of Ingenuity,* p. 213; interview with Dean William W. Hagerty, June 20, 1985; *Engineering–Science News* 6 (September–October 1958).

5. Woolrich, *Men of Ingenuity,* p. 213; interview with Dean Hagerty, June 20, 1985; "New Dean Named," p. 22.

6. Woolrich, *Men of Ingenuity,* pp. 44, 63; "New Dean Named," p. 22; interview with Professor Kreisle, February 8, April 10, 1985; interview with Professor Straiton, May 8, 1985.

7. Interview with Professor Cunningham, May 8, 1985; interview with Dean McKetta, May 10, 1985; interview with Professor Kreisle, February 22, 1985; conversation with Dean Gloyna, April 23, 1985; interview with Professor Lyle G. Clark, June 11, 1985; interview with Dean Hagerty, June 20, 1985.

8. "New Dean Named," p. 22; "Engineering Faculty Minutes," vol. 8: September 1957 to November 1962, minutes of meeting on September 17, 1957, ODE; "Minutes of the Department Chairmen Meetings," vol. 1: September 1958 to December 1960, letter from M. D. Hoover, President of the Engineering Council for Professional Development, to Logan R. Wilson, President of The University of Texas, October 22, 1958, ODE; interview with Dean Hagerty, June 20, 1985.

9. "New Dean Named," p. 22; "Minutes of the Department Chairmen Meetings," vol. 2: September 1958, to April 1965, speech of President Wilson inserted after minutes for September 11, 1958, ODE.

10. Ronnie Dugger, *Our Invaded Universities: Form, Reform, and New Starts; A Nonfiction Play for Five Stages* (New York: W. W. Norton & Company, 1974), pp. 70–71, 74.

11. "Department Chairmen Minutes," vol. 1, October 21, 1959, vol. 2, July 1, 1959; September 22, 1960, ODE; "Engineering Faculty Minutes," vol. 8, February 1, 1962, ODE.

12. William W. Hagerty, "Liberalizing the Education of an Engineer," *Alcalde* 48 (March 1960): 16–17, 28.

13. *Catalog, 1960–1961,* Part IV, p. 14.

14. "Department Chairmen Minutes," vol. 1, September 11, 1958, ODE; "Engineering Faculty Minutes," vol. 8, September 15, 1958, ODE.

15. "Department Chairmen Minutes," vol. 1, October 29, 1958, vol. 2, March 27, 1961, ODE; *Annual Report of the College of Engineering, 1958–1959* (Austin: College of Engineering, The University of Texas at Austin, 1959–1967, 1976–1986), pp. 3–4.

16. Woolrich, *Men of Ingenuity,* pp. 61–62; interview with Dean Hagerty, June 20, 1985, "Mechanical Engineering," mimeograph, n.d. [1963], History File, ODE.

17. Woolrich, *Men of Ingenuity,* pp. 61–62; interview with Dean Hagerty, June 20, 1985; conversation with Dean Gloyna, April 20, 1985.

18. Faculty File: Raymond F. Dawson, ODE; "Engineering Faculty Minutes," vol. 8, May 29, 1959, May 8, 1961, ODE; "Department Chairmen Minutes," vol. 1, October 29, 1958, vol. 2, March 27, 1961, ODE; interview with Professor Focht, February 11, 1985.

19. *Engineering–Science News* 4 (January–February 1954); "Department Chairmen Minutes," vol. 1, January 21, 1959, January 6, 1960, ODE; interview with Dean Hagerty, June 20, 1985.

20. *Engineering–Science News* 5 (May–June 1957); Woolrich, *Men of Ingenuity*, pp. 61–64, 69, 142, 201–203; interviews with Dean Hagerty, June 20 and 22, 1985; interview with Dean McKetta, May 10, 1985; "Department Chairmen Minutes," vol. 1, September 11 and 30, 1958, ODE.

21. McKinney, "Ph.D. and P.E. in Civil Engineering Education," pp. 48–49; Woolrich, *Men of Ingenuity*, p. 62; "Department Chairmen Minutes," vol. 1, July 1, 1959, ODE; interview with Dean Hagerty, June 20, 1985; conversation with Dean Gloyna, April 23, 1985; *Annual Report, 1958–1959*, p. 12; *Annual Report, 1962–1963*, p. 3.

22. "Engineering Faculty Minutes," vol. 8, May 29, 1959, ODE; "The Commttee of 75," *Alcalde* 47 (February 1959): 9–13; "UT Gets 1,684 Report Cards," *Alcalde* 47 (February 1958): 24–25; *Engineering-Science News* 5 (May-June 1957; interview with Dean McKetta, May 10, 1985; Woolrich, *Men of Ingenuity*, pp. 201–203.

23. "Department Chairmen Minutes," vol. 1, Hoover to President Wilson, October 22, 1958, ODE; Woolrich, *Men of Ingenuity*, pp. 75–76, 142; Faculty File: Byron D. Tapley, ODE; "Engineering Faculty Minutes," vol. 9: February 1963 to April 1965, March 5, 1959, ODE; Milton J. Thompson to Harry H. Ransom, Chancellor of The University of Texas, August 25, 1958, in "Annual Report, 1957–1958," History File, ODE.

24. Interview with Dean McKetta, May 10, 1985; interview with Professor Howard F. Rase, June 19, 1985; Faculty File: Matthew Van Winkle, ODE; Woolrich, *Men of Ingenuity*, pp. 113–116.

25. Woolrich, *Men of Ingenuity*, p. 62; interview with Professor James D. McFarland, June 11, 1985; interview with Professor Franklin B. Johnson, June 13, 1985, interview with Dean Hagerty, June 20, 1985; Faculty File: John E. Breen, ODE; *Annual Report, 1958–1959*, p. 11; Woolrich, *Men of Ingenuity*, p. 96.

26. Faculty File: Arwin A. Dougal, ODE; interview with Professor Straiton, May 8, 1985; Woolrich, *Men of Ingenuity*, p. 137; "Plasma is Everywhere," *Alcalde* 54 (April 1966): 16–19.

27. Faculty File: Lyle G. Clark, ODE; interview with Professor Clark, June 11, 1985; interview with Dean Hagerty, June 22, 1985; Woolrich, *Men of Ingenuity*, pp. 142–143; "Engineering Mechanics," mimeograph, n.d. [1963], History File, ODE.

28. "Engineering Faculty Minutes," vol. 2, February 7, 1957, March 7, 1958, ODE; interviews with Dean Hagerty, June 20 and 22, 1985.

29. *Dedication to the Future: Speeches Given at the Dedication of the Engineering Science Building at the University of Texas, October 2, 1964, by J. Herbert Hollomon and Others* (Austin: Privately Printed, 1964), pp. 11–12; "Department Chairmen Minutes," vol. 1, April 19 and May 23, 1960, ODE; *Catalog, 1960–1961*, IV, p. 19; "Focus on the Forty Acres—Nuclear Reactor Bought," *Alcalde* 51 (May 1963): 21; interview with Professor Straiton, May 8, 1985; *Daily Texan*, March 12, 1985; Faculty Files: Arwin A. Dougal, Jack A. Scanlan, ODE.

30. *Daily Texan*, March 12, 1985; Faculty File: Eugene H. Wissler, ODE.

31. Faculty Files: Carl Gatlin, Ben H. Caudle, ODE.

32. Interview with Dean Hagerty, June 20, 1985; "Department Chairmen Minutes," vol. 2, July 29, 1959, March 4 and April 24, 1963, ODE; "Minutes of the Engineering Foundation Advisory Council," vol. 1: May 1959 to October 1976, minutes of meetings on March 30 and June 1, 1963, TSS, ODE.

33. "Engineering Faculty Minutes," vol. 8, May 8, 1961, ODE; Woolrich, *Men of Ingenuity*, pp. 64, 128; *Catalog, 1958–1959*, IV, pp. 14, 21, 25–42, VII, pp. 47, 73; *Catalog, 1962–1963*, IV, pp. 29–42, VII, p. 71; *Catalog, 1964–1965*, IV, pp. 27–41; interviews with Dean Hagerty, June 20 and 22, 1985; Kelly, *31 Years of Research*, p. 18.

34. *Engineering–Science News* 6 (July–August 1958); "Focus on the Forty Acres," *Alcalde* 50 (October 1961): 22–23; "Engineering Faculty Minutes," vol. 8, March 7, 1958, ODE; interview with Professor Cunningham, May 8, 1985; interview with Professor Thompson, June 26, 1985; *Annual Report, 1962–1963*, p. 3.

35. "Focus on the Forty Acres—Computer Is on View," *Alcalde* 52 (February 1964): 16; Woolrich, *Men of Ingenuity*, p. 223; interview with Dean Hagerty, June 22, 1985; interview with Professor Cunningham, May 8, 1985; "Department Chairmen Minutes," vol. 2, May 8 and 23, 1959, ODE; *Annual Report, 1961–1962*, p. 18; *Annual Report, 1962–1963*, p. 12.

36. Interview with Professor Rase, June 19, 1985; Woolrich, *Men of Ingenuity*, pp. 39–40; interview with Professor Clark, June 11, 1985; *Annual Report, 1958–1959*, p. 10; "Minutes of the Engineering Foundation Advisory Council," vol. 1, October 24, 1959, ODE.

37. "Engineering Faculty Minutes," vol. 8, March 7, 1958, vol. 9, November 7, 1957, ODE; Faculty File: William J. Carter, ODE; Woolrich, *Men of Ingenuity*, pp. 18, 64–65, 144–145.

38. "Department Chairmen Minutes," vol. 1, December 17, 1958, April 8, 1959, ODE; "Engineering Faculty Minutes," vol. 9, "Objectives of the Engineering Science Program;" inserted after March 5, 1959, ODE; Woolrich, *Men of Ingenuity*, pp. 144–145.

39. Woolrich, *Men of Ingenuity*, pp. 101, 144–145; "Department Chairmen Minutes," vol. 2,

March 27, 1961, ODE; *Catalog, 1960–1961,* IV, pp. 14, 36–37; *Catalog, 1962–1963,* IV, pp. 38–40; *Catalog, 1966–1967,* IV, p. 15.

40. Interview with Dean Hagerty, June 20, 1985; interview with Professor Clark, June 11, 1985; conversation with Dean Gloyna, April 23, 1985.

41. "Department Chairmen Minutes," vol. 1, report, no date, inserted after April 8, 1959, ODE.

42. "Engineering Faculty Minutes," vol. 8, September 21, 1959, May 8, 1961, ODE; "Department Chairmen Minutes," vol. 2, November 3, 1959, ODE; "Minutes of the Engineering Faculty Advisory Council," vol. 1, August 15 and October 24, 1959, ODE.

43. "Engineering Faculty Minutes," vol. 8, "Annual Report of the Engineering Foundation to the Alumni and Industrial Contributors," inserted after minutes of November 9, 1961, ODE.

44. "Department Chairmen Minutes," vol. 1, November 3 and December 10, 1959, vol. 2, September 22, 1960, ODE; interview with Professor Rase, June 19, 1985; interview with Professor Johnson, June 13, 1985.

45. "Focus on the Forty Acres—Engineering to Receive $975,000 from Ford Foundation Grant," *Alcalde* 49 (December 1960): 16; "Minutes of the Engineering Foundation Advisory Council," January 21, 1961, ODE.

46. Interview with Dean Hagerty, June 20, 1985; interview with Professor Rase, June 19, 1985; interview with Professor Johnson, June 13, 1985; "Department Chairmen Minutes," vol. 1, June 28, 1960, vol. 2, October 11, 1960, ODE; *Annual Report, 1959–1960,* pp. 8–9; *Annual Report, 1961–1962,* p. 8.

47. Interview with Professor Clark, June 11, 1985; interview with Dean Hagerty, June 20, 1985.

48. Office of Government–Sponsored Research, The University of Texas, "Current National Science Foundation Grants, May 1, 1959," "Summary of National Science Foundation Grants, May 1, 1960," "National Science Foundation Grants Pending, May 1, 1960 [notes added]," President's Office Files, BTHC; interview with Dean Hagerty, June 22, 1985; interview with Professor Rase, June 19, 1985; "Engineering Faculty Minutes," vol. 8, February 23, 1962, ODE.

49. *Dedication to the Future,* p. 17; "Basic Research in Engineering to be Given Impetus by New Foundation Unit," *National Science Foundation Newsletter,* November 15, 1961; Office of Government–Sponsored Research, "Current National Science Foundation Grants, May 1, 1959," "Summary of National Science Foundation Grants, May 1, 1960," "National Science Foundation Grants Pending, May 1, 1960 [notes added]," President's Office Files, BTHC; interview with Dean Hagerty, June 22, 1985; conversation with Dean Gloyna, April 23, 1985; interview with Professor Rase, June 19, 1985.

50. Interview with Professor Rase, June 19, 1985; interview with Dean Hagerty, June 22, 1985; conversation with Dean Gloyna, April 23, 1985; "Department Chairmen Minutes," vol. 2, February 19, 1961, ODE.

51. "Focus on the Forty Acres—Engineers Set Record," *Alcalde* 52 (December 1963): 17; "Minutes of the Engineering Foundation Advisory Council," vol. 1, November 4, 1961, January 26, 1962, ODE; conversation with Dean Gloyna, April 23, 1985.

52. Woolrich, *Men of Ingenuity,* pp. 213–214; "Department Chairmen Minutes," vol. 1, January 27, 1960, ODE; *Catalog, 1960–1961,* IV, p. 19; *Catalog, 1964–1965,* IV, p. 18; interview with Professor Fancher, June 19, 1985; *Annual Report, 1959–1960,* pp. 14–15, 21; *Annual Report, 1960–1961,* p. 8.

53. "Engineering Faculty Minutes," vol. 8, November 8, 1956, ODE; interview with Professor Rase, June 19, 1985; Woolrich, *Men of Ingenuity,* pp. 60–61; *Annual Report, 1958–1959,* p. 13.

54. "Engineering Faculty Minutes," vol. 8, May 8, 1961, ODE; "Department Chairmen Minutes," vol. 2, July 29, 1959, ODE; Woolrich, *Men of Ingenuity,* p. 65; *Dedication to the Future,* p. 17; "Minutes of the Engineering Foundation Advisory Council," vol. 1, November 4, 1961, ODE; *Annual Report, 1960–1961,* p. 9.

55. "Engineers Dedicate New Building at 80th Anniversary Celebration," *Alcalde* 53 (December 1964): 22–23; "Department Chairmen Minutes," vol. 1, December 7, 1960, ODE.

56. "Department Chairmen Minutes," vol. 1, September 2 and December 17, 1958, May 20 and December 17, 1959, ODE; interview with Dean Hagerty, June 22, 1985; interview with Professor Johnson, June 13, 1985; interview with Dean McKetta, May 10, 1985.

57. Woolrich, *Men of Ingenuity,* p. 123; *Catalog, 1958–1959,* IV, p. 19; Kelly, *31 Years of Research,* p. 14; Berry, *Pictorial Account,* pp. 151, 399; Frantz, *Forty Acres Follies,* pp. 217–218; interview with Professor Thompson, June 26, 1985.

58. Woolrich, *Men of Ingenuity,* pp. 136–137; *Engineering–Science News* 6 (July–August 1958); "Department Chairmen Minutes," vol. 2, September 24, 1958, March 12, 1964, ODE.

59. "Engineering Faculty Minutes," vol. 8, March 7, 1958, September 21, 1959, November 1, 1962, ODE; "Department Chairmen Minutes," vol. 1, July 29, 1959, March 28, 1960, ODE; "Travis Chapter Engineers Inaugurate New TV Series," *Texas Professional Engineer* 21 (July 1962): 18–19; "Engineering Displays Now Touring State," *Texas Professional Engineer* 21 (March 1963): 19; Woolrich, *Men of Ingenuity,* pp. 64–65; *Annual Report, 1958–1959,* p. 5; *Annual Report, 1960–1961,* p. 17.

60. Interviews with Dean Hagerty, June 20 and 22, 1985; "Department Chairmen Minutes,"

vol. 2, March 12, 1964, ODE; "Engineering Faculty Minutes," vol. 8, November 1, 1962, ODE; "Minutes of the Engineering Foundation Advisory Council," vol. 1, October 24, 1959, October 27, 1962, ODE; *Annual Report, 1961–1962,* p. 1; Straiton, "Electrical Engineering Advanced Degrees Conferred," in possession of Professor Straiton.

61. *The Analog* 2 (February 1959), photocopy in History File, ODE.

62. Interview with Dean Hagerty, June 22, 1985; "Department Chairmen Minutes," vol. 2, October 11, 1960, ODE.

63. "Engineering Faculty Minutes," vol. 9, Myron L. Begeman and William A. Cunningham to Dean Hagerty, November 4, 1963, ODE; *New York Times,* January 15, 1986.

## NOTES TO THE DRIVE FOR TEACHING EXCELLENCE

1. Frederick E. Terman,"Engineering Education in Retrospect and in Prospect," in *Britannica Review of Developments in Engineering Education,* Newman A. Hall, ed. (Chicago: Encyclopedia Britannica, 1970), pp. 3–6; interview with Professor Caudle, June 14, 1985.

2. Derro Evans, "John McKetta: The Academic Man Revisited," *Alcalde* 60 (December 1962): 11; interview with Professor Rase, June 19, 1985; interview with Professor Straiton, May 8, 1985; interview with Professor Cunningham, May 8, 1985; Woolrich, *Men of Ingenuity,* p. 66; "Minutes of the Engineering Foundation Advisory Council," vol. 1, October 23, 1963, ODE; *Catalog, 1964–1965,* IV, pp. 5, 8; "Hagerty Resigns as UT Dean," *Texas Professional Engineer* 21 (July 1963): 5.

3. "Department Chairmen Minutes," vol. 4: July 1965 to June 1971, memorandum, no date, ODE; interview with Professor Straiton, May 8, 1985; interview with Professor Caudle, June 14, 1985; "Engineering Faculty Minutes," vol. 10: May 1958 to May 1969, minutes of the meeting on April 2, 1964, ODE.

4. "Department Chairmen Minutes," vol. 4, February 5, 1968, ODE; interview with Professor Johnson, June 13, 1985; interview with Professor McFarland, June 11, 1985; interview with Professor Clark, June 11, 1985.

5. "Department Chairmen Minutes," vol. 4, July 30, 1965, ODE; "Engineering Faculty Minutes," vol. 10, February 3, May 12, 1969, ODE; "Engineering Faculty Minutes," vol. 11: September 1965 to February 1970, minutes of meeting on September 30, 1965, ODE; "Minutes of the Engineering Foundation Advisory Council," vol. 1, May 29, 1965, ODE; Berry, *Pictorial Account,* p. 334; *Catalog, 1962–1964,* IV; *Catalog, 1966–1968,* IV; *Insight: The Annual Report of the College of Engineering, The University of Texas at Austin, 1968–1969* (Austin: College of Engineering, The University of Texas, 1967–1975), p. 4.

6. "Department Chairmen Minutes," vol. 3: May 1961 to May 1969, minutes of the meeting on May 26, 1964, ODE; Frantz, *Forty Acres Follies,* pp. 199, 213; "Minority Engineering Faculty," TSS, n.d., History File, ODE; Faculty File: Erwin E. Perry, ODE; Woolrich, *Men of Ingenuity,* p. 245; "First Negro Professor at UT Dies at Age 34," *Texas Civil Engineer* 41 (January 1971): 7.

7. "Department Chairmen Minutes," vol. 4, July 30, 1965, ODE; "Engineering Faculty Minutes," vol. 10, September 23 and 26, 1963, May 12, 1969, vol. 11, September 27, 1965, May 12, 1969, ODE; *Phil M. Ferguson,* History File, ODE.

8. "Department Chairmen Minutes," vol. 3, September 17, 18, and 19, 1964, vol. 4, October 19, 1965, ODE; "Engineering Faculty Minutes," vol. 10, September 16, 1964; November 30, 1965, September 26, 1966, ODE; *Annual Report, 1964–1965,* p. 2.

9. "Department Chairmen Minutes," vol. 3, October 3, 1968, ODE; "Engineering Panel," *Texas Engineering and Science Magazine* 3 (December 1966): 38; Hall, ed., *Britannica Review of Developments in Engineering Education,* p. x; interview with Dean McKetta, May 10, 1985; "Goals of Engineering Education," *Texas Civil Engineer* 35 (December 1965): 4.

10. *Dedication to the Future,* pp. 12–15; interview with Professor Cunningham, May 8, 1985.

11. "Engineering Faculty Minutes," vol. 10, September 26, 1966; September 18, 1967; interview with Dean McKetta, May 10, 1985; "History of the Office of Engineering Counselor," TSS, n.d. [1985], History File, ODE; *Insight: 1966–1967,* p. 26; *Insight, 1968–1969,* p. 6.

12. "Annual Report of the College of Engineering, 1955–1956," p. 3, History File, ODE; "Department Chairmen Minutes," vol. 3, February 13, May 12, and October 7, 1964, December 1, 1965, vol. 4w, March 9, 1967, November 14, 1968, April 29, 1969, ODE; "Engineering Faculty Minutes," vol. 10, September 30, 1965, September 26, 1966, September 18, 1967, March 28 and September 16, 1968, ODE; James A. Johnson, Sr. "Ask the Engineers," *Alcalde* 56 (January 1968): 14–15; interview with Professor Caudle, June 14, 1985; interview with Dean McKetta, May 10, 1985; interview with Professor Clark, June 11, 1985, *Insight, 1969–1970,* p. 14; conversation with Professor James E. Stice, September 4, 1985; Leonardt F. Kreisle to Dean John J. McKetta, Jr., July 6, 1967, photocopy in History File, ODE: "Minutes of the Engineering Foundation Advisory Council," vol. 1, June 4, 1966, ODE; *Engineering Teaching Effectiveness Colloquia 1966–1967* (Austin: College of Engineering, The University of Texas at Austin, 1967), pp. 10–12; *Insight, 1965–1966,* p. 14.

13. Augustus B. Kinzel, "The National Academy of Engineering and Engineering Education,"

*The Journal of Engineering Education* 55 (February 1965): 173; "Engineering Faculty Minutes," vol. 10, February 6, 1964, November 30, 1965, January 5, 1968, ODE; "Department Chairmen Minutes," vol. 3, April 2 and May 26, 1964, ODE; "Focus on the Forty Acres—Space Science Added," *Alcalde* 52 (October 1963): 21; *Engineering Teaching Effectiveness Colloquia*, p. 12.

14. "Department Chairmen Minutes," vol. 3, January 6 and July 30, 1965, January 5 and March 20, 1968, vol. 4, February 10, 1966, September 4, 1969, ODE; "Engineering Faculty Minutes," vol. 11, February 2, 1970, ODE; interview with Dean McKetta, May 10, 1985.

15. "Department Chairmen Minutes," vol. 3, April 2, 1964, July 30, 1965, vol. 4, December 1, 1965, February 10, 1966, February 3, 1969, March 17, 1970, ODE; interview with Professor Caudle, June 14, 1985.

16. Interview with Professor Straiton, May 8, 1985; "Department Chairmen Minutes," vol. 3, April 2 and 28, 1964, vol. 4, November 25, 1969, January 8 and 20, 1970, ODE; "Engineering Faculty Minutes," vol. 10, September 18, 1967, ODE; Faculty Files: Arwin A. Dougal, Clarence E. Coates, ODE; *Insight, 1966–1967*, p. 26; "Minutes of the Engineering Foundation Advisory Council,"vol. 1, April 4, 1964, ODE; conversation with Professors Duesterhoft and Smith, September 12, 1985.

17. "Engineering Faculty Minutes," vol. 10, September 26, 1966, September 18, 1967, March 28 and September 16, 1968, ODE; "Engineering Faculty Minutes," vol. 11, September 18 and 26, 1967, ODE; "Department Chairmen Minutes," vol. 3, December 9 and 16, 1963, ODE; "Minutes of the Engineering Foundation Advisory Council," vol. 1, March 20, 1965, October 28, 1967, March 16, 1968, ODE; *Annual Report, 1964–1965*, p. 8.

18. "Department Chairmen Minutes," vol. 4, September 30 and October 19, 1965, December 4, 1967, January 2, 1968, ODE.

19. "Department Chairmen Minutes," vol. 3, May 26, 1964, November 2, 1967, vol. 4, September 30, October 19, 1965, November 2, 1967, January 2, February 23, and March 20, 1968, February 3 and April 1, 1969, September 4 and December 15, 1969, ODE; "Engineering Faculty Minutes," vol. 10, April 2, 1964, November 30, 1965, May 27, 1967, ODE.

20. "Department Chairmen Minutes," vol. 3, September 23, 1963, January 6, 1965; vol. 4, February 10, 1966, March 7 and October 3, 1968, ODE; "Engineering Faculty Minutes," vol. 10, September 16, 1964, ODE; Terman, "Engineering Education in Retrospect and in Prospect," pp. 3–6; interview with Professor Johnson, June 13, 1985; interview with Professor Caudle, June 14, 1985; interview with Professor Rase, June 19, 1985; *Insight, 1968–1969*, p. 14; *Insight, 1971–1972*, pp. 2–7.

21. "Minutes of the Engineering Foundation Advisory Council," vol. 1, May 30, 1964, March 20, 1965, ODE; *Annual Report, 1963–1964*, p. 14; *Annual Report, 1964–1965*, p. 11; *Insight, 1967–1968*, p. 13; *Insight: 1968–1969*, p. 17; "Department Chairmen Minutes," vol. 4, November 2, 1967, ODE; "Engineering Faculty Minutes," vol. 10, September 18, 1967, ODE; "The Engineer," *Texas Engineering and Science Magazine* 4 (December 1967): 30–33; "'The Engineer' is Coming," *Alcalde* 56 (June 1968): 28.

22. "Department Chairmen Minutes," vol. 4, December 15, 1969, January 8, 1970, ODE; "Engineering Faculty Minutes," vol. 11, September 15, 1969, ODE; Anne Hagy and Ann Fortson, "Intruders in Taylor Hall," *Texas Engineering and Science Magazine* 5 (February 1969): 48–49; "Minutes of the Engineering Foundation Advisory Council," vol. 1, January 25, April 4, and May 30, 1964, ODE.

23. Terman, "Engineering Education in Retrospect and in Prospect," p. 12; "Department Chairmen Minutes," vol. 3, October 14, 1963, April 14, 1964, April 15, 1968, vol. 4, March 15, 1967, ODE; "Engineering Faculty Minutes," vol. 10, April 2, 1964, May 27, 1967, March 28, 1968, ODE.

24. "Department Chairmen Minutes," vol. 4, January 2 and March 28, 1968, ODE; "Engineering Faculty Minutes," vol. 10, May 27, 1967, ODE; Anne Hagy, "New Challenges, New Worlds, New Engineers," *Texas Engineering and Science Magazine* 6 (December 1969): 12–13; *Insight, 1967–1968*, pp. 3–4; *Insight, 1968–1969*, p. 11; *Insight, 1969–1970*, p. 8.

25. "Department Chairmen Minutes," vol. 3, January 23, February 21 and 27, March 12, 1964, vol. 4, March 20, 1968, ODE; "Engineering Faculty Minutes," vol. 10, March 28, 1968, ODE; interview with Professor Rase, June 19, 1985; *Catalog, 1968–1969*, IV, pp. 23–24.

26. Billy H. Amstead, "The Modern Engineer," *Texas Engineering and Science Magazine* 1 (April 1965): 20; Johnson, "Ask the Engineers," p. 17; "Department Chairmen Minutes," vol. 3, December 16, 1963, February 13 and March 5, 1964, vol. 4, March 15, 1967, January 9, 1969, ODE; "Engineering Faculty Minutes," vol. 10, April 20, 1965, May 27, 1967, March 5, 1969, ODE; *Catalog, 1964–1965*, IV, pp. 25–27, 34, 38, 39–40, VII, p. 81. "Engineers Must Continue Education to Keep Pace," *Alcalde* 54 (October 1966): 29; *Insight, 1967–1968*, p. 3.

27. Interview with Professor Clark, June 11, 1985; "Engineering Faculty Minutes," vol. 10, March 5, 1969, ODE; "Department Chairmen Minutes," vol. 3, October 20, 1964, February 4, 1965, ODE; *Catalog, 1964–1965*, IV, pp. 25–27, 34, 38, 39–40; VII, p. 81; *Catalog, 1966–1967*, IV, p. 41; *Catalog, 1968–1969*, IV, pp. 46–47; interview with Dean McKetta, May 10, 1985.

28. Interview with Professor Clark, June 11, 1985; conversation with Professor J. Parker Lamb, Jr., August 14, 1985; "Department Chairmen Minutes," vol. 3, May 26, 1964, ODE; "Minutes of the

Engineering Foundation Advisory Council," vol. 1, October 3, 1964, ODE; Eugene B. Konecci, "The Kleberg Professor—Activities and Papers January 1967–July 1969," 2 vols., TSS, photocopy in BTHC.

29. "Engineering Faculty Minutes," vol. 10, March 5, 1969, ODE; "Focus on the Forty Acres," *Alcalde* 55 (January 1967): 17–18; *Catalog, 1966–1967*, IV, p. 32; *Catalog 1968–1969*, IV, p. 37; Johnson, "Ask the Engineers," pp. 14–17; interview with Dean McKetta, May 10, 1985; interview with Professor Rase, June 19, 1985.

30. "Engineering Faculty Minutes," vol. 10, March 5, 1969, ODE; *Catalog, 1964–1965*, IV, pp. 25–27, 34, 38, 39–40; VII, p. 81; *Catalog, 1966–1967*, IV, pp. 30, 35.

31. "Engineering Faculty Minutes," vol. 10, March 5, 1969, ODE; *Catalog, 1964–1965*, VII, p. 81; *Catalog, 1966–1967*, IV, p. 38; *Catalog, 1968–1969*, IV, p. 43; "Minutes of the Engineering Foundation Advisory Council," vol. 1, June 4, 1966, ODE.

32. "Department Chairmen Minutes," vol. 4, March 17, 1970, ODE; Thomas Runge, "Medical Transplants," *Texas Engineering and Science Magazine* 5 (February 1969): 38; Ralph G. Nevins, "Bioengineering," in Hall, ed., *Britannica Review of Developments in Engineering Education*, pp. 252–254; interview with Dean McKetta, May 10, 1985; interview with Professor Rase, June 19, 1985; "Minutes of the Engineering Foundation Advisory Council," vol. 1, March 19, 1966, March 16, 1968, ODE.

33. "Engineering Faculty Minutes," vol. 10, March 5, 1969, ODE; *Catalog, 1964–1965*, IV, pp. 39–40; *Catalog, 1966–1967*, IV, p. 44; *Catalog, 1968–1969*, IV, p. 50; "Department Chairmen Minutes," vol. 3, February 4, 1965, ODE; interview with Dean McKetta, May 10, 1985; "Vice Chairman Appointed," *Texas Engineering and Science Magazine* 3 (October 1966): 36; *Insight, 1967–1968*, pp. 3–4.

34. *Catalog, 1966–1967*, IV, pp. 46–47; *Catalog, 1968–1969*, IV, p. 53; interview with Professor Caudle, June 14, 1985.

35. "Department Chairmen Minutes," vol. 4, January 2 and 15, 1968, May 8, 1969, ODE.

36. "Engineering Faculty Minutes," vol. 10, September 30, November 30, 1965, September 18, 1967, ODE; "Engineers Must Continue Education to Keep Pace," p. 29; Terman, "Engineering Education in Retrospect and in Prospect," pp. 10–11; R. R. O'Neil, "Continuing Education," in Hall, ed., *Britannica Review of Developments in Engineering Education*, pp. 73, 102.

37. "Focus on the Forty Acres—Engineers Start Work Study Program," *Alcalde* 54 (November 1966): 17; "Department Chairmen Minutes," vol. 3, October 14, 1963, July 30, 1965, May 27, 1968, ODE; "Engineering Faculty Minutes," vol. 10, September 30, November 30, 1965, April 4, September 26, 1966, ODE; *Catalog, 1968–1969*, IV, 23–24; Van Leer, "History of Engineering Education," p. 198; Saville, "Achievements in Engineering Education," p. 212; "Annual Report, 1955–1956" p. 2, History File, ODE.

38. Kinzel, "The National Academy of Engineering and Engineering Education," p. 173; interview with Professor Caudle, June 14, 1985; interview with Dean McKetta, May 10, 1985; interview with Professor Thompson, June 26, 1985; interview with Professor Cunningham, May 8, 1985; "Minutes of the Engineering Foundation Advisory Council," vol. 1, October 2, 1965, October 19, 1968, ODE.

39. Kelly, *31 Years of Research*, p. 6; interview with Professor Thompson, June 26, 1985.

40. Kelly, *31 Years of Research*, pp. 17, 22, 23, 26; *Annual Report, 1964–1965*, p. 16; *Insight, 1966–1967*, p. 29.

41. Mary Wightman, "Center for Highway Research: Where 630,000 Ideas Are at Work," *Alcalde* 58 (February 1970): 11–14; "Molding a Bridge," *Texas Engineering and Science Magazine* 8 (October 1971): 16.

42. Andrea Johnson, "Mobile Laboratory," *Texas Engineering and Science Magazine* 5 (April 1969): 20–21; Kelly, *31 Years of Research*, p. 5; *Insight, 1967–1968*, p. 13.

43. "Austin Oaks Completed," *Alcalde* 57 (February 1969): 19; Kelly, *31 Years of Research*, p. 9; interview with Professor Rase, June 19, 1985; interview with Professor Thompson, June 26, 1985.

44. Kelly, *31 Years of Research*, pp. 10–11.

45. "Institute Created," *Texas Engineering and Science Magazine* 3 (October 1967): 47; Berry, *Pictorial Account*, p. 334; "Minutes of the Engineering Foundation Advisory Council," vol. 1, April 2, 1960, ODE.

46. "Department Chairmen Minutes," vol. 4, December 15, 1966, November 2 and December 21, 1967, September 4 and November 25, 1969, January 8, 1970, ODE; Lenda Delk, "Patented Poker Players," *Texas Engineering and Science Magazine* 4 (December 1967): 48–50.

47. "Editor's Note," *Texas Engineering and Science Magazine* 1 (April 1965): 2, 7; "Department Chairmen Minutes," vol. 3, January 14 and April 28, 1964, February 4, 1965, vol. 4, November 14, 1968, March 13 and September 4, 1969, ODE; "Engineering Faculty Minutes," vol. 11, September 15, 1969, ODE.

48. Frantz, *Forty Acres Follies*, p. 312; interview with Dean McKetta, May 10, 1985; conversation with Professor Lamb, August 14, 1985; *Insight, 1968–1969*, p. 3.

49. "Department Chairmen Minutes," vol. 4, September 4, 1969, January 8 and 27, 1970, ODE;

"Engineering Faculty Minutes," vol. 11, September 30, 1965, September 15, 1969, February 2, 1970, ODE; Hagy, "New Challenges, New Worlds, New Engineers," p. 12; Faculty File: Billy H. Amstead, ODE; *Insight, 1968–1969*, p. 3; *Insight, 1969–1970*, pp. 4, 12.

## NOTES FOR TOWARD A POSITION OF ACADEMIC LEADERSHIP

1. *Insight, 1969–1970*, p. 2; "Biographical Data Sketch: Earnest F. Gloyna" TSS, January 1985, History File, ODE.

2. *Insight, 1971–1972*, p. 1.

3. Conversation with Professor Lamb, August 20, 1985; conversation with Dean Gloyna, March 8, 1986.

4. *Insight, 1969–1970*, p. 3, Endpiece; "Minutes of the Engineering Foundation Advisory Council," vol. 1, May 30, 1970, ODE.

5. Interview with Professor Lymon C. Reese, September 25, 1985; *Insight, 1971–1972*, p. 22; *Annual Report, 1983–1984*, pp. 60–61.

6. Conversation with Professor Lamb, August 20, 1985; *Annual Report, 1975–1976*, pp. 7, 27; *Annual Report, 1980–1981*, p. 15; "Engineering Faculty Minutes," vol. 13: April 1973 to October 1980, minutes of meeting on September 28, 1980, ODE; *Annual Report, 1983–1984*, pp. 60–61; *Engineering/84* 5 (Spring 1984).

7. "1985–1986 Committee Assignments," TSS, July 29, 1985, History File, ODE; conversation with Dean Gloyna, March 8, 1986.

8. *Insight, 1971–1972*, p. 22; *Annual Report, 1980–1981*, p. 34; "Engineering Career Assistance Center," TSS, n.d. [1985], History File, ODE; additional information provided by Professor Anthony L. Franzolino.

9. "Engineering Counseling: Dates and Historic Activity," TSS, n.d. [1985], History File, ODE; *Annual Report, 1976–1977*, p. 28; "Engineering Scholarship Program, College of Engineering, The University of Texas at Austin, Annual Report, 1984–1985," TSS, History File, ODE; *Annual Engineering Foundation Report, Recommendations, and College Update for EFAC Approval, September 26, 1985* (Austin: College of Engineering, The University of Texas, 1985), Table 12; "Students Receive Millions in Scholarships, Fellowships," *Alcalde* 72 (May–June 1984): 27; additional information provided by Professor H. Grady Rylander, Jr., Ed D. Davis, and Tom Backus.

10. *Insight, 1969–1970*, p. 14; *Insight, 1972–1973*, pp. 15, 19; *Insight, 1973–1974*, p. 24; "Engineering Faculty Minutes," vol. 13, September 28, 1970, ODE; James E. Stice, "Center for Teaching Effectiveness, University of Texas at Austin," photocopy, n.d., History File, ODE; conversation with Professor Stice, September 12, 1985; James E. Stice, "A Model for Teaching New Teachers How to Teach," *Engineering Education* 75 (November 1984): 83–87; Billy V. Koen et al., "The Keller Plan: A Successful Experiment in Engineering Education," *Engineering Education* 75 (February 1985): 280–284.

11. *Annual Report, 1976–1977*, pp. 3, 28, 30, 35; *Annual Report, 1980–1981*, p. 21; "Engineering Faculty Minutes," vol. 13, December 14, 1977, ODE; conversation with Professor Stice, September 12, 1985; Koen et al., "The Keller Plan," pp. 280–284; John W. Rouse, Jr., "Engineering Education in Texas: New Expectations," *Texas Professional Engineer* 43 (March–April 1984): 14.

12. *Annual Report, 1975–1976*, Frontispiece, p. 19; "Engineering Faculty Minutes," vol. 13, May 6, 1976, ODE; "Department Chairmen Minutes," vol. 6: September 1971 to August 1975, minutes for meeting on July 3, 1975, ODE; "Department Chairmen Minutes," vol. 7: October 1975 to August 1978, January 27, minutes for meeting on April 13, 1976, ODE.

13. *Insight, 1969–1970*, pp. 4, 5; *Insight, 1974–1975*, p. 7; *Annual Report, 1976–1977*, pp. 3, 26; *Annual Report, 1977–1978*, pp. 3, 9; *Annual Report, 1980–1981*, p. 2; *Annual Report, 1984–1985*, p. 2; "Minutes of the Engineering Foundation Advisory Council," vol. 1, October 23, 1976, ODE; interview with Dean McKetta, May 10, 1985; interview with Professor Reese, September 25, 1985; "The University of Texas at Austin Strategic Plan Through 1992–1993," TSS, n.d. [1985], History File, ODE; *Engineering/85* 6 (Spring 1985).

14. Interview with Associate Professor Linda J. Hayes, September 11, 1985; interview with Professor Reese, September 25, 1985; conversation with Professor Myron H. Dorfman, August 16, 1985; *College of Engineering, The University of Texas at Austin, Engineering Research, 1983–1984*, (Austin: College of Engineering, The University of Texas at Austin, 1984), pp. 53, 108, 149, 164, 215, 265.

15. *Annual Engineering Foundation Report, September 26, 1985*, p. 3; *Annual Report of the Department of Civil Engineering, 1984–1985*, (Austin: College of Engineering, The University of Texas at Austin, 1985), p. 63; *Annual Report of the Department of Chemical Engineering, 1984–1985*, (Austin: College of Engineering, The University of Texas at Austin, 1985), p. 62; Louis A. Beecherl to McCaslin, January 14, 1986, History File, ODE.

16. *Insight, 1969–1970*, p. 19; *Insight, 1974–1975*, p. 20; *Annual Report, 1979–1980*, pp. 37, 39; *Annual Report, 1980–1981*, pp. 37, 38; *Annual Report, 1981–1982*, p. 45; *Annual Report, 1982–1983*, p. 32; *Annual Report, 1983–1984*, pp. 52, 53; *Annual Report, 1984–1985*, pp. 2, 33, 35.

17. *Insight, 1973–1974*, pp. 1, 3, 31; *Insight, 1974–1975*, pp. 11, 35; "Minutes of the Engineering Foundation Advisory Council," vol. 1, May 26, October 27, 1973, March 2, 1974, February 21, May 22, 1976, October 31, 1981, ODE; James A. Johnson, "Engineering-Plus," *Alcalde* 62 (January 1974): 35.

18. *Insight, 1974–1975*, pp. 20, 33, 35; *Annual Report, 1975–1976*, pp. 38–39; *Annual Report, 1976–1977*, pp. 39, 40; *Annual Report, 1977–1978*, p. 37; *Annual Report, 1978–1979*, pp. 38, 40; *Annual Report, 1979–1980*, pp. 37, 39; *Annual Report, 1980–1981*, pp. 37, 38; *Annual Report, 1981–1982*, p. 45; *Annual Report, 1982–1983*, p. 32; *Annual Report, 1983–1984*, pp. 52, 53; *Annual Report, 1984–1985*, pp. 2, 33, 35.

19. *Insight, 1973–1974*, pp. 1, 31; *Insight, 1974–1975*, p. 35; "Minutes of the Engineering Foundation Advisory Council," vol. 1, August 6 and October 3, 1970, March 4 and October 21–22, 1972, February 19, May 26, and October 27, 1973, March 2, and May 18, 1974, May 17, 1975, February 21 and May 22, 1976, October 21, 1978, February 24, May 19, and October 6, 1979, October 25, 1980, February 14, 1981, ODE; Beecherl to McCaslin, January 14, 1986, Paul D. Meek to McCaslin, January 13, 1986, John E. Kasch to McCaslin, February 13, 1986, History File, ODE.

20. *Insight, 1974–1975*, p. 33; "Minutes of the Engineering Foundation Advisory Council," vol. 1, October 19, 1974, December 29, 1975, October 23, 1976, October 29, 1977, ODE; *Chair of Free Enterprise Newsletter*, April 1977, September 1978, December 1978, November 1980; *Nexus*, Fall 1984; Robert L. Parker, Sr., to McCaslin, January 16, 1986, History File, ODE.

21. *Annual Report, 1982–1983*, p. 32; "Minutes of the Engineering Foundation Advisory Council," vol. 1, May 20, October 21, 1978, ODE; *Chair of Free Enterprise Newsletter*, April 1977, January, May, September, and December 1978, January and November 1980; *Nexus*, Fall 1982, Spring 1983, Spring and Fall 1985; "Technethics: Engineering Social Responsibilities," *Texas Professional Engineer* 41 (November–December 1982): 14–16; "Energy Expert Discusses Geopolitical Concerns of Energy and Resources," *Texas Professional Engineer* 43 (September–October 1984): 17–21.

22. *Nexus*, Spring and Fall 1985; *Annual Engineering Foundation Report, September 26, 1985*, p. 14.

23. "Faculty Endowments Grow," *Alcalde* 72 (March–April 1984): 31; Don Massa, "History-Making Endowment: 32 Chairs," *Alcalde* 72 (July–August 1984): 6–9; *The University of Texas at Austin, Endowments, College of Engineering*, pamphlet, n.d., History File, ODE; *On Campus*, February 25–March 3, 1985.

24. *Engineering/85* 6 (Spring 1985); "The University of Texas at Austin Strategic Plan Through 1992–1993;" *Annual Engineering Foundation Report, September 26, 1985*, Table 10; *Daily Texan*, February 24, 1986; "Campus Briefs," *Alcalde* 72 (September–October 1983): 33.

25. *Insight, 1973–1974*, p. 2; *Insight, 1974–1975*, pp. 7, 11, 40; *Annual Report, 1981–1982*, p. 2; *Annual Report, 1982–1983*, 3; *Annual Report, 1983–1984*, p. 3; *Annual Report, 1984–1985*, 2. "Department Chairmen Minutes," vol. 5: September 1968 to August 1971, minutes of meeting on September 4, 1970, vol. 6, May 3, 1974, ODE; "Minutes of the Engineering Foundation Advisory Council," vol. 1, February 21, 1976, September 25, 1982, ODE; *Dedication of Ernest Cockrell, Jr. Hall, The University of Texas at Austin*, pamphlet, n.d. [1974], History File, ODE.

26. *Vector*, September 1984; *Daily Texan*, February 24, 1986; conversation with Professor Donald R. Paul, September 18, 1985; conversation with Professor Dorfman, August 16, 1985; "Campus Briefs," p. 33.

27. *Vector*, September 1984; "Smell the New: The Center for Energy Studies Moves to 145,000 Sq. Ft. Building," *Energy Studies* 11 (September–October 1985); Teo Furtado, "King of the Metal Minds," *Alcalde* 74 (May–June 1986): 10–12.

28. *Insight, 1970–1971*, pp. 2–4; *Insight, 1972–1973*, p. 3; *Insight, 1973–1974*, p. 1; *Annual Report, 1977–1978*, p. 1; "Engineering College Research and Graduate Study," *Engineering Education* 75 (March 1985): 328; Paul Dorgan, "Engineering and Engineering Technology Degrees Granted 1984," *Engineering Education* 75 (April 1985): 637.

29. Dorgan, "Engineering and Engineering Technology Degrees Granted 1984," p. 637; "Engineering College Research and Graduate Study," pp. 328, 642.

30. "Minutes of the Engineering Foundation Advisory Council," vol. 1, October 3, 1970, May 20, 1978, ODE; *Insight, 1969–1970*, p. 10; *Insight, 1972–1973*, p. 5; *Insight, 1974–1975*, p. 16; *Annual Report, 1976–1977*, p. 18; *Annual Report, 1984–1985*, pp. 22–23.

31. Interview with Associate Professor Hayes, September 11, 1985; *Annual Report, 1984–1985*, pp. 22–23, 27; *Insight, 1970–1971*, p. 2; *Annual Report, 1976–1977*, pp. 3, 24; *College of Engineering Planning Document, 1986* (Austin: College of Engineering, The University of Texas at Austin, 1986), pp. 62–64; *Daily Texan*, August 14, 1985; "Sixteen Girls in Engineering at UT," p. 13.

32. Almetris M. Duren and Louise Iscoe, *Overcoming: A History of Black Integration at the University of Texas at Austin* (Austin: The University of Texas at Austin, 1979), pp. 4–7; interview with John Hargis, June 20, 1985.

33. Dorgan, "Engineering and Engineering Technology Degrees Granted 1984," p. 637; *Daily Texan*, October 18, 1985; *Engineering/85* 6 (Summer 1985); *Insight, 1971–1972*, pp. 8–9; *Insight, 1973–1974*, pp. 12, 16; *Insight, 1974–1975*, p. 17; *Annual Report, 1975–1976*, pp. 22, 24; *Annual Report,*

*1976–1977*, p. 20; *Annual Report, 1977–1978*, p. 20; *Annual Report, 1978–1979*, p. 20; *Annual Report, 1979–1980*, p. 31; *Annual Report, 1980–1981*, p. 30; *Annual Report, 1981–1982*, p. 33; *Annual Report, 1984–1985*, pp. 22–23, 27; *Planning Document, 1986*, pp. 62–64; *Annual Report, Equal Opportunity in Engineering, 1980–1981* (Austin: College of Engineering, The University of Texas at Austin, 1981–1985); *Annual Report, Equal Opportunity in Engineering, 1984–1985*; additional information provided by Mr. Backus.

34. "Minutes of the Engineering Foundation Advisory Council," vol. 1, February 26, 1977, ODE; *Insight, 1971–1972*, pp. 8–9; *Insight, 1973–1974*, pp. 12, 16; *Insight, 1974–1975*, p. 17; *Annual Report, 1976–1977*, p. 20; *Annual Report, 1977–1978*, p. 20; *Annual Report, 1975–1976*, pp. 22, 24; *Annual Report, 1978–1979*, p. 20; *Annual Report, 1979–1980*, p. 31; *Annual Report, 1984–1985*, pp. 22–23, 27; "Annual Report, Equal Opportunity in Engineering, 1972–1973," p. 4, TSS, History File, ODE; *Annual Report, Equal Opportunity in Engineering, 1984–1985*, p. ii; "Department Chairmen Minutes," vol. 6, July 25, 1974, February 24, 1976, ODE.

35. *Annual Report, 1984–1985*, pp. 22–23, 27; *Insight, 1973–1974*, p. 17; *Insight, 1974–1975*, p. 17; *Annual Report, 1976–1977*, p. 21; *Annual Report, 1977–1978*, 21; *Annual Report, 1975–1976*, pp. 22–23; *Annual Report, 1979–1980*, p. 30; Dorgan, "Engineering and Engineering Technology Degrees Granted 1984," p. 637; *Annual Report, 1980–1981*, p. 2; interview with Associate Professor Hayes, September 11, 1985; conversation with Professor Paul, September 18, 1985; conversation with Professor Lamb, August 20, 1985.

36. *Insight, 1971–1972*, p. 22; *Insight, 1973–1974*, p. 18; *Insight, 1974–1975*, pp. 17, 24; *Annual Report, 1975–1976*, p. 32; *Annual Report, 1976–1977*, p. 21; *Annual Report, 1977–1978*, p. 33; *Annual Report, 1978–1979*, pp. 21, 32; *Annual Report, 1979–1980*, p. 32; *Annual Report, 1980–1981*, pp. 4, 31; *Annual Report, 1981–1982*, pp. 32, 35; *Annual Report, 1984–1985*, p. 23; "Annual Report, Cooperative Engineering Education Program, 1984–1985," TSS, History File, ODE; "Minutes of the Engineering Foundation Advisory Council," vol. 1, February 25, 1984, ODE; additional information provided by Professor Franzolino.

37. "Engineering Faculty Minutes," vol. 13, April 28, August 28, September 28, October 10, 1980, ODE; "Engineering Faculty Minutes," vol. 14: January 1981 to September 1983, minutes of meeting on November 13, 1981, ODE; "Department Chairmen Minutes," vol. 5, September 4, 1970, vol. 7, August 30, 1976, vol. 8: September 1978 to May 1983, minutes of meeting on May 8, 1980, ODE; "Minutes of the Engineering Foundation Advisory Council," vol. 1, October 3, 1970, ODE; *Vector*, September and December 1984; *Daily Texan*, August 14, 1985.

38. "Engineering Faculty Minutes," vol. 13, September 28, October 10, 1980, ODE; "Department Chairmen Minutes," vol. 8, May 8, 1980, ODE; *Planning Document, 1986*, pp. 7–8; *Daily Texan*, August 5, 1985; "Minutes of the Engineering Foundation Advisory Council," vol. 1, February 25, 1984, ODE; *Annual Report, 1981–1982*, p. 2.

39. *Insight, 1970–1971*, pp. 7, 9; *Insight, 1971–1972*, p. 8; *Insight, 1972–1973*, p. 8; *Annual Report, 1982–1983*, pp. 10; *Annual Report, 1984–1985*, pp. 12–15; "Engineering Faculty Minutes," vol. 14, January 5, 1981, ODE; "Department Chairmen Minutes," vol. 5, October 20, 1970, ODE; *Catalog, 1984–1986*, IV, p. 25.

40. *Insight, 1973–1974*, pp. 23–24; "Engineering College Research and Graduate Study," p. 541; *Annual Report, 1978–1979*, p. 33; *Annual Report, 1980–1981*, p. 4; *Annual Report, 1982–1983*, p. 10; *Annual Report, 1984–1985*, pp. 12–15; Dean Gloyna to H. Kenneth Rigsbee, Jr., July 10, 1985, photocopy, History File, ODE; interview with Professor Rase, June 19, 1985; "Engineering Faculty Minutes," vol. 13, May 6, 1976, ODE; "Department Chairmen Minutes," vol. 6, July 25 and August 30, 1974, vol. 7, September 24, 1977, July 3, 1978, vol. 8, September 13, 1978, ODE; "Minutes of the Engineering Foundation Advisory Council," vol. 1, May 20, 1978, ODE.

41. *Insight, 1969–1970*, p. 15; *Insight, 1970–1971*, p. 10; *Insight, 1971–1972*, p. 16; *Annual Report, 1975–1976*, p. 32; *Annual Report, 1976–1977*, p. 36; *Annual Report, 1977–1978*, p. 34; *Annual Report, 1978–1979*, p. 33; *Annual Report, 1979–1980*, p. 24; *Annual Report, 1980–1981*, p. 21; *Annual Report, 1981–1982*, p. 23; *Annual Report, 1984–1985*, p. 31; "Engineering Faculty Minutes," vol. 13, September 5, 1974, ODE; "Department Chairmen Minutes," vol. 8, September 13, 1978, ODE; "History, Continuing Engineering Studies/Engineering Institutes," TSS, n.d. [1985], History File, ODE.

42. Interview with Professor Byron D. Tapley, September 20, 1985; *Annual Report, 1983–1984*, pp. 8–9; *Annual Report, 1977–1978*, p. 7; conversation with Professor Lamb, August 20, 1985; *Annual Report, 1984–1985*, p. 6; *Annual Report, 1982–1983*, p. 4; interview with Professor Victor G. Szebehely, September 12, 1985; *Annual Report of the Department of Aerospace Engineering and Engineering Mechanics, 1984–1985* (Austin: College of Engineering, The University of Texas at Austin, 1985), p. 2; J. Parker Lamb, Jr., "Aerospace Education: From Primitive Planes to Robotic Spacecraft," *Texas Professional Engineer* 43 (July–August 1985): 28–31; additional information provided by Professor Lamb.

43. Interview with Professor Tapley, September 20, 1985; *Annual Report, 1983–1984*, pp. 8–9; *Insight, 1973–1974*, p. 3; *Annual Report 1977–1978*, p. 7; conversation with Professor Lamb, August 20, 1985; *Annual Report, 1984–1985*, p. 6; *Annual Report, 1982–1983*, p. 4; interview with Professor

Szebehely, September 12, 1985; *Annual Report of the Department of Aerospace Engineering and Engineering Mechanics, 1984–1985*, p. 2; additional information provided by Professor Lamb.

44. Conversation with Professor Paul, September 18, 1985; *Insight, 1969–1970*, p. 4; *Insight, 1973–1974*, pp. 4, 7; conversation with Professor Robert S. Schechter, September 12, 1985; *Annual Report 1983–1984*, pp. 10–11; *Annual Report, 1984–1985*, p. 7; *Engineering/1985* 6 (Summer 1985); additional information provided by Professor Rase.

45. Conversation with Professor Paul, September 18, 1985; *Insight, 1969–1970*, p. 4; *Insight, 1973–1974*, pp. 4, 7; conversation with Professor Schechter, September 12, 1985; *Annual Report, 1984–1985*, p. 7; *Annual Report, 1983–1984*, pp. 10–11; "Department Chairmen Minutes," vol. 5, April 21, 1970, ODE; interview with Dean McKetta, May 10, 1985; interview with Professor Rase, June 19, 1985; *Engineering/1985* 6 (Summer 1985); additional information provided by Professor Rase.

46. Conversation with Professor Joseph F. Malina, Jr., August 22, 1985; *Insight, 1974–1975*, p. 11; *Annual Report, 1976–1977*, p. 9; *Annual Report, 1983–1984*, p. 12; additional information provided by Professor Malina.

47. *Insight, 1971–1972*, pp. 11, 12; *Insight, 1972–1973*, p. 10; *Insight, 1973–1974*, p. 7; *Annual Report, 1976–1977*, p. 10; conversation with Professors Duesterhoeft and Smith, September 12, 1985; *Annual Report, 1977–1978*, p. 11; *Annual Report 1984–1985*, p. 9; *Annual Report 1982–1983*, p. 7; interview with Professor Edward J. Powers, Jr., September 5, 1985; additional information provided by Professor Powers.

48. *Insight, 1971–1972*, pp. 11, 12; *Insight, 1972–1973*, p. 10; *Insight, 1973–1974*, p. 7; *Annual Report, 1976–1977*, p. 10; conversation with Professors Duesterhoeft and Smith, September 12, 1985; *Annual Report 1977–1978*, p. 11; "Engineering Excellence: The Key to Economic Development—An Interview with Pike Powers," *Texas Professional Engineer* 42 (November-December 1984): 8–10; "MCC—Putting Texas on the 'High–Tech' Map; An Interview with Admiral Bob Ray Inman," *Texas Professional Engineer* 42 (November–December 1984): 11–13; *Annual Report, 1984–1985*, p. 9; *Annual Report, 1982–1983*, p. 7; "Minutes of the Engineering Foundation Advisory Council," vol. 1, September 24, 1983, ODE; interview with Professor Powers, September 5, 1985; additional information provided by Professor Powers.

49. Interview with Professor H. Grady Rylander, Jr., September 11, 1985; *Insight, 1972–1973*, p. 10; *Insight, 1974–1975*, p. 12; *Annual Report, 1976–1977*, p. 11; *Annual Report, 1977–1978*, p. 12; *Daily Texan*, February 24, 1986; additional information provided by Professor Rylander.

50. *Annual Report, 1984–1985*, p. 10; *Annual Report, 1982–1983*, p. 8; *Master of Science Degree Program in Manufacturing Systems Engineering*, pamphlet, n.d., History File, ODE; interview with Associate Professor Margaret R. Baker, September 23, 1985; additional information provided by Professor Rylander.

51. Conversation with Professor Dorfman, August 16, 1985; conversation with Professor Schechter, September 12, 1985; *Annual Report, 1976–1977*, p. 12; *Annual Report, 1977–1978*, p. 13; *Annual Report, 1979–1980*, p. 12; *Annual Report, 1980–1981*, p. 10; *Annual Report of the Department of Petroleum Engineering, 1984–1985*, pp. 5, 26, 68–69; additional information provided by Professors Augusto L. Podio and Larry W. Lake.

52. *Annual Report, 1982–1983*, p. 9; *Annual Report, 1983–1984*, p. 22; *Annual Report, 1984–1985*, p. 11; conversation with Professor Schechter, September 12, 1985; conversation with Professor Dorfman, August 16, 1985; *Engineering/1985* 6 (Summer 1985); "News Briefs: New Degree in Energy," *Texas Professional Engineer* 39 (April 1981): 23; additional information provided by Professors Podio and Lake.

53. "Engineering Faculty Minutes," vol. 14, memorandum of January 5, 1981, ODE; *Annual Report, 1976–1977*, p. 23; *Annual Report, 1981–1982*, p. 32; *Annual Report, 1983–1984*, p. 20.

54. *Annual Report, 1974–1975*, p. 30; *Annual Report, 1984–1985*, pp. 2, 28; "Engineering and Technical College Research and Graduate Study," *Engineering Education* 76 (March 1986): 420–421, 522, 529–530, 547–548, 557–558, 559, 561, 562–563, 564; "Minutes of the Engineering Foundation Advisory Council," vol. 1, February 27, 1982, ODE; Johnson, "Engineering–Plus," p. 32.

55. *Engineering Digest*, July–October 1979; "Engineering Faculty Minutes," vol. 13, September 28, 1980, ODE; "Department Chairmen Minutes," vol. 5, February 9, 1971, vol. 7, September 23 and 24, November 7, 1977, ODE; "Minutes of the Engineering Foundation Advisory Council," vol. 1, February 27, 1982, ODE; *Insight, 1970–1971*, pp. 13–14; *Insight, 1971–1972*, p. 12; *Annual Report, 1978–1979*, p. 35; *Annual Report, 1979–1980*, p. 25; *Annual Report, 1984–1985*, pp. 28–29; interview with Professor Thompson, June 26, 1985; interview with Professor Reese, September 25, 1985; James J. Kelly, "Balcones," *Alcalde* 63 (July–August 1975): 23–30.

56. *Insight, 1971–1972*, p. 13; *Annual Report, 1978–1979*, p. 7; *Engineering Research, 1983–1984*, pp. 7–8, 10–11, 28–29; interview with Professor Tapley, September 20, 1985; interview with Associate Professor Hayes, September 11, 1985; *Faculty Research and Professional Interest Guide* (Austin: College of Engineering, The University of Texas at Austin, 1985), pp. 11–13; additional information provided by Professor Lamb.

57. *Insight, 1971–1972*, p. 13; *Annual Report, 1978–1979*, p. 7; interview with Professor Szebehely, September 12, 1985; *Faculty Research and Professional Interest Guide*, pp. 11–13; additional information provided by Professor Lamb.

58. *Insight, 1973–1974*, pp. 4, 7; *Annual Report, 1978–1979*, p. 12; *Annual Report, 1984–1985*, p. 2; conversation with Professor Paul, September 18, 1985; *On Campus*, October 14–20, 1985; interview with Professor Rase, June 19, 1985; *Engineering Research, 1983–1984*, pp. 9–10, 27–28; conversation with Professors Duesterhoeft and Smith, September 12, 1985; *Engineering/84* 5 (Summer 1984); *Faculty Research and Professional Interest Guide*, pp. 13–14; additional information provided by Professor Rase.

59. *Insight, 1969–1970*, pp. 4, 18; *Insight, 1971–1972*, p. 12; *Insight, 1972–1973*, p. 11; *Annual Report, 1976–1977*, p. 9; *Annual Report, 1979–1980*, pp. 17, 25; conversation with Professor Malina, August 22, 1985; *Engineering Research, 1983–1984*, pp. 31–32; *Faculty Research and Professional Interest Guide*, pp. 15–18; additional information provided by Associate Dean Thomas W. Kennedy.

60. Interview with Professor Reese, September 25, 1985; conversation with Professor Malina, August 22, 1985; *Faculty Research and Professional Interest Guide*, pp. 15–18; *Engineering Research, 1983–1984*, pp. 12, 20–21, 29–30; *Daily Texan*, October 18, 1985; *Engineering/84* 5 (Spring 1984); John E. Breen and James O. Jirsa, "Structural Engineering," *Discovery: Research and Scholarship at The University of Texas at Austin* 9 (Fall 1984): 28–32; additional information provided by Associate Dean Kennedy.

61. Interview with Professor Joe O. Ledbetter, September 19, 1985; conversation with Professor Malina, August 22, 1985; conversation with Dean Gloyna, March 8, 1986; *Engineering Research, 1983–1984*, p. 31; *Faculty Research and Professional Interest Guide*, pp. 15–18; Ernest T. Smerdon, "Not Enough Water," *Discovery* 9 (Fall 1984): 15–19; additional information provided by Professor Malina.

62. *Annual Report, 1982–1983*, p. 7; conversation with Professors Duesterhoeft and Smith, September 12, 1985; interview with Professor Herbert H. Woodson, September 13, 1985; interview with Professor Powers, September 5, 1985; *Annual Report on Electronics Research at The University of Texas at Austin, No. 32, for the Period April 1, 1984, Through March 31, 1985* (Austin: College of Engineering, The University of Texas at Austin, 1985); *Engineering Research, 1983–1984*, pp. 9–10, 14–16, 18; *Faculty Research and Professional Interest Guide*, pp. 18–21; additional information provided by Professor Powers.

63. "Engineering Excellence: The Key to Economic Development—An Interview with Pike Powers," pp. 8–10; "MCC—Putting Texas on the 'High–Tech' Map; An Interview with Admiral Bob Ray Inman," pp. 11–13; Diane E. Downing, "Thinking for the Future: The Promise of MCC," *Austin* (August 1983), pp. 105–110; *Engineering Research, 1983–1984*, pp. 18–20, 21–22, 24; *Faculty Research and Professional Interest Guide*, pp. 18–21; G. Jack Lipovski, "T∗R∗A∗C," *Discovery* 9 (Summer 1985): 13–16; Ben G. Streetman, "Microelectronics" *Discovery* 9 (Summer 1985): 6; additional information provided by Professor Powers.

64. *Insight, 1971–1972*, pp. 11, 12; *Insight, 1973–1974*, pp. 7, 29; *Annual Report, 1984–1985*, pp. 2, 28; Faculty File: Herbert H. Woodson, ODE; Interview with Professor Woodson, September 13, 1985; *Engineering Research, 1983–1984*, pp. 34–35; *Faculty Research and Professional Interest Guide*, pp. 18–21; Herbert H. Woodson and Jennifer Evans, "Energy Research," *Discovery* 9 (Fall 1984): 11–14.

65. *Insight, 1972–1973*, p. 13; *Annual Report, 1975–1976*, p. 14; *Engineering Research, 1983–1984*, pp. 16–17, 22–23; *Faculty Research and Professional Interest Guide*, pp. 21–24; "Smell the New," pp. 1–3, 6; H. Grady Rylander, "Pulsed Power," *Discovery* 9 (Fall 1984): 8–10; "UT Austin Energy: $5.86 Million Nuclear Lab Approved by UT Regents," *Energy Studies* 9 (September–October 1985): 4.

66. *Faculty Research and Professional Interest Guide*, pp. 21–24; "The Forty Acres—Engineering Experts Fill Endowed Chairs at UT," *Alcalde* 74 (July–August 1986): 25; Damond Benningfield, "The Robot Evolution," *Alcalde* 74 (July–August 1986): 16–17; additional information provided by Professor Rylander.

67. Conversation with Professor Dorfman, August 16, 1985; *Annual Report, 1978–1979*, p. 12; *Engineering Research, 1983–1984*, pp. 12–13, 26; *Faculty Research and Professional Interest Guide*, pp. 25–26; additional information provided by Professors Podio and Lake.

68. "The University of Texas at Austin Strategic Plan Through 1992–1993;" *Prospectus: Separations Research Program, Center for Energy Studies, The University of Texas at Austin* (Austin: Center for Energy Studies, The University of Texas at Austin, 1983), p. 59.

## NOTES TO ENGINEERING LEADERSHIP THROUGH RESEARCH

1. Eckhardt, *Fifty Stars*, pp. 94–95; *Austin Statesman*, December 14, 1897, October 9, 1898; *Dallas News*, October 18, 1896; *Galveston News*, November 25, 1900; John A. Focht, "Memoir," Faculty File: Thomas U. Taylor, ODE; Dean Taylor to President Splawn, May 8, 1926, President's Office Files, BTHC; *Austin Times*, August 12, 1938; Thomas U. Taylor, *The Austin Dam*, UT Bulletin, no. 164 (De-

cember 22, 1910); Taylor, *Silting of the Lake at Austin, Texas*, UT Bulletin, no. 2439 (October 15, 1924); Taylor, "Silting of Lake Worth," *Texas Engineer* 2 (August 1932): 6–12; Taylor, *Annual Flow and Run-Off of Some Texas Streams*, UT Bulletin, no. 1 (January 1, 1915); Taylor, *Rice Irrigation in Texas*, UT Bulletin, no. 16 (Austin: Von Boeckmann, Schutze, and Company, State Printers, 1902); Taylor, *Run-Off and Mean Flow of Some Texas Streams*, UT Bulletin, no. 65 (November 20, 1915).

2. *President's and Faculty Report, 1901–1902*, p. 77; *Record*, July 15, 1910, pp. 152–153; *Daily Texan*, March 15, 1925, March 5, 14, 1926; Berry, *Pictorial History*, p. 71; George L. Dahl, "Power Plant for an Educational Institution," *University of Texas Engineer* 1 (January 1931): 9–10; Eckhardt, *Fifty Who Loved and Served The University*, p. 102; Faculty File: Werner W. Dornberger, ODE; "Architectural Engineering 1905–1963," p. 6, Mimeograph, n.d. [1963], History File, ODE; *Engineering–Science News*, 1 (January–February 1953).

3. James P. Nash, *Road Materials of Texas*, UT Bulletin, no. 62 (November 5, 1915); James P. Nash, *Tests of Concrete Aggregates Used in Texas*, UT Bulletin, no. 1771 (December 20, 1917); James P. Nash, *Road Building Material in Texas*, UT Bulletin, no. 1839 (July 10, 1918); Edward T. Paxton, *Street Paving in Texas*, UT Bulletin, no. 26 (May 5, 1915); *Roads and Pavements*, UT Bulletin, no. 1735 (June 20, 1917) *Roads and Pavements*, UT Bulletin, no. 1922 (April 15, 1919); Robert M. Jameson, *Methods of Sewage Disposal for Texas Cities*, UT Bulletin, no. 362 (October 1, 1914); *Water Supply and Sanitation*, UT Bulletin, no. 1733 (June 10, 1917).

4. John A. Focht, *A Study of Tests of Cylinders and Cores Taken From Concrete Roads in Texas During 1928*, UT Bulletin, no. 2922 (June 8, 1929); *Engineering Digest* 1 (July–October 1979); Frederick E. Giesecke and Stanley P. Finch, *Physical Properties of Dense Concrete as Determined by the Relative Quantity of Cement*, UT Bulletin, no. 1815 (March 10, 1918); Frederick E. Giesecke, H. R. Thomas, and George A. Parkinson, *The Strength of Fine–Aggregate Concrete*, UT Bulletin, no. 1855 (October 1, 1918); Frederick E. Giesecke, H. R. Thomas, and George A. Parkinson, *Progress Report of the Engineering Research Division of the Bureau of Economic Geology and Technology*, UT Bulletin, No. 2215 (April 15, 1922); Stanley P. Finch, George A. Parkinson, and J. E. Hoff, *Preliminary Report on Relation Between Strength of Portland Cement Mortar and Its Temperature at Time of Test*, UT Bulletin, no. 2825 (July 1, 1928); C. Read Granberry, *Testing of Motor Vehicle Headlighting Devices and Investigation of Certain Phases of the Headlight Glare Problem*, UT Bulletin, no. 2813 (April 1, 1928); Raymond F. Dawson, "Civil Engineering," *Discovery* 7 (Summer 1983): 40–42.

5. Byron E. Short, *Heat Transfer and Pressure Drop in Heat Exchangers*, UT Bulletin, no. 3819 (May 15, 1938); Byron E. Short, Willis R. Woolrich, and Luis H. Bartlett, *Specific Heats of Foodstuffs* Circular of the Bureau of Engineering, The University of Texas, no. 3 (December 1942), hereafter cited as BER Circular; *Engineering Digest*, July–October 1979; Howard E. Degler and Alvin H. Willis, *Air Conditioning for the Relief of Cedar–Pollen Hay Fever*, UT Bulletin, no. 3932 (August 22, 1939); Willis R. Woolrich, Francis G. Winters, and James D. McFarland, *Ice Air Conditioning for Intermittent Service*, UT Bulletin, no. 4811 (June 1, 1948); Willis R. Woolrich and David C. Briggs, *The Cooling of Churches*, BER Circular, no. 26 (July 1956); Willis R. Woolrich and H. T. Mei, *Specifying Vapor Barriers for Year–Round Air Conditioning*, Reprint of the Bureau of Engineering, The University of Texas at Austin, no. 49 (1959), henceforth cited as BER Reprint; Carl J. Eckhardt, Jr., and Chapin Winston Yates, *The Influence of Storage Conditions Upon the Physical Properties of Lignite*, UT Bulletin, no. 4240 (October 22, 1942); Texas Industrial and Commercial Research Council, *Power Resources of Texas: Proceedings of the Fourth Industrial Planning Conference, April 12, 1945*, Special Publication of the Bureau of Engineering Research, No. 15 (1945), hereafter cited as BER Special Publication; *Papers Presented at the Food Preservation Conference, March 13–14, 1941*, BER Special Publication, no. 7 (1941); *Proceedings of the Sixth Annual Southwest Air Conditioning Conference, December 11–13, 1950*, BER Special Publication, no. 21 (1951); *Proceedings of the First Annual Texas Traffic Engineering Conference, July 15–20, 1940*, BER Special Publication, no. 5 (1940); *Proceedings of the Fourth Texas Conference on Soil Mechanics and Foundation Engineering, February 21 and 22, 1941*, BER Special Publication, no. 6 (1941); Byron E. Short, "Mechanical Engineering," *Discovery* 7 (Summer 1985): 43–44.

6. *Dr. E. P. Schoch, 1871–1961*, History File, ODE; Eugene P. Schoch, *Chemical Analysis of Texas Rocks and Minerals*, UT Bulletin, no. 1814 (March 5, 1918); interview with Professor Cunningham, May 10, 1985; "Dr. E. P. Schoch Dies," *Texas Professional Engineer* 20 (October 1961): 15; William A. Cunningham, "Chemical Engineering," *Discovery* 7 (Summer 1983): 37–39.

7. Teare, "Graduate Programs and Research," p. 355; W. B. Berry, "Engineering College Research and Graduate Study," *Engineering Education* 75 (March 1985): 318; Susan Goodman and Victor L. Arnold, "High Technology in Texas," *Texas Business Review* 57 (November–December 1983): 290–295; Simpson, "Electronics Industry and Texas," pp. 6–8; Simpson, "Electronics Industry and Texas," pp. 13–16; *Balcones Research Center, Twentieth Anniversary Report*; pp. 1–2; Kelly, *31 Years of Research*, p. 3; *Engineering–Science News* 1 (January–February 1953).

8. Armytage, *A Social History of Engineering*, pp. 311, 314; Finch, *Engineering and Western Civilization*, p. 295.

9. Armytage, *A Social History of Engineering*, pp. 311, 314; Finch, *Engineering and Western Civi-

*lization,* p. 295; *Engineering Digest,* July–October 1979; *Annual Report, 1984–1985,* pp. 28–29; interview with Professor Thompson, June 26, 1985; "Engineering and Technical College Research and Graduate Study," pp. 562–563.

10. *Balcones Research Center, Twentieth Anniversary Report,* pp. 43–45, Kelly, *31 Years of Research,* p. 29; *Engineering Research, College of Engineering, The University of Texas at Austin, 1985–1986,* draft; *Annual Report of the Department of Aerospace Engineering and Engineering Mechanics, 1984–1985,* pp. 22–23; additional information provided by Professor Lamb.

11. *Balcones Research Center, Twentieth Anniversary Report,* pp. 43–45, Kelly, *31 Years of Research,* pp. 11; Damond Benningfield, "To Space and Back," *Alcalde* 70 (September–October 1981): 20–23; Damond Benningfield, "UT's Link with the Space Shuttle," *Alcalde* 72 (January–February 1984): 12–15; *Engineering Research, 1985–1986,* draft; *Annual Report of the Department of Aerospace Engineering and Engineering Mechanics, 1984–1985,* pp. 22–23; additional information provided by Professor Lamb.

12. *Balcones Research Center, Twentieth Anniversary Report,* pp. 43–45, Kelly, *31 Years of Research,* pp. 11, 29; Benningfield, "UT's Link with the Space Shuttle," pp. 12–15; *Engineering Research, 1985–1986,* draft; *Annual Report of the Department of Aerospace Engineering and Engineering Mechanics, 1984–1985,* pp. 22–23; additional information provided by Professor Lamb.

13. *Engineering Research, 1985–1986,* draft; *Annual Report of the Department of Aerospace Engineering and Engineering Mechanics, 1984–1985,* p. 24.

14. *Engineering Research, 1985–1986,* draft; *Annual Report of the Department of Aerospace Engineering and Engineering Mechanics, 1984–1985,* p. 24; *Faculty Research and Professional Interest Guide,* pp. 11–13.

15. Dana Young and Robert P. Felgar, Jr., *Tables of Characteristic Functions Representing Normal Modes of Vibration of a Beam,* UT Bulletin, no. 4904 (July 1, 1949); *Balcones Research Center, Twentieth Anniversary Report,* pp. 173–181, 207–208; Kelly, *31 Years of Research,* pp. 11, 19, 30; *Annual Report of the Department of Aerospace Engineering and Engineering Mechanics, 1984–1985,* p. 22.

16. Anita Howard, "Balcones Research Center—Science City," *Alcalde* 74 (March–April 1986): 14; Kelly, *31 Years of Research,* p. 11; additional information provided by Professor Lamb.

17. Information provided by Professor Lamb.

18. *Engineering Research, 1985–1986,* draft; conversation with Dean Gloyna, June 19, 1986; additional information supplied by Professor Lamb.

19. Howard F. Rase and James R. Fair, *Process Design of Light Hydrocarbon Cracking Units,* BER Reprint, no. 27 (1954); Howard F. Rase and C. C. Oldenburg, *Kinetics of Aldehyde Hydrogenation: Vapor–Phase Flow System and Supported Nickel Catalyst,* BER Reprint, no. 43 (1958); "Book Authored by UT Professor," *Texas Professional Engineer* 15 (August 1956): 21; Kenneth A. Kobe and Katherine C. Hellwig, *Sodium Sulfite from Caustic Cell Liquor: Sodium Sulfite–Sodium Chloride–Water System,* BER Reprint, no. 31 (1955); Kenneth A. Kobe, Horace R. Crawford, and Robert W. Stephenson, *Critical Properties and Vapor Pressures of Some Ketones,* BER Reprint, no. 32 (1955); Kenneth A. Kobe and Thomas R. Perkins, *A Simplified Method for Designing Light Hydrocarbon Cracking Units,* BER Reprint, no. 35 (1956); Kenneth A. Kobe et al., *Thermochemistry of Petrochemicals,* BER Reprint, no. 44 (1958); Kobe and Robert L. Pennington, *The Thermodynamic Properties of Acetone,* BER Reprint no. 41 (1957); John J. McKetta, Jr., and T. L. Kang, *Thermodynamic Properites of Sulfur Dioxide,* BER Reprint, no. 59 (1961); William A. Cunningham, *Hydrogen Sulfide in West Texas,* BER Reprint, no. 12 (1950); William A. Cunningham and W. C. Mills, *Deionization of Water for Ice Manufacture,* UT Bulletin, no. 5621 (November 1, 1956); additional information provided by Professor Rase.

20. Information provided by Professor Rase.

21. Information provided by Professor Rase.

22. "SRP Researchers Study Polymer Membranes for Separating Gases," *Energy Studies* 9 (March–April 1984): 1–3; *Annual Report of the Department of Chemical Engineering, 1984–1985,* p. vi; *Engineering Research, 1985–1986,* draft; additional information provided by Professor Rase.

23. *Engineering Research, 1985–1986,* draft; additional information provided by Professor Rase.

24. *Prospectus: Separations Research Program;* "SRP Researchers Study Polymer Membranes," pp. 1–3; *On Campus,* October 14–20, 1985; *Annual Report of the Department of Chemical Engineering, 1984–1985,* p. vi; *Engineering Research, 1985–1986,* draft; additional information provided by Professor Rase.

25. Raymond F. Dawson, *Settlement Studies of the San Jacinto Monument,* BER Circular, no. 5 (1947); Raymond F. Dawson, *The Design of Building Footings on Expansive Clay Soils,* BER Reprint, no. 17 (1952); *Engineering Digest,* July–October 1979; *Balcones Research Center, Twentieth Anniversary Report,* pp. 7, 275; Robert L. Stone and Paul D. Martino, *Limestone–Marl Mixtures for Extruded and Dry Pressed Building Brick,* BER Reprint, no. 36 (1956); Robert L. Stone and E. Joseph Weiss, *Three–Sheet Minerals in Clays,* BER Reprint, no. 24 (1954); Dawson, *Vertical Movement of House Number 6—Acme Ceramic House Project,* BER Circular, no. 23 (September 1953); *Researches on Livability in Hot Climates,* BER Reprint, no. 18 (May 1953); Short, "Mechanical Engineering," pp. 45–46.

26. *Engineering Research, 1985–1986*, draft; interview with Professor Reese, September 25, 1985; Lymon C. Reese, "Contributions of Faculty in Engineering at UT Austin to the Offshore Industry," *Texas Professional Engineer* 34 (March–April 1985): 21; Kelly, *31 Years of Research*, p. 19; *Faculty Research and Professional Interest Guide*, pp. 15–18.

27. *Engineering Research, 1985–1986*, draft; interview with Professor Reese, September 25, 1985; Reese, "Contributions," p. 21; Kelly, *31 Years of Research*, p. 19.

28. *Balcones Research Center, Twentieth Anniversary Report*, pp. 119–129, 211–212; Kelly, *31 Years of Research*, pp. 24, 30; *Phil M. Ferguson*, History File, ODE; "Civil Engineering Laboratory Established at Research Center," *Texas Professional Engineer* 10 (October 1951): 10–11; Reese, "Contributions," p. 21.

29. *Balcones Research Center, Twentieth Anniversary Report*, pp. 257–275; Kelly, *31 Years of Research*, p. 9; "Shock Waves Study at UT," *Texas Professional Engineer* 19 (July 1960): 5.

30. *Balcones Research Center, Twentieth Anniversary Report*, pp. 257–275; Kelly, *31 Years of Research*, p. 9; "Focus on the Forty Acres—Austin Oaks Completed," *Alcalde* 57 (February 1969): 19.

31. Kelly, *31 Years of Research*, pp. 24, 30; "Blueprint—Texas UT Engineers Test Bridge Cable," *Texas Professional Engineer* 38 (December 1979–January 1980): 71; "Bridge," *Civil Engineering* 54 (July 1984): 31–33; Breen and Jirsa, "Structural Engineering," pp. 28–32.

32. *Engineering Research, 1985–1986*, draft; *Balcones Research Center, Twentieth Anniversary Report*, pp. 277–281; Kelly, *31 Years of Research*, p. 14; *Faculty Research and Professional Interest Guide*, pp. 15–18.

33. *Engineering Research, 1985–1986*, draft; *Daily Texan*, October 18, 1985; *Faculty Research and Professional Interest Guide*, pp. 15–18.

34. Wightman, "Center for Highway Research," 11–14; "DOT and CATS Make Tracks," *Alcalde* 63 (July–August 1976): 15; *Annual Report of the Department of Civil Engineering, 1984–1985*, p. 43; *Balcones Research Center, Twentieth Anniversary Report*, pp. 211–212; Hilton Hagan, "A History of the Texas Highway Department," *Texas Professional Engineer* 34 (November–December 1985): 14; *Engineering Research, 1985–1986*, draft; G. K. Sprinkle and Leigh Sander, "UT Research: Arena of Discovery," *Alcalde* 71 (May–June 1983): 20.

35. *Annual Report of the Department of Civil Engineering, 1984–1985*; *Balcones Research Center, Twentieth Anniversary Report*, pp. 211–212; Hagan, "Texas Highway Department," p. 14; *Engineering Research 1985–1986*, draft; Sprinkle and Sander, "Arena of Discovery," p. 20.

36. "Construction Booming at Off-Campus Center," *Texas Professional Engineer* 11 (September 1952): 20–21; "UT Engineer Builds New Device," *Texas Professional Engineer* 11 (November 1952): 14; Phil M. Ferguson to Dean Woolrich, August 9, 1957, in "Annual Report of the College of Engineering, 1956–1957," pp. 2–3; *Balcones Research Center, Twentieth Anniversary Report*, pp. 29, 103–114, 183–202; Kelly, *31 Years of Research*, pp. 5, 8; "The Urgent Problem in Texas: Water," *Alcalde* 53 (May 1965): 14–18; "Water: Do We Have Enough?" *Alcalde* 73 (May–June 1985): 10–16.

37. W. Wesley Eckenfelder, Jr., and Davis L. Ford, *The Effect of Process Variables on Sludge Floe Formation and Settling Characteristics*, Technical Report of the Environmental Health Engineering Laboratory, no. 11–6604 (November 1, 1966), hereafter cited as EHEL Technical Report; Joseph F. Malina, Jr., and Joe Clifton Mosely II, *Relationships Between Selected Physical Parameters and Cost Responses for the Deep-Well Disposal of Aqueous Industrial Wastes*, EHEL Technical Report, no. 07–6801 (August 1968); Joseph F. Malina, Jr., and Lawrence P. Gazda, *Land Disposal of Municipal Solid Wastes in Selected Standard Metropolitan Statistical Areas in Texas*, EHEL Technical Report, no. 01–6901 (January 1969); E. Gus Fruh and Ernest M. Davis, *Water Quality of the Highland Lakes: Determination of the Effect of Urbanization on Impoundment Water Quality*, EHEL Technical Report, no. 69–10 (April 1969); Joe J. Ledbetter and Torsten Rothman, *Droplet Size of Cooling Tower Fog*, EHEL Technical Report, no. 11–6802 (December 1968); Patrick R. Atkins and Ivan David Besner, *The Dispersion of Lead and Carbon Monoxide from a Heavily-Traveled Highway*, EHEL Technical Report, no. 70–08 (May 1970); Earnest F. Gloyna and Neal E. Armstrong, *Radioactivity Transport in Water: Numerical Solutions of Radionuclide Transport Equations and Role of Plants in SR-85 Transport*, EHEL Technical Report, no. 12–6703 (January 1968); Neal E. Armstrong and Anita J. Dawson, *Final Report, Exchange of Carbon, Nitrogen and Phosphorus in Lavaca Bay, Texas Marshes, Volume 2: The Role of Plants in Nutrient Exchange in the Lavaca Bay Brackish Marsh System*, EHEL Technical Report, no. 75–06 (August 31, 1975); Kelly, *31 Years of Research*, pp. 5, 8; *Engineering Research, 1985–1986*, draft; "Water: Do We Have Enough?" pp. 10–16; *Faculty Research and Professional Interest Guide*, pp. 15–18.

38. Kelly, *31 Years of Research*, pp. 5, 8; *Engineering Research 1985–1986*, draft; "Water: Do We Have Enough?" pp. 14–16; Smerdon, "Not Enough Water," pp. 15–19; *Faculty Research and Professional Interest Guide*, pp. 15–18.

39. Ernest M. Siegel, *Wavelength of Oscillations Along Transmission Lines and Antennae*, UT Bulletin, no. 4031 (August 15, 1940); *Balcones Research Center, Twentieth Anniversary Report*, pp. 149–150; Kelly, *31 Years of Research*, pp. 22–23, 25, 26.

40. Kenneth H. Jehn, *Some Aspects of Engineering Meteorology*, BER Reprint, no. 19 (1953);

"Invention Defines Paths in Atmosphere," *Texas Professional Engineer* 10 (May 1951): 9; *Proceedings of the Conference on Radio Meteorology, November 9–12, 1953*, BER Special Publication, no. 24 (1953); *Balcones Research Center, Twentieth Anniversary Report*, pp. 69–73; Kelly, *31 Years of Research*, pp. 17, 22.

41. Kelly, *31 Years of Research*, pp. 17, 22; *Balcones Research Center, Twentieth Anniversary Report*, pp. 69–73; "They Can 'See' the Wind," *Alcalde* 50 (May 1962): 12–13.

42. *Balcones Research Center, Twentieth Anniversary Report*, pp. 167–171; Kelly, *31 Years of Research*, p. 26; "Ricochet Romance with Old Man Moon," *Alcalde* 48 (November 1959): 12–13; *Engineering Research, 1985–1986*, draft; *Annual Report of the Department of Electrical and Computer Engineering, 1984–1985* (Austin: College of Engineering, The University of Texas at Austin, 1985), pp. 30–31; conversation with Professor David S. Evans, Department of Astronomy, The University of Texas at Austin, January 15, 1986.

43. *Balcones Research Center, Twentieth Anniversary Report*, pp. 150–161; Kelly, *31 Years of Research*, p. 23; *Faculty Research and Professional Interest Guide*, pp. 18–21; *Annual Report of the Department of Electrical and Computer Engineering, 1984–1985*, pp. 30–31; *Engineering Research, 1985–1986*, draft.

44. *Balcones Research Center, Twentieth Anniversary Report*, pp. 162–166; Kelly, *31 Years of Research*, pp. 22, 26; *Engineering Research, 1985–1986*, draft; *Annual Report of the Department of Electrical and Computer Engineering, 1984–1985*, pp. 30–31.

45. *Engineering Research, 1985–1986*, draft; *Annual Report on Electronics Research, No. 32*; *Annual Report of the Department of Electrical and Computer Engineering, 1984–1985*, pp. 32–33; Edward J. Powers, Jr., "A Brief History of the DOD Joint Services Electronics Program at The University of Texas at Austin," TSS, October 30, 1985, History File, ODE; *Faculty Research and Professional Interest Guide*, pp. 18–21; additional information provided by Professor Powers.

46. *Engineering Research, 1985–1986*, draft; *Annual Report of the Department of Electrical and Computer Engineering, 1984–1985*, pp. 32–33; Powers, "A Brief History of the DOD Joint Services Electronics Program"; *Annual Report on Electronics Research, No. 32*; additional information provided by Professor Powers.

47. *Engineering Research, 1985–1986*, draft; *Annual Report of the Department of Electrical and Computer Engineering, 1984–1985*, pp. 32–33; Streetman, "Microelectronics," p. 6; *Annual Report on Electronics Research, No. 32*; Powers, "A Brief History of the DOD Joint Services Electronics Program"; additional information provided by Professor Powers.

48. *Engineering Research, 1985–1986*, draft; *Annual Report of the Department of Electrical and Computer Engineering, 1984–1985*, pp. 32–33; Powers, "A Brief History of the DOD Joint Services Electronics Program"; *Annual Report on Electronics Research, No. 32*; additional information provided by Professor Powers.

49. *Engineering Research, 1985–1986*, draft; *Annual Report of the Department of Electrical and Computer Engineering, 1984–1985*, pp. 32–33; Powers, "A Brief History of the DOD Joint Services Electronics Program"; *Faculty Research and Professional Interest Guide*, pp. 18–21; *Annual Report on Electronics Research, No. 32*; additional information provided by Professor Powers.

50. *Engineering Research, 1985–1986*, draft; *Annual Report of the Department of Electrical and Computer Engineering, 1984–1985*, pp. 32–33; Powers, "A Brief History of the DOD Joint Services Electronics Program"; *Annual Report on Electronics Research, No. 32*; additional information provided by Professor Powers.

51. *Annual Report of the Department of Electrical and Computer Engineering, 1984–1985*, pp. 32–33; *Annual Report on Electronics Research, No. 32*; additional information provided by Professor Powers.

52. Streetman, "Microelectronics," pp. 6–9; *Annual Report of the Department of Electrical and Computer Engineering, 1984–1985*, pp. 35–36.

53. *Engineering Research, 1985–1986*, draft; *Annual Report of the Department of Electrical and Computer Engineering, 1984–1985*, p. 34.

54. Lipovski, "T*R*A*C," pp. 13–16; additional information provided by Professor Powers.

55. Woodson, "Alternative Sources of Energy," pp. 5–7, 17; Woodson, "Energy Sources of the Future," pp. 8–11; Sprinkle and Sander, "Arena of Discovery," pp. 10–21; Damond Benningfield, "Fascinating Fusion," *Alcalde* 69 (May–June 1981): 16–18; Johnson, "Engineering–Plus," pp. 29–35; "Grant Expands Energy Research," *Alcalde* 63 (September–October 1976): 20; *Annual Report of the Department of Electrical and Computer Engineering, 1984–1985*, p. 29; *Engineering Research, 1985–1986*, draft.

56. *Balcones Research Center, Twentieth Anniversary Report*, pp. 15, 213–215; Kelly, *31 Years of Research*, p. 7; Short, "Mechanical Engineering," p. 45.

57. Kelly, *31 Years of Research*, p. 7.

58. Kelly, *31 Years of Research*, p. 7; Jim Hicks, "Energy Update," *Alcalde* 64 (May–June 1977): 43; Sprinkle and Sander, "Arena of Discovery," p. 14.

59. *Annual Report of the Department of Mechanical Engineering, 1984–1985* (Austin: College of Engineering, The University of Texas at Austin, 1985), p. 26; *Engineering Research, 1985–1986*, draft; "UT–Austin Energy: Center for Electromechanics Explores Pulsed Power and How to Use It," *Energy Studies* 8 (November–December 1982): 4, 6; "UT Austin Energy: Center for Electromechanics Wins IR

100 Award for Homoplanar Generator," *Energy Studies* 9 (November–December 1983): 4; Sprinkle and Sander, "Arena of Discovery," pp. 10–21; Rylander, "Pulsed Power," pp. 8–10; Anita Howard, "Bill Weldon's View of the Future," *Alcalde* 74 (March–April 1986): 15.

60. *Annual Report of the Department of Mechanical Engineering, 1984–1985,* p. 26; *Engineering Research, 1985–1986,* draft; "Center for Electromechanics Explores Pulsed Power," pp. 4, 6; "Texas Rail Guns," *Texas Times* 1 (Winter 1985): 24–27; Sprinkle and Sander, "Arena of Discovery," pp. 10–21; *Daily Texan,* October 30, 1985.

61. *Engineering Research, 1985–1986,* draft; Sprinkle and Sander, "Arena of Discovery," pp. 10–21; *Faculty Research and Professional Interest Guide,* pp. 21–24.

62. Hicks, "Energy Update," p. 43; Sprinkle and Sander, "Arena of Discovery," p. 14; "Indirect Evaporative Cooling System May Cut Summer Energy Peaks," *Energy Studies* 10 (November–December 1984): 1–2; "CES Update: Conservation and Solar Energy" *Energy Studies* 10 (November–December 1984): 5–6; "Conservation Power Plant: Center Researchers Help City of Austin Save Energy," *Energy Studies* 10 (September–October 1984): 1–3; "CES Update: Conservation and Solar Energy," *Energy Studies* 10 (July–August 1985): 3; "4 Home Water Heating Alternatives Evaluated," *Energy Studies* 11 (November–December 1985): 1–2; *Faculty Research and Professional Interest Guide,* pp. 21–24.

63. *Engineering Research, 1985–1986,* draft; Harris L. Marcus, "Electronic Packaging," *Discovery* 9 (Fall 1985): 30–33; *Faculty Research and Professional Interest Guide,* pp. 21–24; "Engineering Experts Fill Endowed Chairs," p. 25.

64. *Engineering Research, 1985–1986,* draft; conversation with Dean Gloyna, June 19, 1986; Benningfield, "Robot Evolution," pp. 16–18; *Faculty Research and Professional Interest Guide,* pp. 21–24.

65. *Engineering Research, 1985–1986,* draft; Thompson, "University Research Aids Oil Industry," pp. 10–12; Woolrich, *Men of Ingenuity,* p. 165; Power to Dean Woolrich, August 26, 1957, in "Annual Report, 1955–1956," History File, ODE; *Annual Report of the Department of Petroleum Engineering, 1984–1985,* pp. 56–57; Fancher, Whiting, and Cretsinger, *The Oil Resources of Texas;* conversation with Professor Fancher, April 29, 1986.

66. Hicks, "Energy Update," pp. 42–43; Sprinkle and Sander, "Arena of Discovery," p. 10–14; "CES Update: Geothermal Energy," *Energy Studies* 9 (July–August 1984): 4–5; "CES Update: Geothermal Studies," *Energy Studies* 11 (November–December 1985): 2–3; *Balcones Research Center, Twentieth Anniversary Report,* pp. 99–101; Myron H. Dorfman, "The Outlook for Geopressured–Geothermal Energy and Associated Natural Gas," *Energy Studies* 8 (March–April 1983): 6–8; *Engineering Research, 1985–1986,* draft; Kelly, *31 Years of Research,* p. 10; *Co–Production of Natural Gas and Water: Program Information* (Chicago: The Gas Research Institute, 1985); *Annual Report of the Department of Petroleum Engineering, 1984–1985,* p. 27.

67. Sprinkle and Sander, "Arena of Discovery," pp. 10–14; *Engineering Research, 1985–1986,* draft; Kelly, *31 Years of Research,* p. 10; *Co–Production of Natural Gas and Water; Annual Report of the Department of Petroleum Engineering, 1984–1985,* p. 27; *Faculty Research and Professional Interest Guide,* pp. 25–26.

68. Sprinkle and Sander, "Arena of Discovery," pp. 10–14; *Engineering Research, 1985–1986,* draft; Kelly, *31 Years of Research,* p. 10; *Co–Production of Natural Gas and Water; Annual Report of the Department of Petroleum Engineering, 1984–1985,* p. 27.

69. Information provided by Professors Podio and Lake and Senior Lecturer Martin E. Chenevert.

70. Powers, "A Brief History of the DOD Joint Services Electronics Program"; Johnson, "Engineering–Plus," pp. 29–35; Sprinkle and Sander, "Arena of Discovery," pp. 10–21; "New Dialysis Process Frees Patients from Kidney Machines," *Alcalde* 69 (September–October 1980): 24; Grady Rylander, M.D., "Biomedical Engineering—What's Going On in Central Texas," *Texas Professional Engineer* 34 (December 1975), 6–7; *Engineering Research, 1985–1986,* draft.

71. Johnson, "Engineering–Plus," pp. 29–35; Carol Thurston, "The Marriage of Medicine and Engineering," *Alcalde* 62 (May 1974): 16–19; Sprinkle and Sander, "Arena of Discovery," pp. 10–21; Damond Benningfield, "UT Professor Attacks G–Forces to Protect Pilots," *Alcalde* 71 (September–October 1982): 6; Rylander, "Biomedical Engineering," pp. 6–7; *Engineering Research, 1985–1986,* draft.

72. *Applied Research Laboratories, The University of Texas at Austin* (Austin: Applied Research Laboratories, The University of Texas at Austin, 1983); *Balcones Research Center, Twentieth Anniversary Report,* pp. 21, 25, 51–55, 205–206; Kelly, *31 Years of Research,* p. 6; Short, "Mechanical Engineering," p. 45.

73. *Balcones Research Center, Twentieth Anniversary Report,* pp. 21, 25, 51–55, 205–206; *Applied Research Laboratories;* Kelly, *31 Years of Research,* p. 6.

74. Damond Benningfield, "ARL: Focuses on Research," *Alcalde* 69 (January–February 1981): 24–27; *Balcones Research Center, Twentieth Anniversary Report,* pp. 38–39, 51–55, 205–206; *Financial Statement for Fiscal Year Ending August 31, 1984* (Austin: The University of Texas at Austin, 1985),

pp. 106–107; *Applied Research Laboratories;* "Engineering and Technical College Research and Graduate Study," p. 563.

75. Benningfield, "ARL: Focuses on Research," pp. 24–27; *Balcones Research Center, Twentieth Anniversary Report,* pp. 38–39, 51–55, 205–206; *Distinguished Graduates, College of Engineering, The University of Texas at Austin* (Austin: College of Engineering, The University of Texas at Austin, 1978–1986 ), p. 39; *Applied Research Laboratories.*

76. Herbert H. Woodson, "Alternative Sources of Energy: Where Do We Go from Here?" *Texas Professional Engineer* 22 (March 1973): 5–7, 17; Woodson, "Energy Sources of the Future," *Texas Professional Engineer* 34 (February 1975): 8–11; Johnson, "Engineering–Plus," pp. 29–35; Sprinkle and Sander, "Arena of Discovery," pp. 10–21; *Annual Report of the Department of Electrical and Computer Engineering, 1984–1985,* p. 29; *Engineering Research, 1985–1986,* draft; Woodson and Evans, "Energy Research," pp. 11–14.

77. *Engineering Research, 1985–1986,* draft; conversation with Dean Gloyna, June 19, 1986.


## NOTES TO THE CHILDREN OF ALEC

1. *Cactus, 1908,* p. 101; *Cactus, 1913,* pp. 87–88; *Cactus, 1919,* p. 207; "Taylor's Quarter-Centennial Book," pp. 385, 392–399, 421, Taylor Papers, BTHC; Taylor, *Fifty Years,* pp. 250–252; "A Spontaneous Dedication of Dean Taylor's Office in the New Engineering Building," *Alcalde* 22 (1933–1934): 8; *Daily Texan,* November 24, 1912.

2. *Cactus, 1897,* p. 50.

3. *Cactus, 1901,* p. 145; *Cactus, 1902,* p. 182; *Cactus, 1903,* pp. 69, 84; *Record,* January 8, 1911, p. 234; *Cactus, 1907,* p. 185; *Cactus, 1909,* pp. 192, 194; *Cactus, 1915,* p. 296; *Cactus, 1918,* p. 108; Berry, *Pictorial History,* p. 208.

4. Taylor, *Fifty Years,* p. 97; *Cactus, 1921,* p. 399; *Cactus, 1922,* p. 394; *Cactus, 1928,* p. 250; *Cactus, 1930,* pp. 228, 230, 234, 242, 250, 260; *Cactus, 1933* p. 267; *Cactus, 1936,* no pagination.

5. Berry, *Pictorial Account,* p. 65; Berry, *Traditions,* pp. 67–70; Carl J. Eckhardt, Jr., *The Promise of Greatness:* Early Experiences at The University of Texas (Austin: Privately Printed, 1978), p. 25; Frantz, *Forty Acres Follies,* pp. 95–100; Dean Taylor to President Benedict, January 19, 1933, Taylor Papers, BTHC; Taylor, *Fifty Years,* p. 267; *Cactus, 1928,* p. 368.

6. Taylor, *Fifty Years,* pp. 116–123.

7. Taylor, *Fifty Years,* pp. 154–164; Berry, *Pictorial Account,* p. 299; Charles F. Morrison, "The Battle of the Tower," *Alcalde* 44 (April 1956): 188–189; Berry, *Traditions,* pp. 65–66; *Daily Texan,* September 20, 1984.

8. "Taylor's Quarter-Centennial Book," pp. 169–170, Taylor Papers, BTHC.

9. Taylor, *Fifty Years,* pp. 227–229; Woolrich, *Men of Ingenuity,* pp. 185–186.

10. Woolrich, *Men of Ingenuity,* pp. 190–191.

11. Taylor, *Fifty Years,* pp. 209–210; *Cactus, 1913,* p. 85; *Cactus, 1922,* p. 145; McFarland, "Development," p. 4, History File, ODE; *Daily Texan,* December 7 and 9, 1930, December 18, 1934.

12. Taylor, *Fifty Years,* pp. 201–202; alternate verse and chorus from "Program of the T. U. Taylor Quarter–Centennial Banquet, Given by the Engineers of the University of Texas in Honor of the 'Old Man' at the Driskill Hotel, February 21, 1913," photocopy in History File, ODE; "Taylor's Quarter–Centennial Book," pp. 327–333, Taylor Papers, BTHC; *Cactus, 1904,* p. 53; *Cactus, 1905,* p. 191; interview with Professor Kreisle, April 8, 1985; a more detailed account of Alec's career can be found in John A. Focht, "History of the Travels, Trials, and Tribulations of Alexander Fredericke Claire," TSS, November 1, 1978, History File, ODE.

13. Taylor, *Fifty Years,* pp. 202–203; *Cactus, 1923,* p. 83; Mary Waller, "Dr. Focht Remembers," *Vector* 32 (January 1985), p. 1; John A. Focht, *The Story of Alec, Patron Saint of the College of Engineering,* pamphlet, n.d., History File, ODE; interview with Professor Kreisle, April 8, 1985.

14. Taylor, *Fifty Years,* pp. 184–185; Focht, *Story of Alec,* History File, ODE; "Taylor's Quarter–Centennial Book," p. 243, Taylor Papers, BTHC.

15. *Cactus, 1910,* p. 285; *Cactus, 1913,* p. 85; *Cactus, 1914,* no pagination; *Cactus, 1915,* pp. 42–43; *Cactus, 1916,* p. 176; *Record,* April 22, 1911, p. 368; interview with Professor Focht, February 11, 1985.

16. *Cactus, 1917,* p. 174; *Cactus, 1918,* pp. 139–140; *Cactus, 1923,* p. 83; Focht, *Story of Alec,* History File, ODE; *Texas Engineering Notes* 1 (February 1917); Dick King, "Orange and White Clown," *Alcalde* 55 (November 1966): 30; *Austin News,* May 8, 1927.

17. Taylor, *Fifty Years,* pp. 203–204; *Cactus, 1923,* p. 83; *Austin News,* May 8, 1927; *Cactus, 1928,* p. 138; interview with Professor Kreisle, April 8, 1985; interview with Professor Focht, February 11, 1985.

18. Focht, *Story of Alec,* History File, ODE; interview with Professor Focht, February 11, 1985; interview with Professor Kreisle, April 8, 1985.

19. Focht, *Story of Alec,* History File, ODE; Berry, *Traditions,* pp. 89–90; interview with Pro-

fessor Kreisle, April 8, 1985; conversation with Professor Eckhardt, April 15, 1985; *Daily Texan*, May 20, 1938.

20. Focht, *Story of Alec*, History File, ODE; Berry, *Traditions*, pp. 89–90; interview with Professor Kreisle, April 8, 1985; conversation with Professor Eckhardt, April 15, 1985; *Engineering Digest*, November 1974; *Engineering Digest*, January–March 1979.

21. Taylor, *Fifty Years*, p. 210; "Taylor's Quarter–Centennial Book," p. 224, Taylor Papers, BTHC.

22. Taylor, *Fifty Years*, pp. 75–76, 255; *Cactus, 1983*, pp. 28, 36, 114; Focht, "A Tribute," p. 5; Woolrich, *Men of Ingenuity*, p. 49; "Engineering Faculty Minutes," vol. 1, January 20 and February 5, 1914, January 15, 1924, ODE; *Austin News*, December 11, 1928.

23. Taylor, *Fifty Years*, pp. 263, 266; Banks L. McLaurin, "The Engineers' Loan Fund," *Journal of Architecture, Engineering, and Industry* 7 (January 1946): 6; *Record*, April 22, 1911, p. 367; Berry, *Traditions*, pp. 79–80; "Engineering Faculty Minutes," vol. 4, September 16, 1950, ODE; "Minutes of the Engineering Foundation Advisory Council," vol. 2: October 1976– , minutes of meeting on September 25, 1982, ODE; *Austin American–Statesman*, March 20, 1938; John A. Focht to Collector of Internal Revenue, July 9, 1963, Focht to Burnell Waldrip, October 4, 1972, Focht to John D. Miller, March 21 and October 4, 1972, photocopies in History File, ODE.

24. Taylor, *Fifty Years*, pp. 296–297.

25. James D. McFarland, "The Ramshorn Association," TSS, May 8, 1939, History File, ODE; *Cactus, 1908*, p. 101; Dean Taylor to James D. McFarland et al., April 28, 1937, McFarland to John A. Focht, April 29, 1937, Carl J. Eckhardt et al., to James C. Cline, President of the Student Engineering Council, January 20, 1961, "Constitution of the Ramshorn Association, Adopted May 21, 1937," photocopies in History File, ODE.

26. Dean Woolrich to McFarland et al., August 5, 1946, McFarland to ———, March 25, 1947, "Ramshorn Program," n.d., "Minutes of the Ramshorn Association Staff and Spring Program Committee Meeting, February 19, 1948," "Constitution of the Ramshorn Association, Amended January 23, 1956," Eckhardt to Cline, January 20, 1961, photocopies in History File, ODE; J. C. Smith, "The Ramshorn Club," *Journal of Architecture, Engineering, and Industry* 10 (Summer 1950): 19–21; "Department Chairmen Minutes," vol. 2, April 30, 1959, ODE.

27. "Engineering Power Show Faculty Committee Chairmen," TSS, May 4, 1956, Robert C. McWherter to ———, March 27, 1950, photocopies in History File, ODE; "Engineering Faculty Minutes," vol. 3, May 20, 1938, April 3, 1945, ODE; "Department Chairmen Minutes," vol. 1, November 6, 1958, ODE.

28. Berry, *Pictorial Account*, pp. 195, 208; *Cactus, 1983*, p. 498; John A. Focht, "The Engineering Students' Association," *Journal of Architecture, Engineering, and Industry* 1 (December 1938): 5; "Engineering Power Show at UT", *Texas Professional Engineer* 16 (May 1957): 13; "Power Show," *Texas Engineering and Science Magazine* 1 (April 1965): 42–44.

29. Woolrich, *Men of Ingenuity*, pp. 191–192; interview with Professor Kreisle, April 10, 1985; "Harkleroad New Ramshorn Club President," *Texas Professional Engineer* 15 (January 1957): 4.

30. Woolrich, *Men of Ingenuity*, pp. 191–192; interview with Professor Kreisle, April 10, 1985; Charlie D. Anderson to ———, November 5, 1952, Anderson to Board of Directors, Texas Union, The University of Texas, November 22, 1952, photocopies in History File, ODE.

31. Woolrich, *Men of Ingenuity*, p. 192; "Engineering Faculty Minutes," vol. 7, November 25, 1952, ODE; Anderson to ———, November 5 and November 22, 1952, Dick Bailey to ———, December 5, 1952, photocopies in History File, ODE.

32. Woolrich, *Men of Ingenuity*, p. 193; Jerry Garrett to R. Don Foster, February 20 and March 4, 1953, Ernest Kistler, "Report on Student Engineering Council Work for the 1954 Fall Semester," TSS, n.d., Lynn Evans to Jitter Nolan, May 31, 1955, "Suggestions for the Administration of the Taylor T Room," TSS, n.d., photocopies in History File, ODE; "Engineering Faculty Minutes," vol. 7, November 8, 1956, ODE; "Taylor's T Room," *Alcalde* 45 (February 1957): 13; *Cactus, 1983*, p. 329; interview with Professor Kreisle, April 8, 1985; "Annual Report, 1956–1957," p. 2, History File, ODE.

33. *Student Engineering Council: Thirty Years on Forty Acres*, pamphlet, n.d., *1973 Awards Convocation, College of Engineering*, pamphlet, n.d. [1973], ——— to Dean Gloyna, December 5, 1985, History File, ODE; *Cactus, 1983*, p. 329.

34. *Cactus, 1929*, p. 380; *Cactus, 1938*, p. 68; *Cactus, 1958*, pp. 474, 491; *Cactus, 1985*, p. 259.

35. *Cactus, 1933*, p. 182; *Cactus, 1934*, p. 141; *Cactus, 1935*, p. 111; *Cactus, 1936*, no pagination; *Cactus, 1938*, p. 60; *Cactus, 1939*, pp. 288, 293; *Cactus, 1940*, p. 304; *Cactus, 1946*, pp. 390, 397, 400; H. Wayne Wilson to Dean Gloyna, November 27, 1985, ——— to Dean Gloyna, December 2, 1985, History File, ODE; *Cactus, 1931*, pp. 229, 268; *Cactus, 1932*, p. 263; *Cactus, 1933*, p. 21; *Cactus, 1938*, p. 176; *Cactus, 1965*, p. 422; *Cactus, 1970*, p. 279.

36. *Cactus, 1909*, p. 191; *Cactus, 1920*, p. 183; *Cactus, 1923*, pp. 370–371; *Cactus, 1926*, p. 307; *Cactus, 1928*, p. 399; *Cactus, 1929*, p. 379; *Cactus, 1936*, no pagination; *Cactus, 1965*, p. 411; *Cactus, 1970*, pp. 221, 232; "First Anniversary of Ramshorn," *Texas Professional Engineer* 16 (March 1957): 22;

to Dean Gloyna, December 2, 1985, Michelle Stillman to Dean Gloyna, December 3, 1985, Tina Telly to Dean Gloyna, December 4, 1985; Scott Schwab to Dean Gloyna, December 11, 1985, History File, ODE.

37. *Cactus, 1946,* p. 466; *Cactus, 1958,* p. 496; ——— to Dean Gloyna, November 26, 1985, ——— to Dean Gloyna, December 2, 1985, ——— to Dean Gloyna, December 6, 1985, History File, ODE.

38. *Cactus, 1902,* p. 67; *Cactus, 1917,* p. 123; *Cactus, 1923,* p. 284; *Cactus, 1924,* p. 99; *Cactus, 1928,* p. 250; *Cactus, 1975,* p. 391; Taylor, *Fifty Years,* p. 168; Frantz, *Forty Acres Follies,* p. 90; "USS 'Two Tons of Fun' Goes to ASCE Spring Convention," *Vector* 34 (Spring 1986): 7; "Blood, Sweat, and Beers a Winning Combination," *Alcalde* 70 (September–October 1981): 25; "A Great Day for the Races, Saturday, April 24, 1981," *Texas Civil Engineer* 51 (May 1981): 6–7.

39. Frantz, *Forty Acres Follies,* p. 64; *Record, 1908,* p. 56; Eckhardt, *Fifty Stars,* pp. 52–53; Berry, *Pictorial Account,* pp. 339–340, 348; Morse, *Students' History,* p. 64; *Dedication Program, Texas Memorial Stadium, Thanksgiving, 1924,* History File, ODE; *Insight, 1969–1970,* p. 11.

40. Frantz, *Forty Acres Follies,* p. 64; *Record, 1908,* p. 56; Eckhardt, *Fifty Stars,* pp. 52–53; Berry, *Pictorial Account,* pp. 339–340, 348; Morse, *Students' History,* p. 64; Bill Frisbie, "All–American Doug Dawson," *Alcalde* 72 (January–February 1984): 9; *Insight, 1969–1970,* p. 11.

41. *Cactus, 1895,* p. 79; *Cactus, 1983,* p. 373; *Dr. E. P. Schoch,* History File, ODE; Berry, *Pictorial Account,* pp. 201, 286, 295; Berry, *Traditions,* pp. 15–17, 19–21, 29, 43–44, 60; "Scholarship's Symbolic Scepter: The Mace," *Alcalde* 52 (June 1964): 13–15; interviews with Professor Kreisle, February 8 and April 8, 1985; conversation with Professor Eckhardt, April 17, 1985; Linda Carr, "The Seal Makers," *Alcalde* 57 (October 1968): 12–13, 32; Candace Klein, "Whatever Turns You Orange," *Alcalde* 65 (January–February 1978): 44–46.

42. *Cactus, 1983,* p. 411; *Engineering Digest,* April 1975.

# APPENDICES

## FACULTY OF THE COLLEGE OF ENGINEERING, 1888–1986

### Deans

| | |
|---|---|
| Thomas U. Taylor | 1906*–1936 |
| Willis R. Woolrich | 1936 –1958 |
| Byron E. Short, Acting Dean | 1948 –1949 |
| William W. Hagerty | 1958 –1963 |
| John J. McKetta, Jr. | 1963 –1969 |
| Billy H. Amstead, Acting Dean | 1969 –1970 |
| Earnest F. Gloyna | 1970 – |

*Taylor directed the activities of the Department of Engineering from 1895 until 1906, when he was officially designated as Dean.

### Assistant Deans

| | |
|---|---|
| Edward C. H. Bantel | 1913–1943 |
| Charles E. Rowe | 1943–1950 |
| John A. Focht | 1950–1959 |
| Billy H. Amstead | 1959–1969 |
| William R. Hudson | 1969–1970 |

### Assistant Dean for Continuing Professional Education and Special Projects

| | |
|---|---|
| William G. Lesso | 1978–1981 |

### Associate Deans

| | Specified Responsibilities | |
|---|---|---|
| William R. Hudson | Advanced Programs | 1970–1971 |
| Eugene H. Wissler | Academic Affairs | 1970–1976 |
| Lymon C. Reese | Advanced Programs | 1971–1979 |
| J. Parker Lamb, Jr. | Academic Affairs | 1976–1981 |
| Thomas W. Kennedy | Advanced Programs | 1979–1981 |
| | Research and Planning | 1981–1986 |
| | Research and Facilities | 1986– |

| Charles A. Sorber | Professional Education and Career Development | 1980–1981 |
| | Academic Affairs | 1981–1986 |
| Herbert H. Woodson | Development and Planning | 1986– |
| Mario J. Gonzalez, Jr. | Academic Affairs | 1986– |

## Chairmen, Engineering Schools and Departments

### CIVIL ENGINEERING† 1903–

| Departmental Status | Chairman | Period of Appointment |
| --- | --- | --- |
| School of Civil Engineering | Thomas U. Taylor | 1903–1920 |
| Department of Civil | Thomas U. Taylor | 1920–1924 |
| Engineering | Edward C. H. Bantel | 1924–1933 |
| | John A. Focht | 1933–1935 |
| | Banks L. McLaurin | 1935–1937 |
| | Stanley P. Finch | 1937–1943 |
| | Phil M. Ferguson | 1943–1957 |
| | Ernest W. Steel | 1957–1958 |
| | Walter L. Moore | 1958–1965 |
| | Lymon C. Reese | 1965–1971 |
| | L. Hudson Matlock | 1972–1976 |
| | Joseph F. Malina, Jr. | 1976– |

†A civil engineering curriculum was offered from the inception of the Department of Engineering at The University of Texas.

### MINING ENGINEERING 1903–1913

| Departmental Status | Chairman | Period of Appointment |
| --- | --- | --- |
| School of Mines | William B. Phillips | 1903–1905 |
| | Charles E. Rowe | 1905–1913 |

### ELECTRICAL ENGINEERING 1903–

| Departmental Status | Chairman | Period of Appointment |
| --- | --- | --- |
| School of Electrical | Arthur C. Scott | 1903–1911 |
| Engineering | Newton H. Brown | 1911–1914 |
| | John M. Bryant | 1914–1917 |
| | James A. Correll | 1917–1919 |
| | John M. Bryant | 1919–1920 |
| Department of Electrical | John M. Bryant | 1920–1928 |
| Engineering | James A. Correll | 1928–1937 |
| | Joseph W. Ramsay | 1937–1938 |
| | Robert W. Warner | 1938–1945 |
| | Burns N. Gafford | 1945–1964 |
| | Clarence L. Coates | 1964–1966 |
| | Archie W. Straiton | 1966–1971 |
| | Herbert H. Woodson | 1971–1981 |
| Department of Electrical | Edward J. Powers, Jr. | 1981– |
| and Computer | | |
| Engineering | | |

## ARCHITECTURE 1905–1951†

| Departmental Status | Chairman | Period of Appointment |
|---|---|---|
| School of Architectural Engineering and Drawing | George A. Endress | 1905–1907 |
| | Olaf Ellingson | 1907–1909 |
| School of Architecture and Drawing | Louis C. Wagner | 1909–1910 |
| School of Architecture | Hugo F. Kuehne | 1910–1912 |
| | Frederick E. Giesecke | 1912–1920 |
| Department of Architecture | Frederick E. Giesecke | 1920–1922 |
| | Robert L. White* | 1923 |
| | Frederick E. Giesecke | 1924–1927 |
| | Thomas U. Taylor* | 1927–1928 |
| | Goldwin Goldsmith | 1928–1935 |
| | Walter T. Rolfe | 1935–1946 |
| | Hugh L. McMath | 1946–1947 |
| Department of Architecture and Planning, School of Architecture | Hugh L. McMath | 1947–1951 |

†The School of Architecture became autonomous in 1951

## DRAWING 1911–1968

| Departmental Status | Chairman | Period of Appointment |
|---|---|---|
| School of Mechanical Drawing | Henry G. Livesay | 1910–1911 |
| School of Drawing | Charles E. Rowe | 1911–1920 |
| Department of Drawing | Charles E. Rowe | 1920–1933 |
| | Walter H. McNeill | 1933–1937 |
| | Charles E. Rowe | 1937–1940 |
| | Walter H. McNeill | 1941–1951 |
| | James D. McFarland | 1951–1968 |

## MECHANICAL ENGINEERING 1914–

| Departmental Status | Chairman | Period of Appointment |
|---|---|---|
| School of Mechanical Engineering | Forrest E. Cardullo | 1914–1915 |
| | Thomas U. Taylor | 1915–1916 |
| | Hal C. Weaver | 1916–1918 |
| | James A. Correll* | 1918–1919 |
| | Hal C. Weaver | 1919–1920 |
| Department of Mechanical Engineering | Hal C. Weaver | 1920–1929 |
| | Alex Vallance* | 1929–1930 |
| | Howard E. Degler | 1930–1945 |
| | Byron E. Short | 1945–1947 |
| | Myron L. Begeman | 1947–1949 |
| | Venton L. Doughtie | 1949–1951 |
| | Byron E. Short | 1952–1953 |

*Acting Chairman

| | | |
|---|---|---|
| | Myron L. Begeman | 1953–1957 |
| | Venton L. Doughtie | 1957–1962 |
| | Harry L. Kent, Jr.* | 1962–1963 |
| | Carl Gatlin | 1963–1964 |
| | William R. Upthegrove | 1964–1970 |
| | J. Parker Lamb, Jr. | 1970–1976 |
| | H. Grady Rylander, Jr. | 1976– |

## PETROLEUM ENGINEERING 1930–

| Departmental Status | Chairman | Period of Appointment |
|---|---|---|
| Department of Petroleum Engineering | Frederick B. Plummer | 1930–1936 |
| | Harry H. Power | 1936–1956 |
| | George Fancher | 1956–1959 |
| | Harry H. Power | 1959–1960 |
| | Carl Gatlin | 1960–1963 |
| | Ben H. Caudle | 1963–1966 |
| | Kenneth E. Gray | 1966–1975 |
| | Robert S. Schechter | 1975–1978 |
| | Myron H. Dorfman | 1978–1985 |
| | Gary A. Pope | 1985– |

## CHEMICAL ENGINEERING 1917–

| Departmental Status | Chairman | Period of Appointment |
|---|---|---|
| Chemical Engineering† Department of Chemical Engineering | Eugene P. Schoch | 1917–1938 |
| | Eugene P. Schoch | 1938–1942 |
| | William A. Cunningham | 1942–1945 |
| | Kenneth A. Kobe | 1945–1947 |
| | William A. Cunningham | 1947–1949 |
| | John J. McKetta, Jr. | 1949–1951 |
| | Matthew Van Winkle | 1951–1953 |
| | William A. Cunningham | 1953–1955 |
| | John J. McKetta, Jr. | 1955–1957 |
| | Kenneth A. Kobe* | 1957–1958 |
| | John J. McKetta, Jr. | 1958–1963 |
| | Howard F. Rase | 1963–1968 |
| | Eugene H. Wissler | 1968–1970 |
| | Robert S. Schechter | 1970–1973 |
| | David M. Himmelblau | 1973–1977 |
| | Donald R. Paul | 1977–1985 |
| | Thomas F. Edgar | 1985– |

†Administered by the Department of Chemistry with a curriculum established by the College of Engineering

## CERAMIC ENGINEERING 1945–1959

| Departmental Status | Chairman | Period of Appointment |
|---|---|---|
| Department of Ceramic Engineering | Forrest K. Pence | 1945–1950 |
| | E. Joseph Weiss* | 1950–1951 |
| | Robert L. Stone | 1951–1959 |

*Acting Chairman

## AEROSPACE ENGINEERING 1942–1968

| Departmental Status | Chairman | Period of Appointment |
|---|---|---|
| Department of Aeronautical Engineering | Milton J. Thompson | 1942–1944 |
| | Millard V. Barton | 1945–1946 |
| | Milton J. Thompson | 1946–1958 |
| Department of Aerospace Engineering | Milton J. Thompson | 1958–1966 |
| | Byron D. Tapley | 1966–1968 |

## ENGINEERING MECHANICS 1947–1968

| Departmental Status | Chairman | Period of Appointment |
|---|---|---|
| Department of Engineering Mechanics | Dana Young | 1947–1950 |
| | Banks L. McLaurin | 1950–1952 |
| | Millard V. Barton* | 1952–1954 |
| | Banks L. McLaurin | 1954–1958 |
| | Enrico G. Volterra | 1958–1959 |
| | Milton J. Thompson* | 1959–1961 |
| | Harold J. Plass, Jr. | 1961–1966 |
| | Lyle G. Clark | 1966–1968 |

## AEROSPACE ENGINEERING AND ENGINEERING MECHANICS 1968–

| Departmental Status | Chairman | Period of Appointment |
|---|---|---|
| Department of Aerospace Engineering and Engineering Mechanics | Byron D. Tapley | 1968–1977 |
| | Victor G. Szebehely | 1977–1981 |
| | J. Parker Lamb, Jr. | 1981– |

## ARCHITECTURAL ENGINEERING 1947–1969

| Departmental Status | Chairman | Period of Appointment |
|---|---|---|
| Department of Architectural Engineering, School of Architecture | James J. Pollard | 1947–1949 |
| | Werner W. Dornberger | 1949–1951 |
| Department of Architectural Engineering, College of Engineering | Werner W. Dornberger | 1951–1954 |
| | James J. Pollard | 1954–1956 |
| | Werner W. Dornberger* | 1956–1957 |
| | James J. Pollard | 1957–1961 |
| | Franklin B. Johnson | 1961–1969 |

*Acting Chairman

---

**TENURED FACULTY BEGINNING SERVICE UNDER DEAN THOMAS U. TAYLOR, 1895–1936**

Thomas U. Taylor                                                                    1888–1941
    Adjunct Professor of Mathematics to Professor of Civil Engineering
    Dean, 1906–1936

Eugene P. Schoch                                                                    1896–1961
    Instructor in Chemistry to Professor of Chemical Engineering
    Professor Emeritus, 1954–1961

Edward C. H. Bantel                                                                 1901–1965
    Instructor to Professor of Civil Engineering
    Professor Emeritus, 1952–1965

William B. Phillips                                                                 1902–1905
    Professor of Mining Engineering

Arthur C. Scott                                                                     1903–1911
    Professor of Electrical Engineering

Stanley P. Finch                                                                    1905–1971
    Instructor to Professor of Civil Engineering
    Professor Emeritus, 1952–1971

Charles E. Rowe                                                                     1905–1965
    Instructor in Mining Engineering to Professor of Drawing
    Professor Emeritus, 1960–1965
    Assistant Dean, 1943–1950

James A. Correll                                                                    1909–1937
    Instructor to Professor of Electrical Engineering

Richard G. Tyler                                                                    1910–1912,
    Instructor in Civil Engineering to Associate Professor of             1916–1920
      Highway and Sanitary Engineering

Hal C. Weaver                                                                       1910–1929
    Instructor in Electrical Engineering to Professor of Mechanical Engineering

Newton H. Brown                                                                     1911–1914
    Professor of Electrical Engineering

Joseph W. Ramsay                                                                    1911–1939
    Instructor to Professor of Electrical Engineering

Frederick E. Giesecke                                                               1912–1927
    Professor of Architecture

Samuel E. Gideon                                                                    1913–1945
    Associate Professor to Professor of Architecture

John M. Bryant                                                                      1914–1928
    Professor of Electrical Engineering

Forrest E. Cardullo                                                                 1914–1916
    Professor of Mechanical Engineering

Raymond Everett                                                                     1915–1948
    Adjunct Professor to Professor of Architecture

Walter H. McNeill                                                                   1918–1951
    Instructor to Professor of Drawing

Armour T. Granger                                                                   1920–1928
    Instructor to Associate Professor of Civil Engineering

Alex Vallance                                                                       1921–1938
    Instructor to Associate Professor of Mechanical Engineering

Burns N. Gafford                                                                    1923–1976
    Instructor to Professor of Electrical Engineering
    Professor Emeritus, 1966–1976

Robert L. White                                                                     1923–1949
    Adjunct Professor to Professor of Architecture

Burnett F. Treat                                                      1924–1958
    Instructor to Associate Professor of Mechanical Engineering

William F. Helwig                                                    1925–1926,
    Instructor to Associate Professor of Electrical Engineering      1949–1964

Banks L. McLaurin                                                     1925–1961
    Instructor to Professor of Civil Engineering and Engineering Mechanics
    Professor Emeritus, 1961

Carl J. Eckhardt, Jr.                                                 1926–
    Instructor to Professor of Mechanical Engineering
    Director of Physical Plant, The University of Texas, 1931–1973
    Professor Emeritus, 1973–

John A. Focht                                                        1926–
    Professor of Civil and Highway Engineering
    Assistant Dean, 1950–1959
    Professor Emeritus, 1964–

C. Read Granberry                                                    1926–1962
    Instructor to Professor of Electrical Engineering

Byron E. Short                                                       1926–
    Instructor to Professor of Mechanical Engineering
    Professor Emeritus, 1973–

James D. McFarland                                                   1927–
    Instructor in Drawing to Professor of Engineering Graphics
    Professor Emeritus, 1969–

Raymond F. Dawson                                                    1928–
    Bureau of Engineering Research to Professor of Civil Engineering
    Professor Emeritus, 1970–

Phil M. Ferguson                                                     1928–
    Associate Professor to Professor of Civil Engineering
    Dean T. U. Taylor Professor in Civil Engineering, 1969–1973
    Professor Emeritus, 1977–

Goldwin Goldsmith                                                    1928–1949
    Professor of Architecture

Walter T. Rolfe                                                      1928–1946
    Professor of Architecture

Leland C. Barclay                                                    1929–1981
    Instructor to Associate Professor of Civil Engineering
    Associate Professor Emeritus, 1976–1981

Venton L. Doughtie                                                   1929–
    Adjunct Professor to Professor of Mechanical Engineering
    Professor Emeritus, 1967–

Howard E. Degler                                                     1930–1948
    Professor of Mechanical Engineering

Hugh L. McMath                                                       1930–1951*
    Instructor to Professor of Architecture

Fred B. Plummer                                                      1930–1947
    Professor of Petroleum Engineering

Myron L. Begeman                                                     1932–1971
    Associate Professor to Professor of Mechanical Engineering
    Professor Emeritus, 1965–1971

Werner W. Dornberger                                                 1934–1971
    Instructor in Architecture to Professor of Architectural
        Engineering
    Professor Emeritus, 1971

William A. Cunningham                                                1935–
    Instructor in Chemistry to Professor of Chemical Engineering
    Professor Emeritus, 1971–

| | |
|---|---|
| George H. Fancher<br>    Professor of Petroleum Engineering | 1935–1960 |
| Claude R. Hocott<br>    Instructor in Chemistry to Professor of Petroleum Engineering | 1935–1936,<br>1974– |

*The School of Architecture separated from the College of Engineering in 1951.

## TENURED* FACULTY BEGINNING SERVICE UNDER DEAN WILLIS R. WOOLRICH, 1936–1958

| | |
|---|---|
| Willis R. Woolrich<br>    Professor of Mechanical Engineering<br>    Dean, 1936–1958<br>    Professor Emeritus, 1966–1977 | 1936–1958,<br>1966–1977 |
| John Griswold<br>    Instructor in Chemistry to Professor of Chemical Engineering | 1936–1948 |
| Harry H. Power<br>    Professor of Petroleum Engineering<br>    Professor Emeritus, 1964–1982 | 1936–1982 |
| Leonard R. Benson<br>    Instructor to Assistant Professor of Mechanical Engineering<br>    Professor Emeritus, 1964– | 1937– |
| Quintin B. Graves<br>    Instructor to Associate Professor of Civil Engineering | 1937–1946 |
| Jack Lenhart<br>    Instructor to Professor of Engineering Graphics<br>    Professor Emeritus, 1978– | 1937– |
| Harry L. Kent, Jr.<br>    Assistant Professor to Professor of Mechanical Engineering<br>    Professor Emeritus, 1974– | 1938– |
| Robert W. Warner<br>    Professor of Electrical Engineering | 1938–1961 |
| Rinaldo A. Bacon<br>    Instructor to Professor of Mechanical Engineering | 1939–1968 |
| Ralph A. Galbraith<br>    Assistant Professor to Associate Professor of Electrical Engineering | 1939–1944 |
| Edwin W. Hamlin<br>    Professor of Electrical Engineering | 1939–1947 |
| Hugo Leipziger–Pearce<br>    Instructor to Professor of Architecture† | 1939–1951 |
| Judson S. Swearingen<br>    Assistant Professor to Professor of Chemical Engineering | 1939–1943 |
| Roscoe Guernsey<br>    Instructor to Associate Professor of Civil Engineering | 1940–1952 |
| Forrest K. Pence<br>    Assistant Professor of Chemical Engineering to Professor of<br>        Ceramic Engineering | 1940–1954 |
| Howard E. Brown<br>    Instructor to Associate Professor of Mechanical Engineering<br>    Associate Professor Emeritus, 1981– | 1941– |
| J. Robert Buffler<br>    Assistant Professor to Professor of Architecture | 1941–1951 |
| James R. Holmes<br>    Instructor to Associate Professor of Drawing | 1941–1976 |

Kenneth A. Kobe                                          1941–1958
    Professor of Chemical Engineering

J. Neils Thompson                                        1941–
    Instructor to Professor of Civil Engineering

Milton J. Thompson                                       1941–1971
    Professor of Aeronautical Engineering to Professor of
      Aerospace Engineering and Engineering Mechanics

Millard V. Barton                                        1942–1954
    Professor of Aeronautical Engineering and Engineering Mechanics

Dana Young                                               1942–1950
    Professor of Civil Engineering and Engineering Mechanics

Luis H. Bartlett                                         1943–1946
    Assistant Professor to Associate Professor of Mechanical Engineering

Frederick E. Brooks                                      1943–1957
    Assistant Professor to Professor of Electrical Engineering

William J. Carter                                        1943–
    Instructor to Professor of Mechanical Engineering
    Professor Emeritus, 1978–

Cullen M. Crain                                          1943–1957
    Instructor to Associate Professor of Electrical Engineering

Leonardt F. Kreisle                                      1943–
    Instructor of Drawing to Professor of Mechanical Engineering

Warren A. Meyer                                          1943–1951
    Instructor to Assistant Professor of Aeronautical Engineering

Archie W. Straiton                                       1943–
    Associate Professor of Electrical Engineering to Professor of
      Electrical and Computer Engineering

John R. Watt                                             1943–1972
    Instructor to Associate Professor of Mechanical Engineering

Roy R. Krezdorn                                          1944–1978
    Assistant Professor to Associate Professor of Electrical Engineering

William M. Newton                                        1944–1947
    Associate Professor of Chemical Engineering

Horace E. Staph                                          1944–1960
    Instructor to Assistant Professor of Mechanical Engineering

Andrew J. McCrocklin                                     1945–1952
    Instructor to Assistant Professor of Electrical Engineering

Billy H. Amstead                                         1946–
    Instructor to Professor of Mechanical Engineering
    Assistant Dean, 1959–1969
    Acting Dean, 1969–1970
    President, The University of Texas in the Permian
    Basin, 1970–1975
    Professor Emeritus, 1981–

Leland L. Antes                                          1946–1952
    Assistant to Associate Professor of Electrical Engineering

William C. Duesterhoeft                                  1946–
    Instructor to Professor of Electrical and Computer Engineering
    B. N. Gafford Professor in Electrical Engineering, 1982–

John P. German                                           1946–1954
    Instructor to Assistant Professor of Drawing

William K. Griffis                                       1946–1951
    Assistant Professor of Mechanical Engineering

Kenneth H. Jehn                                                    1946–1980
   Instructor to Professor of Meteorology

Jacob M. Lebeaux                                                   1946–1952
   Instructor to Assistant Professor of Petroleum Engineering

Noel C. McGuire                                                    1946–
   Assistant Professor to Associate Professor of Drawing
   Associate Professor Emeritus of Engineering Graphics, 1978–

John J. McKetta, Jr.                                               1946–1951,
   Assistant Professor to Professor of Chemical Engineering      1953–1969,
   Dean, 1963–1969                                             1970–
   Executive Vice-Chancellor for Academic Affairs, The
     University of Texas System, 1969–1970
   Joe J. King Professor in Engineering, 1968–1970
   E. P. Schoch Professor in Engineering, 1970–1981
   Joe C. Walter, Jr., Chair in Engineering, 1981–

Carl W. Morgan                                                     1946–1985
   Instructor to Professor of Civil Engineering

Eugene A. Ripperger                                                1946–1982
   Instructor in Engineering Mechanics to Professor of
     Aerospace Engineering and Engineering Mechanics

Harold W. Smith                                                    1946–
   Instructor in Electrical Engineering to Professor of Electrical
     and Computer Engineering

Anthony A. Benish                                                  1947–1951
   Assistant Professor of Civil Engineering

Edith Clarke                                                       1947–1957
   Associate Professor to Professor of Electrical Engineering

Benjamin B. Ewing                                                  1947–1956
   Instructor to Assistant Professor of Civil Engineering

Earnest F. Gloyna                                                  1947–
   Instructor to Professor of Civil Engineering
   Joe J. King Professor in Engineering, 1970–1982
   Dean, 1970–
   Bettie Margaret Smith Chair in Environmental Health Engineering, 1982–

James D. McClung                                                   1947–1953
   Assistant Professor of Drawing

Walter L. Moore                                                    1947–
   Associate Professor to Professor of Civil Engineering
   Professor Emeritus, 1984–

James J. Pollard                                                   1947–1961
   Professor of Architectural Engineering

H. Grady Rylander, Jr.                                             1947–
   Assistant Professor to Professor of Mechanical Engineering
   Jack S. Josey Professor in Energy Studies, 1978–1980
   E. P. Schoch Professor in Engineering, 1981–1983
   Joe J. King Professor in Engineering, 1983–

Jack A. Scanlan                                                    1947–1967
   Instructor to Associate Professor of Mechanical Engineering

John N. Seaman                                                     1947–1951
   Assistant Professor of Aeronautical Engineering

Wilbert E. Shallene                                                1947–1959
   Assistant Professor of Drawing

Robert F. Shurtz                                                   1947–1951
   Assistant Professor of Ceramic Engineering

Arthur R. Teasdale                                                 1947–1951
   Assistant Professor to Associate Professor of Electrical Engineering

Matthew Van Winkle                                                      1947–1977
    Associate Professor to Professor of Chemical Engineering
    Henry Beckman Professor in Chemical Engineering, 1971–1975
    Professor Emeritus, 1976–1977

John C. Westkaemper                                                     1947–
    Instructor of Aeronautical Engineering to Professor of
        Aerospace Engineering and Engineering Mechanics

L. Hudson Matlock                                                       1948–1978
    Instructor to Professor of Civil Engineering

Robert D. Slonneger                                                     1948–1954
    Instructor to Assistant Professor of Mechanical Engineering

Raymond C. Staley                                                       1948–1960
    Instructor to Assistant Professor of Meteorology

James W. Turnbow                                                        1948–1959
    Instructor to Assistant Professor of Engineering Mechanics

Joseph W. Dalley                                                        1949–1959
    Instructor to Assistant Professor of Aeronautical Engineering

William H. Hartwig                                                      1949–1982
    Instructor to Professor of Electrical Engineering

Bernard J. Lerner                                                       1949–1954
    Assistant Professor of Chemical Engineering

Robert D. Turpin                                                        1949–1966
    Instructor in Civil Engineering

E. Joseph Weiss                                                         1949–1964
    Assistant Professor of Ceramic Engineering to Professor of
        Chemical Engineering

Harold J. Plass, Jr.                                                    1950–1967
    Assistant Professor to Professor of Engineering Mechanics

Ernest W. Steel                                                         1950–1960
    Instructor to Assistant Professor of Civil Engineering

A. Anthony Toprac                                                       1950–1974
    Assistant Professor to Adjunct Professor of Civil Engineering

Bob M. Fannin                                                          1951–
    Assistant Professor of Electrical Engineering to Professor of
        Electrical and Computer Engineering

Wayne E. Long                                                           1951–1978
    Professor of Mechanical Engineering
    Professor Emeritus, 1971–1978

William H. Shutts                                                       1951–1958
    Assistant Professor of Aeronautical Engineering

Robert L. Stone                                                         1951–1959
    Associate Professor to Professor of Ceramic Engineering

Eldred W. Hough                                                         1952–1961
    Professor of Petroleum Engineering

Frank W. Jessen                                                         1952–1972
    Professor of Petroleum Engineering

Howard F. Rase                                                          1952–
    Assistant Professor to Professor of Chemical Engineering
    William A. (Bill) Cunningham Professor in Engineering, 1974–

Frank G. Bryant                                                         1953–1959
    Assistant Professor of Civil Engineering

William W. Dingle                                                       1954–1959,
    Assistant Professor of Petroleum Engineering, Lecturer in        1965–1977
        Petroleum Engineering

Kermit E. Brown                                                      1955–1966
    Assistant Professor of Petroleum Engineering

Elmer L. Hixson                                                     1954–
    Assistant Professor of Electrical Engineering to Professor of
      Electrical and Computer Engineering

Franklin B. Johnson                                                 1955–
    Assistant Professor to Professor of Architectural Engineering

Alfred H. LaGrone                                                   1955–
    Associate Professor of Electrical Engineering to Professor of
      Electrical and Computer Engineering

Norman Lamont                                                      1955–1962
    Assistant Professor of Petroleum Engineering

Lymon C. Reese                                                     1955–
    Assistant Professor to Professor of Civil Engineering
    Dean T. U. Taylor Professor in Engineering, 1973–1981
    Nasser I. Al–Rashid Chair in Civil Engineering, 1981–1984

Robert S. Schechter                                                1955–
    Assistant Professor to Professor of Chemical and of
      Petroleum Engineering
    Ernest Cockrell, Jr., Memorial Professor in Engineering,
      1975–1981
    Ernest Cockrell, Sr., Centennial Chair in Engineering,
      1981–1984
    Getty Oil Company Centennial Chair in Petroleum Engineering, 1984–

Carl C. Steyer                                                     1955–1959
    Assistant Professor of Engineering Mechanics

Eric H. Bucknall                                                   1956–1966
    Professor of Mechanical Engineering

Clayton W. Chance                                                 1956–1968
    Assistant Professor of Drawing

Bill G. Eppes                                                      1956–1962
    Assistant Professor of Electrical Engineering

Sylvain J. G. Pirson                                               1956–1983
    Professor of Petroleum Engineering
    Professor Emeritus, 1975–1983

Eugene H. Wissler                                                  1956–
    Assistant Professor to Professor of Chemical Engineering
    Associate Dean, 1970–1976
    Henry Beckman Professor in Chemical Engineering, 1973–
    Associate Dean of the Graduate School, The University of
      Texas at Austin, 1981–

David M. Himmelblau                                               1957–
    Assistant Professor to Professor of Chemical Engineering
    Bob R. Dorsey Professor of Engineering, 1978–

Kenneth C. Rathbun                                                1957–1961
    Associate Professor of Mechanical Engineering

Paul J. Root                                                       1957–1961
    Assistant Professor of Petroleum Engineering

Herbert A. Rundell                                                1957–1961
    Assistant Professor of Mechanical Engineering

Enrico G. Volterra                                                1957–1973
    Professor of Engineering Mechanics

---

*The rank of Instructor is included only for faculty prior to 1950.
†The School of Architecture separated from the College of Engineering in 1951.

## TENURED* FACULTY BEGINNING SERVICE UNDER DEAN WILLIAM W. HAGERTY, 1958–1963

William W. Hagerty                                                      1958–1963
    Professor of Engineering Mechanics
    Dean, 1958–1963

Richard W. Furlong                                                     1958–
    Assistant Professor to Professor of Civil Engineering
    Donald J. Douglass Centennial Professor of Engineering, 1982–

Joe O. Ledbetter                                                      1958–
    Assistant Professor to Professor of Civil Engineering

Clyde E. Lee                                                          1958–
    Assistant Professor to Professor of Civil Engineering
    Phil M. Ferguson Professor in Civil Engineering, 1981–1983
    Nasser I. Al–Rashid Centennial Professor in Transportation
      Engineering, 1983–
    Hussein M. Alharthy Centennial Professor in Civil
      Engineering, 1984–1985

Richard T. Smith                                                      1958–1961
    Associate Professor of Electrical Engineering

Edward J. Wagner                                                      1958–1981
    Associate Professor of Electrical Engineering
    Associate Professor Emeritus, 1978–1981

Shao W. Yuan                                                          1958–1968
    Professor of Aerospace Engineering

William F. Bradley                                                    1959–1973
    Professor of Chemical Engineering

James R. Brock                                                        1959–
    Assistant Professor to Professor of Chemical Engineering
    Kenneth A. Kobe Professor in Chemical Engineering, 1981–

Carl Gatlin                                                           1959–1964
    Associate Professor to Professor of Petroleum
      Engineering

Edwin C. Lowenberg                                                    1959–1964
    Assistant Professor to Associate Professor of Electrical
      Engineering

William A. Youngblood                                                 1959–1962
    Associate Professor of Electrical Engineering

Lyle G. Clark                                                         1960–
    Professor of Mechanical Engineering to Professor of
      Aerospace Engineering and Engineering Mechanics

Joseph F. Malina, Jr.                                                 1960–
    Assistant Professor to Professor of Civil Engineering
    C. W. Cook Professor in Environmental Engineering

Hugo Steinfink                                                        1960–
    Associate Professor to Professor of Chemical Engineering
    Jewel McAlister Smith Professor in Engineering, 1981–

Byron D. Tapley                                                       1960–
    Assistant Professor of Engineering Mechanics to Professor of
      Aerospace Engineering and Engineering Mechanics
    W. R. Woolrich Professor in Engineering, 1974–1984
    Clare Cockrell Williams Chair in Engineering, 1984–

Charles S. Beightler                                                  1961–
    Assistant Professor to Professor of Mechanical Engineering

Kenneth B. Bishoff                                                          1961–1967
    Assistant Professor to Associate Professor of Chemical Engineering

Roy R. Craig, Jr.                                                          1961–
    Assistant Professor of Engineering Mechanics to Professor of
      Aerospace Engineering and Engineering Mechanics

Arwin A. Dougal                                                          1961–
    Professor of Electrical Engineering to Professor of Electrical
      and Computer Engineering

Charles H. Roth, Jr.                                                          1961–
    Assistant Professor of Electrical Engineering to Professor of
      Electrical and Computer Engineering

Baxter F. Womack                                                          1961–
    Assistant Professor of Electrical Engineering to Professor of
      Electrical and Computer Engineering

Ned H. Burns                                                          1962–
    Assistant Professor to Professor of Civil Engineering
    Assistant Counselor, 1968–1970
    Zarrow Centennial Professor in Engineering, 1983–

John E. Breen                                                          1962–
    Assistant Professor to Professor of Civil Engineering
    John J. McKetta Energy Professor in Engineering, 1977–1981
    Carol Cockrell Curran Chair in Engineering, 1981–1984
    Nasser I. Al–Rashid Chair in Civil Engineering, 1984–

Kenneth E. Gray                                                          1962–
    Assistant Professor to Professor of Petroleum Engineering
    Halliburton Annual Professor in Petroleum Engineering, 1968–1982
    Zarrow Centennial Professor in Petroleum Engineering, 1982–

J. Parker Lamb, Jr.                                                          1962–
    Assistant Professor of Mechanical Engineering to Professor of
      Mechanical Engineering and Professor of Aerospace
      Engineering and Engineering Mechanics
    Ernest Cockrell, Jr. Memorial Professor in Engineering, 1981–

Lawrence R. Mack                                                          1962–
    Assistant Professor of Civil Engineering and Engineering
      Mechanics to Associate Professor of Aerospace Engineering
      and Engineering Mechanics

Frank D. Masch                                                          1962–1975
    Assistant Professor to Professor of Civil Engineering

Ching–Hsie Yew                                                          1962–
    Assistant Professor of Engineering Mechanics to Professor of
      Aerospace Engineering and Engineering Mechanics

---

* Associate Professor or Professor on or before April 1986.

---

## TENURED* FACULTY BEGINNING SERVICE UNDER DEAN JOHN J. McKETTA, 1963–1969, AND ACTING DEAN BILLY H. AMSTEAD, 1969–1970

Francis X. Bostick                                                          1963–
    Assistant Professor of Electrical Engineering to Professor of
      Electrical and Computer Engineering

Ben H. Caudle                                                          1963–
    Associate Professor to Professor of Petroleum Engineering
    B. J. Lancaster Professor in Petroleum Engineering, 1981–

Clarence L. Coates                                                          1963–1971
    Professor of Electrical Engineering

Amos Eddy                                                                       1963–1969
    Assistant Professor to Associate Professor of Meteorology

John P. Stark                                                                   1963–
    Assistant Professor to Professor of Mechanical Engineering

Terry J. Wagner                                                                 1963–
    Assistant Professor of Electrical Engineering to Professor of
      Electrical and Computer Engineering

H. Alan Walls                                                                   1963–
    Assistant Professor to Professor of Mechanical Engineering
    Director of Planning Services, The University of Texas at Austin, 1982–

Melvin A. Wilkov                                                                1963–1984
    Associate Professor of Aerospace Engineering and Engineering Mechanics

J. K. Aggarwal                                                                  1964–
    Assistant Professor of Electrical Engineering to Associate
      Professor of Electrical and Computer Engineering
    John J. McKetta Energy Professor in Engineering, 1981–

David W. Fowler                                                                 1964–
    Assistant Professor to Professor of Architectural Engineering
    Dean T. U. Taylor Professor in Engineering, 1981–

Ervin S. Perry                                                                  1964–1971
    Assistant Professor to Associate Professor of Civil Engineering

John W. Porter                                                                  1964–
    Assistant Professor of Aerospace Engineering to Associate
      Professor of Aerospace Engineering and Engineering Mechanics

Donald S. Swanson                                                              1964–1974
    Assistant Professor to Associate Professor of Electrical Engineering

William R. Upthegrove                                                          1964–1970
    Professor of Mechanical Engineering

Ashley J. Welch                                                                 1964–
    Assistant Professor to Professor of Biomedical Engineering
    Marion E. Forsman Centennial Professor in Engineering, 1985–

W. Wesley Eckenfelder, Jr.                                                      1965–1969
    Professor of Civil Engineering

Richard R. Ensminger                                                           1965–1973
    Assistant Professor to Associate Professor of Aerospace Engineering

Wallace T. Fowler                                                               1965–
    Assistant Professor to Professor of Engineering Mechanics

Stephen J. Gage                                                                 1965–1973
    Assistant Professor to Associate Professor of Mechanical Engineering

Bernard Haurwitz                                                                1965–1968
    Professor of Atmospheric Science

William R. Hudson                                                               1965–
    Assistant Professor to Professor of Civil Engineering
    Assistant Dean, 1969–1970
    Associate Dean for Advanced Programs, 1970–1971
    Dewitt C. Greer Centennial Professor in Transportation Engineering, 1981–

Thomas W. Kennedy                                                               1965–
    Assistant Professor to Professor of Civil Engineering
    Associate Dean for Advanced Programs, 1979–1981
    Associate Dean for Research and Planning, 1981–1986
    Associate Dean for Research and Facilities, 1986–
    Engineering Foundation Professor in Engineering, 1981–

Edward J. Powers, Jr.                                                           1965–
    Assistant Professor of Electrical Engineering to Professor of

Electrical and Computer Engineering
B. N. Gafford Professor in Electrical Engineering, 1981–1982
Texas Atomic Energy Research Foundation Professor in Engineering, 1982–

Herbert L. Taylor                                                              1965–1980
    Associate Professor of Electrical Engineering

Margaret R. Baker                                                             1966–
    Assistant Professor of Drawing to Associate Professor of Engineering Graphics

Eric B. Becker                                                                1966–
    Assistant Professor of Aerospace Engineering to Professor of
      Aerospace Engineering and Engineering Mechanics

John J. Bertin                                                                1966–
    Assistant Professor to Professor of Aerospace Engineering
      and Engineering Mechanics
    Bettie Margaret Smith Professor in Engineering, 1981–

Harry H. Calvit                                                               1966–1973
    Associate Professor of Aerospace Engineering and Engineering Mechanics

John R. Cogdell                                                               1966–
    Assistant Professor of Electrical Engineering to Associate
      Professor of Electrical and Computer Engineering

Robert H. Flake                                                               1966–
    Assistant Professor of Electrical Engineering to Professor of
      Electrical and Computer Engineering

E. Gus Fruh                                                                   1966–1979
    Assistant Professor to Professor of Civil Engineering

William D. Gregg                                                              1966–1980
    Assistant Professor to Associate Professor of Electrical Engineering

David G. Hull                                                                 1966–
    Assistant Professor of Aerospace Engineering to Professor of
      Aerospace Engineering and Engineering Mechanics
    M. J. Thompson Regents' Professor in Aerospace
    Engineering and Engineering Mechanics, 1985–

Eugene B. Konecci                                                             1966–1971
    Professor of Aerospace Engineering and Professor of Management

Demetrios G. Lainiotis                                                        1966–1973
    Associate Professor to Professor of Electrical Engineering

Ronald O. Stearman                                                            1966–
    Associate Professor of Aerospace Engineering to Professor of
      Aerospace Engineering and Engineering Mechanics

Morris Stern                                                                  1966–
    Associate Professor of Engineering Mechanics to Professor of
      Aerospace Engineering and Engineering Mechanics

Norman K. Wagner                                                              1966–
    Assistant Professor to Associate Professor of Meteorology

Joseph A. Yura                                                                1966–
    Assistant Professor to Professor of Civil Engineering
    Warren S. Bellows Centennial Professor in Civil Engineering, 1982–

Joel O. Hougen                                                                1967–1980
    Professor of Chemical Engineering
    Alcoa Professor in Chemical Engineering, 1967–1974
    Professor Emeritus, 1980–

Paul A. Jensen                                                                1967–
    Assistant Professor to Professor of Mechanical Engineering
    Jack S. Josey Professor in Energy Studies, 1982–1984
    Hughes Tool Company Centennial Professor in Mechanical Engineering, 1984–

William G. Lesso                                                              1967–
    Associate Professor to Professor of Mechanical Engineering

Assistant Dean, 1978–1981
E. C. H. Bantel Professor for Professional Practice, 1980–1982

Donald R. Paul                                                                      1967–
  Assistant Professor to Professor of Chemical Engineering
  T. Brockett Hudson Professor in Chemical Engineering, 1978–1985
  Melvin H. Gertz Regents' Chair in Chemical Engineering, 1985–

Ilya Prigogine                                                                       1967–
  Professor of Chemical Engineering and Professor of Physics
  Nobel Prize for Chemistry, 1977

Kenneth M. Ralls                                                                     1967–
  Assistant Professor to Professor of Mechanical Engineering

Chittoor V. Ramamoorthy                                                          1967–1972
  Professor of Electrical Engineering

Thomas M. Runge                                                                      1967–
  Professor of Biomedicine

Dimiter I. Tchernev                                                              1967–1975
  Associate Professor of Electrical Engineering

John J. Allan III                                                                1968–1977
  Associate Professor of Mechanical Engineering

A. Marc Bedford                                                                      1968–
  Assistant Professor to Professor of Aerospace Engineering
    and Engineering Mechanics

Robert W. Bené                                                                       1968–
  Assistant Professor of Electrical Engineering to Professor of
    Electrical and Computer Engineering

Thomas H. Courtney                                                               1968–1974
  Assistant Professor to Associate Professor of Mechanical Engineering

Dewitt C. Greer                                                                  1968–1973
  Professor of Civil Engineering
  Engineering Foundation Professor in Engineering Practice, 1970–1972
  Professor Emeritus, 1973–

Lawrence L. Hoberock                                                             1968–1978
  Assistant Professor to Associate Professor of Mechanical Engineering

Billy V. Koen                                                                        1968–
  Assistant Professor to Professor of Mechanical Engineering

E. Lothar Koschmieder                                                                1968–
  Assistant Professor to Associate Professor of Meteorology

Lew Kowarski                                                                     1968–1970
  Professor of Mechanical Engineering

Paul E. Nacozy                                                                   1968–1985
  Assistant Professor to Professor of Aerospace Engineering
    and Engineering Mechanics

Augusto L. Podio                                                                     1968–
  Assistant Professor to Professor of Petroleum Engineering
  Halliburton Annual Professor in Petroleum Engineering, 1982–1984
  H. B. (Burt) Harkins, Jr., Professor in Petroleum Engineering, 1984–

Phillip C. Richardson                                                            1968–1981
  Assistant Professor to Professor of Biomedical Engineering

James E. Stice                                                                       1968–
  Associate Professor to Professor of Chemical Engineering
  Director, Center for Teaching Effectiveness, The University of
    Texas at Austin, 1973–
  T. Brockett Hudson Professor in Chemical Engineering, 1985–

Victor G. Szebehely                                                                  1968–
  Professor of Aerospace Engineering and Engineering Mechanics

L. B. (Preach) Meaders Professor in Engineering, 1978–1983
Dula D. Cockrell Centennial Chair in Engineering, 1983–1984
Richard B. Curran Centennial Chair in Engineering, 1984–

George B. Thurston                                                          1968–
    Professor of Mechanical Engineering

Fred B. Vogt                                                               1968–1974
    Professor of Biomedical Engineering

Gerald Wagner                                                             1968–1978
    Assistant Professor to Associate Professor of Mechanical Engineering

Rodger M. Walser                                                          1968–
    Assistant Professor of Electrical Engineering to Professor of
      Electrical and Computer Engineering
    J. H. Herring Centennial Professor in Engineering, 1985–

William S. Butler                                                         1969–1975
    Associate Professor to Professor of Civil Engineering

E. Linn Draper                                                            1969–1978
    Assistant Professor to Associate Professor of Mechanical
      Engineering

C. Philip Johnson                                                         1969–
    Associate Professor of Civil Engineering

B. Franklin McCullough                                                    1969–
    Assistant Professor to Professor of Civil Engineering
    Phil M. Ferguson Professor in Civil Engineering, 1983–1984
    Adnan Abou–Ayyash Centennial Professor in Transportation
      Engineering, 1984–

Bob E. Schutz                                                             1969–
    Assistant Professor to Professor of Aerospace Engineering
      and Engineering Mechanics

Stephen G. Wright                                                         1969–
    Assistant Professor to Professor of Civil Engineering
    Ashley H. Priddy Centennial Professor in Engineering, 1985–

---

*Associate Professor or Professor on or before April 1986

---

## TENURED* FACULTY BEGINNING SERVICE UNDER DEAN EARNEST F. GLOYNA, 1970–

Dale G. Bettis                                                            1970–1982
    Assistant Professor to Associate Professor of Aerospace
      Engineering and Engineering Mechanics

Michael J. Humenick                                                       1970–1981
    Associate Professor of Civil Engineering

William L. Oberkampf                                                      1970–1979
    Assistant Professor to Associate Professor of Mechanical Engineering

Roy E. Olson                                                              1970–
    Professor of Civil Engineering
    L. P. Gilvin Centennial Professor in Civil Engineering, 1984–

Philip S. Schmidt                                                         1970–
    Assistant Professor to Professor of Mechanical Engineering

Richard E. Speece                                                         1970–1974
    Professor of Civil Engineering

Neal E. Armstrong                                                         1971–
    Associate Professor of Civil Engineering

Thomas F. Edgar                                                           1971–
    Assistant Professor to Professor of Chemical Engineering

Paul D. and Betty Robertson Meek Centennial Professor in
  Chemical Engineering, 1983–

Anthony J. Healey                                                    1971–1981
  Associate Professor to Professor of Mechanical Engineering

Ronald L. Panton                                                    1971–
  Professor of Mechanical Engineering

Gary C. Vliet                                                        1971–
  Associate Professor to Professor of Mechanical Engineering
  W. R. Woolrich Professor in Engineering, 1985–

C. Michael Walton                                                  1971–
  Associate Professor to Professor of Civil Engineering

Herbert H. Woodson                                                  1971–
  Professor of Electrical and Computer Engineering
  Alcoa Professor in Engineering, 1973–1974
  Texas Atomic Energy Research Foundation Professor in
    Engineering, 1980–1982
  Ernest H. Cockrell Centennial Chair in Engineering, 1982–
  Associate Dean for Development and Planning, 1986–

Leo R. Beard                                                        1972–1982
  Lecturer to Professor of Civil Engineering

John D. Borcherding                                                1972–
  Assistant Professor to Associate Professor of Civil Engineering

James O. Jirsa                                                      1972–
  Associate Professor to Professor of Civil Engineering
  Stanley P. Finch Centennial Professor in Engineering, 1982–1984
  Phil M. Ferguson Professor in Civil Engineering, 1984–1986
  Hussein M. Alharthy Centennial Professor in Civil Engineering, 1986–

Robert P. Popovich                                                  1972–
  Assistant Professor to Professor of Chemical Engineering
  E. P. Schoch Professor in Engineering, 1983–

Gerard A. Rohlich                                                  1972–1984
  Professor of Public Affairs, Civil Engineering
  C. W. Cook Professor in Environmental Engineering,
    1972–1980

Joel W. Barlow                                                      1973–
  Assistant Professor to Professor of Chemical Engineering
  Z. D. Bonner Professor in Chemical Engineering, 1984–

Kenneth R. Diller                                                  1973–
  Assistant Professor to Professor of Biomedical Engineering

Jerold W. Jones                                                    1973–
  Assistant Professor of Civil Engineering to Professor of
    Mechanical Engineering

Roy M. Knapp                                                        1973–1979
  Assistant Professor to Associate Professor of Petroleum Engineering

J. Tinsley Oden                                                    1973–
  Professor of Aerospace Engineering and Engineering
    Mechanics
  Carol and Henry Groppe Professor in Chemical Engineering, 1979–

Walter S. Reed                                                      1973–
  Assistant Professor to Associate Professor of Mechanical
    Engineering

Kenneth H. Stokoe II                                              1973–
  Assistant Professor to Professor of Civil Engineering
  Brunswick-Abernathy Regents' Professor in Soil Dynamics
    and Geotechnical Engineering, 1985–

Stephen A. Szygenda                                                      1973–1980,
    Professor of Electrical and Computer Engineering                     1983–
    Clint W. Murchison, Sr., Chair of Free Enterprise, 1986–

Edward W. Thompson                                                       1973–1980
    Assistant Professor to Associate Professor of Electrical Engineering

J. Wesley Barnes                                                         1974–
    Assistant Professor to Professor of Mechanical Engineering

Michael F. Becker                                                       1974–
    Assistant Professor to Associate Professor of Electrical and
        Computer Engineering

A. Bruce Buckman                                                        1974–
    Associate Professor of Electrical and Computer Engineering

Kanianthra M. Chandy                                                    1974–
    Associate Professor to Professor of Electrical and Computer Engineering

Hal B. H. Cooper                                                        1974–1982
    Assistant Professor to Associate Professor of Civil Engineering

Myron H. Dorfman                                                        1974–
    Assistant Professor to Professor of Petroleum Engineering
    H. B. (Burt) Harkins, Jr., Professor in Petroleum Engineering, 1980–1983
    W. A. (Tex) Moncrief, Jr., Centennial Endowed Chair in
        Petroleum Engineering, 1983–

Zwy Eliezer                                                             1974–
    Assistant Professor to Professor of Mechanical Engineering

Karl H. Frank                                                           1974–
    Assistant Professor to Associate Professor of Civil Engineering

Norman M. Martin                                                        1974–
    Professor of Philosophy and Professor of Electrical and
        Computer Engineering

Richard W. Miksad                                                      1974–
    Assistant Professor of Meteorology to Professor of Civil Engineering

Calin M. Popescu                                                        1974–1976,
    Associate Professor of Architectural Engineering                     1980–

Lee E. Baker                                                            1975–
    Professor of Biomedical Engineering
    Robert L. Parker, Sr., Centennial Professor in Engineering, 1982–

Raynor L. Duncombe                                                      1975–
    Lecturer to Professor of Aerospace Engineering and
        Engineering Mechanics

Harris L. Marcus                                                        1975–
    Professor of Mechanical Engineering
    Harry L. Kent, Jr., Professor in Mechanical Engineering, 1981–

Steven I. Marcus                                                        1975–
    Assistant Professor of Electrical Engineering to Professor of
        Electrical and Computer Engineering

Martin L. Baughman                                                      1976–
    Assistant Professor of Electrical Engineering to Associate
        Professor of Electrical and Computer Engineering

Roger A. Broucke                                                        1976–
    Associate Professor to Professor of Aerospace Engineering
        and Engineering Mechanics

Gerald J. Lipovski                                                      1976–
    Associate Professor to Professor of Electrical and Computer
        Engineering

Larry W. Mays                                                                    1976–
  Assistant Professor to Associate Professor of Civil Engineering

Jason L. Speyer                                                                  1976–
  Associate Professor to Professor of Aerospace Engineering
    and Engineering Mechanics
  Harry H. Power Professor in Engineering, 1982–

T. William Thompson                                                         1976–1986
  Assistant Professor to Associate Professor of Petroleum Engineering

Richard L. Tucker                                                               1976–
  Professor of Architectural Engineering
  C. T. Wells Professor in Project Management, 1982–

Gary L. Wise                                                                    1976–
  Assistant Professor of Electrical Engineering to Professor of
    Electrical and Computer Engineering

Graham F. Carey                                                                 1977–
  Assistant Professor to Professor of Aerospace Engineering
    and Engineering Mechanics

Dale E. Klein                                                                   1977–
  Assistant Professor to Associate Professor of Mechanical Engineering

Richard Klingner                                                               1977–
  Assistant Professor to Associate Professor of Civil Engineering

Leon S. Lasdon                                                             1977–1986
  Professor of Mechanical Engineering and General Business

Randy B. Machemehl                                                             1977–
  Assistant Professor to Associate Professor of Civil Engineering

Miroslaw Malek                                                                 1977–
  Assistant Professor to Associate Professor of Electrical and
    Computer Engineering

Gary A. Pope                                                                   1977–
  Assistant Professor to Professor of Petroleum Engineering
  Halliburton Annual Professor in Petroleum Engineering, 1984–1985
  J. H. Herring Centennial Professor in Engineering, 1985–

Gary T. Rochelle                                                               1977–
  Assistant Professor to Associate Professor of Chemical Engineering

Polichronis D. Spanos                                                      1977–1985
  Assistant Professor to Associate Professor of Aerospace
    Engineering and Engineering Mechanics

Ronald E. Barr                                                                 1978–
  Assistant Professor to Associate Professor of Mechanical Engineering

Randall J. Charbeneau                                                          1978–
  Assistant Professor to Associate Professor of Civil Engineering

John H. Davis                                                                  1978–
  Assistant Professor to Associate Professor of Electrical and
    Computer Engineering

Linda J. Hayes                                                                 1978–
  Assistant Professor to Associate Professor of Aerospace
    Engineering and Engineering Mechanics

John R. Howell                                                                 1978–
  Professor of Mechanical Engineering
  E. C. H. Bantel Professor for Professional Practice, 1982–

Tatsuo Itoh                                                                    1978–
  Associate Professor to Professor of Electrical and Computer Engineering
  Hayden Head Professor in Engineering, 1983–

Davor Juricic                                                           1978–
    Professor of Mechanical Engineering

Larry W. Lake                                                          1978–
    Assistant Professor to Professor of Petroleum Engineering
    Halliburton Annual Professor in Petroleum Engineering, 1985–

José M. Roesset                                                       1978–
    Professor of Civil Engineering
    Paul D. and Betty Robertson Meek Centennial Professor in
      Engineering, 1983–

Joseph J. Beaman                                                      1979–
    Assistant Professor to Associate Professor of Mechanical Engineering

David L. Bourell                                                      1979–
    Assistant Professor to Associate Professor of Mechanical Engineering

Royal E. Collins                                                      1979–1984
    Professor of Petroleum Engineering
    Frank W. Jessen Professor in Petroleum Engineering, 1981–1983
    W. A. (Monty) Moncrief Centennial Endowed Chair in
      Petroleum Engineering, 1983–1984

John G. Ekerdt                                                        1979–
    Assistant Professor to Associate Professor of Chemical Engineering

James R. Fair                                                         1979–
    Professor of Chemical Engineering
    Ernest and Virginia Cockrell Chair in Engineering, 1979–1985
    John J. McKetta Energy Chair in Engineering, 1985–

Robert Herman                                                        1979–
    Professor of Civil Engineering, Physics
    L. P. Gilvin Centennial Professor in Civil Engineering, 1982–1984

Nolan E. Hertel                                                      1979–
    Assistant Professor to Associate Professor of Mechanical Engineering

Edward R. Holley                                                     1979–
    Professor of Civil Engineering
    Stanley P. Finch Centennial Professor in Engineering, 1984–

Ramon Carrasquillo                                                  1980–
    Assistant Professor to Associate Professor of Civil Engineering

Stelios Kyriakides                                                  1980–
    Assistant Professor to Associate Professor of Aerospace
      Engineering and Engineering Mechanics

Desmond F. Lawler                                                   1980–
    Assistant Professor to Associate Professor of Civil Engineering

Howard M. Liljestrand                                               1980–
    Assistant Professor to Associate Professor of Civil Engineering

Ronald D. Matthews                                                  1980–
    Assistant Professor to Associate Professor of Mechanical Engineering

Ekwere J. Peters                                                    1980–
    Assistant Professor to Associate Professor of Petroleum Engineering

Charles A. Sorber                                                   1980–1986
    Associate Professor to Professor of Civil Engineering
    Associate Dean for Professional Education and Career
      Development, 1980–1981
    Associate Dean for Academic Affairs, 1981–1986
    L. B. (Preach) Meaders Professor in Engineering, 1985–1986

David E. Daniel, Jr.                                                1981–
    Assistant Professor to Associate Professor of Civil Engineering

Douglas R. Lloyd                                                                          1981–
        Assistant Professor to Associate Professor of Chemical Engineering

David R. Maidment                                                                        1981–
        Assistant Professor to Associate Professor of Civil Engineering

Kurt M. Marshek                                                                           1981–
        Associate Professor to Professor of Mechanical Engineering

Kamy Sepehrnoori                                                                         1981–
        Assistant Professor to Associate Professor of Petroleum Engineering

Willem C. J. van Rensburg                                                                1981–
        Professor of Petroleum Engineering
        George H. Fancher Professor in Petroleum Engineering, 1983–

Chuan-lin Wu                                                                              1981–
        Assistant Professor to Associate Professor of Electrical and
            Computer Engineering

David B. Ashley                                                                           1982–
        Associate Professor of Civil Engineering

Margaret N. Maxey                                                                        1982–
        Professor of Bioethics
        Director, Clint W. Murchison, Sr., Chair of Free Enterprise, 1982–

Ernest T. Smerdon                                                                         1982–
        Professor of Civil Engineering, Public Affairs

Ben G. Streetman                                                                          1982–
        Professor of Electrical and Computer Engineering
        Janet S. Cockrell Centennial Chair in Engineering, 1982–1986
        Earnest F. Gloyna Regents' Chair in Engineering, 1986–

William J. Koros                                                                          1984–
        Professor of Chemical Engineering
        Paul D. and Betty Robertson Meek and American Petrofina
            Foundation Professor in Chemical Engineering, 1985–

Harvey G. Cragon                                                                         1984–
        Professor of Electrical and Computer Engineering
        Ernest Cockrell, Jr., Centennial Chair in Engineering, 1984–

Raymond C. Loehr                                                                         1985–
        Professor of Civil Engineering
        Hussein M. Alharthy Centennial Chair in Civil Engineering,
            1985–

Delbert Tesar                                                                            1985–
        Professor of Mechanical Engineering
        Carol Cockrell Curran Chair in Engineering, 1985–

Mario J. Gonzalez, Jr.                                                                   1986–
        Professor of Electrical and Computer Engineering
        Associate Dean for Academic Affairs, 1986–

John B. Goodenough                                                                      1986–
        Professor of Mechanical Engineering and of Electrical and
            Computer Engineering
        Virginia H. Cockrell Centennial Chair in Engineering, 1986–

Irwin W. Sandberg                                                                        1986–
        Professor of Electrical and Computer Engineering
        Cockrell Family Regents' Chair in Engineering, Number One, 1986–

Al F. Tasch, Jr.                                                                         1986–
        Professor of Electrical and Computer Engineering
        Cockrell Family Regents' Chair in Engineering, Number Four, 1986–

---

*Associate Professor or Professor on or before April 1986

**DEGREES GRANTED BY THE COLLEGE OF ENGINEERING, 1888–1985**

| Cal. Year | B.S. AeE | B.S. ASE | B.S. Arch | B. of Arch | B.S. ArE | B.S. CrE | B.S. ChE | B.S. CE Maj | CE | B.S. CE | EE | B.S. EE | B.S. ME | B.S. PPE |
|---|---|---|---|---|---|---|---|---|---|---|---|---|---|---|
| 1888 | | | | | | | | 1 | | | | | | |
| 1889 | | | | | | | | 2 | | | | | | |
| 1890 | | | | | | | | | | | | | | |
| 1891 | | | | | | | | 2 | | | | | | |
| 1892 | | | | | | | | 3 | | | | | | |
| 1893 | | | | | | | | 4 | | | | | | |
| 1894 | | | | | | | | | 1 | | | | | |
| 1895 | | | | | | | | | 3 | | | | | |
| 1896 | | | | | | | | | 3 | | 1 | | | |
| 1897 | | | | | | | | | 3 | | | | | |
| 1898 | | | | | | | | | 2 | | | | | |
| 1899 | | | | | | | | | | | | | | |
| 1900 | | | | | | | | | 4 | | | | | |
| 1901 | | | | | | | | | | | | | | |
| 1902 | | | | | | | | | 3 | | | | | |
| 1903 | | | | | | | | | 8 | | | | | |
| 1904 | | | | | | | | | 4 | | | | | |
| 1905 | | | | | | | | | 16 | | 2 | | | |
| 1906 | | | | | | | | | 17 | | 4 | | | |
| 1907 | | | | | | | | | 9 | | 1 | | | |
| 1908 | | | | | | | | | 15 | | 7 | | | |
| 1909 | | | | | | | | | 15 | | 7 | | | |
| 1910 | | | | | | | | | 7 | | 16 | | | |
| 1911 | | | | | | | | | 15 | | 14 | | | |
| 1912 | | | | | | | | | 11 | | 15 | 1 | | |
| 1913 | | | 1 | | | | | | 8 | | 15 | | | |
| 1914 | | | | | | | | | 12 | | 11 | | | |
| 1915 | | | 4 | | | | | | 7 | 2 | 16 | | | |
| 1916 | | | 2 | | | | | | 3 | 7 | 8 | 11 | | |
| 1917 | | | 6 | | | | | | 5 | 10 | 2 | 13 | | |
| 1918 | | | 5 | | | | | | 2 | 3 | | 6 | | |
| 1919 | | | 2 | | | | 2 | | | 3 | | 3 | 3 | |
| 1920 | | | 4 | | | | 1 | | | 7 | | 11 | 2 | |
| 1921 | | | 5 | | | | 6 | | | 13 | | 8 | 7 | |
| 1922 | | | 8 | | | | 9 | | | 13 | | 15 | 10 | |
| 1923 | | | 12 | | | | 6 | | | 19 | | 28 | 9 | |
| 1924 | | | 3 | | | | 9 | | | 22 | | 18 | 14 | |
| 1925 | | | 10 | | | | 5 | | | 21 | | 18 | 9 | |
| 1926 | | | 13 | | | | 6 | | | 13 | | 19 | 16 | |
| 1927 | | | 4 | | | | 11 | | | 14 | | 24 | 8 | |
| 1928 | | | 11 | | 6 | | 7 | | | 10 | | 18 | 15 | |
| 1929 | | | | 7 | 4 | | 13 | | | 12 | | 20 | 9 | |
| 1930 | | | | 6 | 8 | | 9 | | | 10 | | 8 | 6 | |
| 1931 | | | | 12 | 5 | | 8 | | | 7 | | 27 | 11 | 2 |
| 1932 | | | | 12 | 5 | | 8 | | | 22 | | 25 | 15 | 2 |
| 1933 | | | | 12 | 4 | | 15 | | | 16 | | 25 | 7 | 9 |
| 1934 | | | | 16 | 2 | | 11 | | | 19 | | 15 | 35 | 8 |
| 1935 | | | | 9 | 4 | | 23 | | | 20 | | 22 | 18 | 8 |
| 1936 | | | | 13 | 5 | | 20 | | | 24 | | 12 | 18 | 9 |
| 1937 | | | | 7 | 1 | | 35 | | | 20 | | 18 | 23 | 23 |

| B.S. PE | B.S. NS & T | E of Mines | B.S. E & UE | B. of Int Arch | B.S. M & IndE | B.S. Met | B of ES | Total | 5-yr CE | 5-yr EE | MS | PhD | Total | Grand Total |
|---|---|---|---|---|---|---|---|---|---|---|---|---|---|---|
|  |  |  |  |  |  |  |  | 1 |  |  |  |  |  | 1 |
|  |  |  |  |  |  |  |  | 2 |  |  |  |  |  | 2 |
|  |  |  |  |  |  |  |  | — |  |  |  |  |  | — |
|  |  |  |  |  |  |  |  | 2 |  |  |  |  |  | 2 |
|  |  |  |  |  |  |  |  | 3 |  |  |  |  |  | 3 |
|  |  |  |  |  |  |  |  | 4 |  |  |  |  |  | 4 |
|  |  |  |  |  |  |  |  | 1 |  |  |  |  |  | 1 |
|  |  |  |  |  |  |  |  | 3 |  |  |  |  |  | 3 |
|  |  |  |  |  |  |  |  | 4 |  |  |  |  |  | 4 |
|  |  |  |  |  |  |  |  | 3 |  |  |  |  |  | 3 |
|  |  |  |  |  |  |  |  | 2 |  |  |  |  |  | 2 |
|  |  |  |  |  |  |  |  | — |  |  |  |  |  | — |
|  |  |  |  |  |  |  |  | 4 |  |  |  |  |  | 4 |
|  |  |  |  |  |  |  |  | — |  |  |  |  |  | — |
|  |  |  |  |  |  |  |  | 3 |  |  |  |  |  | 3 |
|  |  |  |  |  |  |  |  | 8 |  |  |  |  |  | 8 |
|  |  |  |  |  |  |  |  | 4 |  |  |  |  |  | 4 |
|  |  |  |  |  |  |  |  | 18 |  |  |  |  |  | 18 |
|  |  | 1 |  |  |  |  |  | 22 |  |  |  |  |  | 22 |
|  |  | 1 |  |  |  |  |  | 11 |  |  |  |  |  | 11 |
|  |  | 1 |  |  |  |  |  | 23 |  |  |  |  |  | 23 |
|  |  | 2 |  |  |  |  |  | 24 |  |  |  |  |  | 24 |
|  |  | 2 |  |  |  |  |  | 25 |  |  |  |  |  | 25 |
|  |  | 2 |  |  |  |  |  | 31 |  |  |  |  |  | 31 |
|  |  |  |  |  |  |  |  | 27 |  | 1 |  |  | 1 | 28 |
|  |  | 3 |  |  |  |  |  | 27 |  | 1 |  |  | 1 | 28 |
|  |  | 2 |  |  |  |  |  | 25 |  | 1 |  |  | 1 | 26 |
|  |  | 2 |  |  |  |  |  | 31 |  |  |  |  |  | 31 |
|  |  |  |  |  |  |  |  | 31 |  | 2 |  |  | 2 | 33 |
|  |  |  |  |  |  |  |  | 36 | 1 | 3 |  |  | 4 | 40 |
|  |  |  |  |  |  |  |  | 16 |  |  |  |  |  | 16 |
|  |  |  |  |  |  |  |  | 13 |  |  |  |  |  | 13 |
|  |  |  |  |  |  |  |  | 25 | 3 |  |  |  | 3 | 28 |
|  |  |  |  |  |  |  |  | 39 | 3 | 2 |  |  | 5 | 44 |
|  |  |  |  |  |  |  |  | 55 |  | 1 | 4 |  | 5 | 60 |
|  |  |  |  |  |  |  |  | 74 | 2 |  | 5 |  | 7 | 81 |
|  |  |  |  |  |  |  |  | 66 |  |  | 7 |  | 7 | 73 |
|  |  |  |  |  |  |  |  | 63 |  |  | 7 |  | 7 | 70 |
|  |  |  |  |  |  |  |  | 67 |  |  | 5 |  | 5 | 72 |
|  |  |  |  |  |  |  |  | 61 |  |  | 4 |  | 4 | 65 |
|  |  |  |  |  |  |  |  | 67 |  |  | 7 |  | 7 | 74 |
|  |  |  |  |  |  |  |  | 65 |  |  | 11 |  | 11 | 76 |
|  |  |  |  | 3 |  |  |  | 50 |  |  | 14 |  | 14 | 64 |
|  |  |  |  | 1 |  |  |  | 73 |  |  | 13 |  | 13 | 86 |
|  |  |  | 1 | 2 |  |  |  | 92 |  |  | 18 |  | 18 | 110 |
|  |  |  | 1 | 1 | 2 |  |  | 92 |  |  | 11 |  | 11 | 103 |
|  |  |  |  | 2 | 2 |  |  | 110 |  |  | 14 |  | 14 | 124 |
|  |  |  | 2 |  |  |  |  | 106 |  |  | 14 |  | 14 | 120 |
|  |  |  |  | 1 |  |  |  | 102 |  |  | 14 |  | 14 | 116 |
|  |  |  |  | 1 |  |  |  | 128 |  |  | 13 | 4 | 17 | 145 |

| Cal. Year | B.S. AeE | B.S. ASE | B.S. Arch | B. of Arch | B.S. ArE | B.S. CrE | B.S. ChE | B.S. CE Maj | CE | B.S. CE | EE | B.S. EE | B.S. ME | B.S. PPE |
|---|---|---|---|---|---|---|---|---|---|---|---|---|---|---|
| 1938 |  |  |  | 10 | 6 |  | 33 |  |  | 18 |  | 27 | 31 | 42 |
| 1939 |  |  |  | 9 | 9 |  | 54 |  |  | 13 |  | 27 | 30 | 65 |
| 1940 |  |  |  | 8 | 1 |  | 50 |  |  | 21 |  | 22 | 29 |  |
| 1941 |  |  |  | 12 | 7 |  | 66 |  |  | 28 |  | 25 | 37 |  |
| 1942 |  |  |  | 8 | 3 |  | 60 |  |  | 39 |  | 37 | 52 |  |
| 1943 | 3 |  |  | 9 | 7 |  | 61 |  |  | 24 |  | 38 | 62 |  |
| 1944 | 8 |  |  | 1 | 4 |  | 41 |  |  | 15 |  | 31 | 24 |  |
| 1945 | 5 |  |  |  | 3 |  | 13 |  |  | 15 |  | 11 | 18 |  |
| 1946 | 5 |  |  | 4 | 5 |  | 13 |  |  | 21 |  | 59 | 49 |  |
| 1947 | 29 |  |  | 8 | 8 |  | 79 |  |  | 63 |  | 76 | 100 |  |
| 1948 | 20 |  |  | 14 | 21 | 15 | 105 |  |  | 77 |  | 97 | 131 |  |
| 1949 | 33 |  |  | 35 | 47 | 17 | 95 |  |  | 113 |  | 134 | 131 |  |
| 1950 | 27 |  |  | 50 | 49 | 14 | 79 |  |  | 105 |  | 131 | 143 |  |
| 1951 | 12 |  |  | 60 | 35 | 9 | 55 |  |  | 65 |  | 82 | 87 |  |
| 1952 | 13 |  |  |  | 30 | 7 | 34 |  |  | 55 |  | 52 | 61 |  |
| 1953 | 8 |  |  |  | 33 | 5 | 43 |  |  | 39 |  | 43 | 61 |  |
| 1954 | 16 |  |  |  | 26 | 6 | 31 |  |  | 38 |  | 39 | 62 |  |
| 1955 | 15 |  |  |  | 22 | 4 | 21 |  |  | 28 |  | 32 | 43 |  |
| 1956 | 28 |  |  |  | 29 |  | 46 |  |  | 39 |  | 64 | 91 |  |
| 1957 | 29 |  |  |  | 30 | 7 | 56 |  |  | 68 |  | 91 | 111 |  |
| 1958 | 43 |  |  |  | 38 | 5 | 70 |  |  | 69 |  | 146 | 148 |  |
| 1959 | 31 |  |  |  | 34 | 7 | 76 |  |  | 59 |  | 135 | 127 |  |
| 1960 |  | 43 |  |  | 42 | 9 | 64 |  |  | 54 |  | 107 | 112 |  |
| 1961 |  | 35 |  |  | 27 | 6 | 55 |  |  | 69 |  | 122 | 117 |  |
| 1962 |  | 31 |  |  | 25 | 1 | 64 |  |  | 60 |  | 111 | 116 |  |
| 1963 |  | 39 |  |  | 24 |  | 46 |  |  | 42 |  | 92 | 92 |  |
| 1964 |  | 29 |  |  | 22 |  | 61 |  |  | 28 |  | 107 | 62 |  |
| 1965 |  | 43 |  |  | 17 |  | 51 |  |  | 49 |  | 118 | 71 |  |
| 1966 |  | 55 |  |  | 20 |  | 49 |  |  | 39 |  | 100 | 62 |  |
| 1967 |  | 54 |  |  | 33 |  | 58 |  |  | 38 |  | 106 | 75 |  |
| 1968 |  | 55 |  |  | 21 |  | 60 |  |  | 47 |  | 85 | 63 |  |
| 1969 |  | 69 |  |  | 19 |  | 57 |  |  | 40 |  | 129 | 70 |  |
| 1970 |  | 70 |  |  | 21 |  | 72 |  |  | 147 |  | 117 | 117 |  |
| 1971 |  | 74 |  |  | 22 |  | 53 |  |  | 40 |  | 123 | 103 |  |
| 1972 |  | 51 |  |  | 29 |  | 56 |  |  | 38 |  | 116 | 124 |  |
| 1973 |  | 33 |  |  | 42 |  | 72 |  |  | 88 |  | 129 | 118 |  |
| 1974 |  | 23 |  |  | 28 |  | 60 |  |  | 80 |  | 153 | 87 |  |
| 1975 |  | 34 |  |  | 64 |  | 89 |  |  | 139 |  | 180 | 117 |  |
| 1976 |  | 21 |  |  | 32 |  | 51 |  |  | 74 |  | 137 | 80 |  |
| 1977 |  | 23 |  |  | 36 |  | 65 |  |  | 102 |  | 128 | 92 |  |
| 1978 |  | 18 |  |  | 51 |  | 63 |  |  | 121 |  | 146 | 135 |  |
| 1979 |  | 27 |  |  | 55 |  | 102 |  |  | 105 |  | 166 | 123 |  |
| 1980 |  | 32 |  |  | 60 |  | 103 |  |  | 117 |  | 182 | 192 |  |
| 1981 |  | 51 |  |  | 66 |  | 100 |  |  | 120 |  | 195 | 156 |  |
| 1982 |  | 48 |  |  | 59 |  | 106 |  |  | 121 |  | 196 | 185 |  |
| 1983 |  | 62 |  |  | 59 |  | 96 |  |  | 112 |  | 261 | 179 |  |
| 1984 |  | 58 |  |  | 50 |  | 112 |  |  | 119 |  | 289 | 169 |  |
| 1985 |  | 65 |  |  | 49 |  | 110 |  |  | 107 |  | 263 | 200 |  |

| B.S. PE | B.S. NS & T | E of Mines | B.S. E & UE | B. of Int Arch | B.S. M & IndE | B.S. Met | B of ES | Total | 5–yr CE | 5–yr EE | MS | PhD | Total | Grand Total |
|---|---|---|---|---|---|---|---|---|---|---|---|---|---|---|
|  |  |  |  |  |  |  |  | 167 |  |  | 9 |  | 9 | 176 |
|  |  |  |  |  |  |  |  | 207 |  |  | 24 | 5 | 29 | 236 |
| 65 |  |  |  |  |  |  |  | 196 |  |  | 20 | 3 | 23 | 219 |
| 65 |  |  |  |  |  |  |  | 240 |  |  | 26 | 2 | 28 | 268 |
| 53 |  |  |  |  |  |  |  | 252 |  |  | 14 | 4 | 18 | 270 |
| 21 |  |  |  |  |  |  |  | 225 |  |  | 11 | 6 | 17 | 242 |
| 14 |  |  |  |  |  |  |  | 138 |  |  | 11 | 1 | 12 | 150 |
| 4 | 1 |  |  |  |  |  |  | 70 |  |  | 5 | 6 | 11 | 81 |
| 13 | 1 |  |  |  |  |  |  | 170 |  |  | 11 | 3 | 14 | 184 |
| 42 | 17 |  |  |  |  |  |  | 422 |  |  | 51 | 2 | 53 | 475 |
| 48 | 22 |  |  |  |  |  |  | 550 |  |  | 55 | 3 | 58 | 608 |
| 94 | 5 |  |  |  |  |  |  | 704 |  |  | 68 | 6 | 74 | 778 |
| 96 | 2 |  |  |  |  |  |  | 696 |  |  | 60 | 9 | 69 | 765 |
| 77 |  |  |  |  |  | 1 |  | 483 |  |  | 82 | 5 | 87 | 570 |
| 61 |  |  |  |  |  | 2 |  | 315 |  |  | 67 | 12 | 79 | 394 |
| 65 |  |  |  |  |  | 3 |  | 300 |  |  | 42 | 8 | 50 | 350 |
| 45 |  |  |  |  |  | 2 |  | 265 |  |  | 53 | 7 | 60 | 325 |
| 57 |  |  |  |  |  | 2 |  | 224 |  |  | 51 | 17 | 68 | 292 |
| 63 |  |  |  |  |  | 2 |  | 362 |  |  | 53 | 10 | 63 | 425 |
| 82 |  |  |  |  |  | 5 |  | 479 |  |  | 73 | 7 | 80 | 559 |
| 109 |  |  |  |  |  | 3 |  | 631 |  |  | 77 | 11 | 88 | 719 |
| 108 |  |  |  |  |  | 8 |  | 585 |  |  | 58 | 12 | 70 | 655 |
| 81 |  |  |  |  |  | 2 |  | 514 |  |  | 72 | 14 | 86 | 600 |
| 51 |  |  |  |  |  | 7 |  | 489 |  |  | 104 | 10 | 114 | 603 |
| 31 |  |  |  |  |  | 1 |  | 440 |  |  | 90 | 26 | 116 | 556 |
| 23 |  |  |  |  |  | 4 | 12 | 374 |  |  | 80 | 37 | 117 | 491 |
| 14 |  |  |  |  |  |  | 9 | 332 |  |  | 96 | 36 | 132 | 464 |
| 19 |  |  |  |  |  |  | 22 | 390 |  |  | 95 | 49 | 144 | 534 |
| 9 |  |  |  |  |  |  | 20 | 354 |  |  | 125 | 60 | 185 | 539 |
| 9 |  |  |  |  |  |  | 16 | 389 |  |  | 120 | 59 | 179 | 568 |
| 14 |  |  |  |  |  |  | 18 | 363 |  |  | 155 | 78 | 233 | 596 |
| 18 |  |  |  |  |  |  | 8 | 410 |  |  | 162 | 74 | 236 | 646 |
| 13 |  |  |  |  |  |  | 15 | 572 |  |  | 183 | 81 | 264 | 836 |
| 23 |  |  |  |  |  |  | 16 | 454 |  |  | 124 | 71 | 195 | 649 |
| 24 |  |  |  |  |  |  | 15 | 453 |  |  | 190 | 75 | 265 | 718 |
| 26 |  |  |  |  |  |  | 15 | 523 |  |  | 141 | 39 | 180 | 703 |
| 21 |  |  |  |  |  |  | 17 | 469 |  |  | 160 | 53 | 213 | 682 |
| 40 |  |  |  |  |  |  | 22 | 685 |  |  | 254 | 70 | 324 | 1,009 |
| 33 |  |  |  |  |  |  | 18 | 446 |  |  | 178 | 47 | 225 | 671 |
| 48 |  |  |  |  |  |  | 23 | 517 |  |  | 180 | 65 | 245 | 762 |
| 85 |  |  |  |  |  |  | 20 | 639 |  |  | 180 | 38 | 218 | 857 |
| 88 |  |  |  |  |  |  | 31 | 697 |  |  | 206 | 43 | 249 | 946 |
| 56 |  |  |  |  |  |  | 19 | 761 |  |  | 196 | 40 | 236 | 997 |
| 109 |  |  |  |  |  |  | 29 | 826 |  |  | 238 | 45 | 283 | 1,109 |
| 125 |  |  |  |  |  |  | 30 | 870 |  |  | 238 | 57 | 295 | 1,165 |
| 168 |  |  |  |  |  |  | 36 | 973 |  |  | 336 | 60 | 396 | 1,369 |
| 146 |  |  |  |  |  |  | 29 | 972 |  |  | 289 | 59 | 348 | 1,320 |
| 148 |  |  |  |  |  |  |  | 942 |  |  | 325 | 74 | 399 | 1,341 |

## ENDOWED POSITIONS, SCHOLARSHIPS, AND FACILITIES IN THE COLLEGE OF ENGINEERING

| | Name of Chair | Date of Regents' Acceptance | History of Holder Name |
|---|---|---|---|
| 1. | Nasser I. Al–Rashid Chair in CE | 7–11–80 | Lymon C. Reese John E. Breen |
| 2. | Hussein M. Alharthy Centennial Chair in CE | 6–17–83 | Raymond C. Loehr |
| 3. | Dula D. Cockrell Centennial Chair in Engr. (Matching) # | 8–12–82 | Victor G. Szebehely Open |
| 4. | Ernest Cockrell, Jr., Centennial Chair in Engr. # | 2–11–83 | Harvey G. Cragon |
| 5. | Ernest Cockrell, Sr., Chair in Engr. # | 2–29–80 | Robert S. Schechter Open |
| 6. | Ernest H. Cockrell Centennial Chair in Engr. | 2–12–82 | Herbert H. Woodson |
| 7. | Ernest and Virginia Cockrell Chair in Engr. | 2–09–79 | James R. Fair Open |
| 8. | Cockrell Family Regents' Chair in Engr. #1 (Matching added) ## | 2–15–85 | Irwin W. Sandberg |
| 9. | Cockrell Family Regents' Chair in Engr. #2 ## | 2–15–85 | Open |
| 10. | Cockrell Family Regents' Chair in Engr. #3 ## | 2–15–85 | Open |
| 11. | Cockrell Family Regents' Chair in Engr. #4 (Matching) ## | 2–15–85 | Al F. Tasch, Jr. |
| 12. | Cockrell Family Regents' Chair in Engr. #5 (Matching) ## | 2–15–85 | Open |
| 13. | Cockrell Family Regents' Chair in Engr. #6 (Matching added) ## | 2–15–85 | Open |
| 14. | Cockrell Family Regents' Chair in Engr. #7 (Matching added) * ## | 2–15–85 | Open |
| 15. | Cockrell Family Regents' Chair in Engr. #8 (Matching) * ## | 2–15–85 | Open |
| 16. | Janet S. Cockrell Centennial Chair in Engr. | 2–12–82 | Ben G. Streetman Open |
| 17. | Virginia H. Cockrell Centennial Chair in Engr. (Matching) # | 2–11–83 | John B. Goodenough |
| 18. | Carol Cockrell Curran Chair in Engr. | 2–13–81 | John E. Breen Delbert Tesar |
| 19. | Richard B. Curran Centennial Chair in Engr. | 2–11–83 | Victor G. Szebehely |

**History of Holder (Cont'd)**

| Dept. | Date | Restrictions | Donor |
|---|---|---|---|
| CE<br>" | 1981–84<br>1984– | CE | Nasser I. Al–Rashid |
| CE | Jan 85– | CE | Hussein M. Alharthy |
| AsE–EM | 1983–84 | None | University matching gift of Cockrell Foundation |
| ECE | 1984– | None | Cockrell Foundation |
| ChE and PE | 1981–84 | None | Cockrell Foundation |
| ECE | 1982– | None | Cockrell Foundation |
| ChE | 1979–85 | None | Cockrell Foundation |
| ECE | Jan 1986– | Microelectronics, Computer, MS&E, or Mfg. Systems | |
| | | Microelectronics, Computer, MS&E, or Mfg. Systems | |
| | | Microelectronics, Computer, MS&E, or Mfg. Systems | |
| ECE | 1986– | Microelectronics, Computer, MS&E, or Mfg. Systems | |
| | | Microelectronics, Computer, MS&E, or Mfg. Systems | |
| | | Microelectronics, Computer, MS&E, or Mfg. Systems | |
| | | Microelectronics, Computer, MS&E, or Mfg. Systems | |
| | | Microelectronics, Computer, MS&E, or Mfg. Systems | |
| ECE | 1982–86 | None | Cockrell Foundation |
| ME and ECE | 1986– | None | University matching gift of Cockrell Foundation |
| CE<br>ME | 1981–84<br>Jan 1985 | None | Cockrell Foundation |
| AsE–EM | 1984– | None | Cockrell Foundation |

| | Name of Chair | Date of Regents' Acceptance | History of Holder Name |
|---|---|---|---|
| 20. | Melvin H. Gertz Regents' Chair in ChE (Matching added) ## | 8–10–84 | Donald R. Paul |
| 21. | Getty Oil Co. Centennial Chair in PE (Matching) | 8–12–82 | Robert S. Schechter |
| 22. | Earnest F. Gloyna Regents' Chair in Engr. (Matching added) ## | 2–15–85 | Ben G. Streetman |
| 23. | John J. McKetta, Jr. Centennial Energy Chair in Engr. (Matching added) * ## | 4–13–84 | James R. Fair |
| 24. | W. A. (Monty) Moncrief Centennial Endowed Chair in PE | 8–12–82 | Royal E. Collins Open |
| 25. | W. A. (Tex) Moncrief, Jr., Centennial Endowed Chair in PE (Matching) | 8–12–82 | Myron H. Dorfman |
| 26. | Motorola Regents' Chair in Electrical and Computer Engr. ## | 2–15–85 | Open |
| 27. | Clint W. Murchison, Sr., Chair of Free Enterprise * ## | 8–09–85 | Margaret N. Maxey (Director) Stephen A. Szygenda |
| 28. | Rashid Engineering Regents' Chair (Matching added) ## | 2–15–85 | Open |
| 29. | Schlumberger Centennial Chair in EE | 2–11–83 | Open |
| 30. | Bettie Margaret Smith Chair in EHE (CE) | 10–09–81 | Earnest F. Gloyna |
| 31. | Judson S. Swearingen Regents' Chair in Engr. (Matching added) ## | 2–15–85 | Open |
| 32. | Robert B. Trull Chair in Engr. ** | 8–14–81 | Morris Fine |
| 33. | Joe C. Walter, Jr., Chair in Engr. ** | 8–14–81 | John J. McKetta, Jr. |
| 34. | Clare Cockrell Williams Centennial Chair in Engr. | 2–11–83 | Byron D. Tapley |

* Not fully funded.
** Limited funds available because of stock.
# $1.4 million chairs approved by regents 6–15–84.
## $1 million chairs.

**History of Holder (Cont'd)**

| Dept. | Date | Restrictions | Donor |
|-------|------|--------------|-------|
| ChE | 1985– | ChE | |
| ChE and PE | 1984– | PE | University matching gift of Getty Oil Co. |
| ECE | 1986– | Microelectronics, Computer, MS&E, or Mfg. Systems | |
| ChE | 1985– | None | Multiple individual and industrial donors and University matching funds |
| PE | 1983–84 | PE | W. A. (Tex) Moncrief, Jr. |
| PE | 1983– | PE | University matching gift of W. A. (Tex) Moncrief, Jr. |
| | | Microelectronics or Computer | |
| ECE | 1982– | None | Engineering Foundation Advisory Council and |
| ECE | 1986– | | multiple individual and industrial donors |
| | | Microelectronics, Computer, MS&E, or Mfg. Systems | |
| | | ECE | Schlumberger Foundation |
| CE | 1982– | Environmental Health Engr. | Bettie Margaret Smith |
| | | MS&E or Mfg. Systems | |
| ME | Feb/Mar 1986 only | None | Robert B. Trull |
| ChE | 1981– | None | Houston Oil and Minerals |
| AsE–EM | 1984– | None | Cockrell Foundation |

## ENDOWED POSITIONS, SCHOLARSHIPS, AND FACILITIES IN THE COLLEGE OF ENGINEERING

| | Name of Professorship | Date of Regents' Acceptance | History of Holder Name |
|---|---|---|---|
| 1. | Adnan Abou–Ayyash Centennial Prof. in Transp. Engr. (Matching added) | 6–17–83 | B. Frank McCullough |
| 2. | Nasser I. Al–Rashid Centennial Prof. in Transp. Engr. (Matching added) | 2–11–83 | Clyde E. Lee |
| 3. | Hussein M. Alharthy Centennial Prof. in CE (Matching) | 6–17–83 | Clyde E. Lee James O. Jirsa |
| 4. | E.C.H. Bantel Prof. for Professional Practice | 10–12–79 | William G. Lesso John R. Howell |
| 5. | Henry Beckman Prof. in ChE | 3–13–65 | M. Van Winkle Eugene H. Wissler |
| 6. | Warren S. Bellows Centennial Prof. in CE | 2–12–82 | Joseph A. Yura |
| 7. | Z. D. Bonner Prof. in ChE | 12–07–79 | Joel W. Barlow |
| 8. | Brunswick–Abernathy Regents' Prof. in Soil Dynamics and Geotechnical Engr. (Matching added) | 8–10–84 | Kenneth H. Stokoe II |
| 9. | Ernest Cockrell, Jr., Memorial Prof. in Engr. | 4–28–75 | Robert S. Schechter  J. Parker Lamb, Jr. |
| 10. | C. W. Cook Prof. in Environmental Engr. | 7–70 | Gerard A. Rohlich Joseph F. Malina, Jr. |
| 11. | W. A. (Bill) Cunningham Prof. in Engr. | 2–16–74 | Howard F. Rase |
| 12. | Bob R. Dorsey Prof. in Engr. | 2–11–77 | David M. Himmelblau |
| 13. | Donald J. Douglass Centennial Prof. in Engr. (Matching) | 8–12–82 | Richard W. Furlong |
| 14. | Engr. Foundation Prof. in Engr. | 9–05–80 | Thomas W. Kennedy |
| 15. | George H. Fancher Prof. in PE | 8–14–81 | W. C. J. van Rensburg |
| 16. | Phil M. Ferguson Prof. in CE | 4–10–81 | Clyde E. Lee B. Frank McCullough James O. Jirsa |
| 17. | Stanley P. Finch Centennial Prof. in Engr. (Matching) | 2–12–82 | James O. Jirsa Edward R. Holley |
| 18. | Marion E. Forsman Centennial Prof. in Engr. * | 12–08–83 | Ashley J. Welch |
| 19. | E. Gus Fruh Visiting Prof. in CE | 8–10–84 | Open |

**History of Holder (Cont'd)**

| Dept. | Date | Restrictions | Donor |
|---|---|---|---|
| CE | 1984– | Transportation Engineering | University matching and a gift of Adnan Abou–Ayyash |
| CE | 1983– | Transportation Engineering | University matching and a gift of Nasser I. Al–Rashid |
| CE | 1984–85 Jan 1986 | CE "On Leave" support for research and studies | University matching gift of Hussein M. Alharthy |
| ME ME | 1980–82 1982– | None | Engineering Foundation |
| ChE ChE | 1971–75 1973– | ChE | Henry J. Beckman |
| CE | 1982– | CE | Family of Warren S. Bellows |
| ChE | 1984– | ChE | Z. D. Bonner |
| CE | 1985– | Soil Dynamics and Geotechnical Engr. | |
| ChE and PE ME and AsE–EM | 1975–81 1981– | None | Cockrell Foundation |
| CE " | 1972–80 1980– | Environmental Health Engr. | C. W. Cook |
| ChE | 1974– | None | Multiple individual donors |
| ChE | 1978– | None | Bob R. Dorsey |
| CE | 1982– | None | University matching gift of Donald J. Douglass |
| CE | 1981– | None | Ford Foundation |
| PE | 1983– | PE | R. B. Trull and George H. Fancher |
| CE " " | 1981–83 1983–84 1984– | CE | Engineering Foundation and Phil M. Ferguson |
| CE " | 1982–84 1984– | None | University matching gift of the family of Warren S. Bellows |
| ECE | 1985– | None | Marion E. Forsman |

CE

| | Name of Chair | Date of Regents' Acceptance | History of Holder Name |
|---|---|---|---|
| 20. | B. N. Gafford Prof. in EE | 4–10–81 | Edward J. Powers, Jr. <br> William C. Duesterhoeft |
| 21. | L. P. Gilvin Centennial Prof. in CE (Matching) | 4–08–82 | Robert Herman <br> Roy E. Olson |
| 22. | Dewitt C. Greer Centennial Prof. in Transp. Engr. | 10–09–81 | W. Ronald Hudson |
| 23. | Carol and Henry Groppe Prof. in ChE | 10–20–78 | J. Tinsley Oden |
| 24. | Halliburton Annual Prof. in PE | Spring 1968 | Kenneth E. Gray <br> Augusto L. Podio <br> Gary A. Pope <br> Larry W. Lake |
| 25. | H. B. (Burt) Harkins, Jr., Prof. in PE | 10–12–79 | Myron H. Dorfman <br> Augusto L. Podio |
| 26. | Hayden Head Prof. in Engr. | 10–09–81 | Tatsuo Itoh |
| 27. | J. H. Herring Centennial Prof. in Engr. (Matching) | 4–15–83 | Rodger M. Walser |
| 28. | J. H. Herring Centennial Prof. in PE | 4–15–83 | Gary A. Pope |
| 29. | T. Brockett Hudson Prof. in ChE | 10–20–78 | Donald R. Paul <br> James E. Stice |
| 30. | Hughes Tool Co. Centennial Prof. in ME (Matching added) | 4–08–82 | Paul A. Jensen |
| 31. | Frank W. Jessen Prof. in PE | 4–10–81 | Royal E. Collins <br> Open |
| 32. | Josey Centennial Prof. in Energy Resources (Matching) * | 2–11–83 | Open |
| 33. | Jack S. Josey Prof. in Energy Studies | 10–01–76 | H. Grady Rylander, Jr. <br> Paul A. Jensen <br> Open |
| 34. | Harry L. Kent, Jr., Prof. in ME | 4–10–81 | Harris L. Marcus |
| 35. | Joe J. King Prof. in Engr. | 3–20–68 | John J. McKetta, Jr. <br> Earnest F. Gloyna <br> H. Grady Rylander, Jr. |
| 36. | Kenneth A. Kobe Prof. in ChE | 4–10–81 | James R. Brock |

**History of Holder (Cont'd)**

| Dept. | Date | Restrictions | Donor |
|---|---|---|---|
| ECE<br>" | 1981–82<br>1982– | ECE | Engineering Foundation and multiple individual donors |
| CE<br>" | 1982–84<br>1984– | CE | University matching gift of Sun Co., Inc., and multiple individual donors |
| CE | 1981– | Transportation Engineering | Multiple individual donors |
| AsE–EM | 1979– | ChE | E. H. Groppe, Jr. |
| PE<br>PE<br>PE<br>PE | 1968–82<br>1982–84<br>1984–85<br>1985– | Annual—not endowed | Halliburton Education Foundation, Inc. |
| PE<br>" | 1980–83<br>1984– | PE | Harkins and Co. and multiple individual donors |
| ECE | 1983– | None | Celanese Co. |
| ECE | 1985– | None | University matching gift of J. H. Herring and Marathon Oil Foundation, Inc. |
| PE | 1985– | PE | J. H. Herring and Marathon Oil Foundation, Inc. |
| ChE<br>ChE | 1978–85<br>1985– | ChE | Multiple individual donors |
| ME | 1984– | ME | University matching and a gift of Hughes Tool Co. |
| PE | 1981–83 | PE | Engineering Foundation and multiple individual donors |
|  |  | Energy resources | University matching gift of Mr. and Mrs. Jack S. Josey |
| ME<br>" | 1978–80<br>1982–84 | Shared with Natural Sciences and Business (each two–year terms)—rotates back to Engineering in Fall 1990 | Mr. and Mrs. Jack S. Josey |
| ME | 1981– | ME | Engineering Foundation and multiple individual donors |
| ChE<br>CE<br>ME | 1968–70<br>1970–82<br>1983– | None | Joe J. King |
| ChE | 1981– | ChE | Engineering Foundation and multiple individual donors |

| | Name of Professorship | Date of Regents' Acceptance | History of Holder Name |
|---|---|---|---|
| 37. | B. J. Lancaster Prof. in PE | 4–10–81 | Ben H. Caudle |
| 38. | John J. McKetta, Jr., Energy Prof. in Engr. | 12–10–76 | John E. Breen<br>J. K. Aggarwal |
| 39. | L. B. (Preach) Meaders Prof. in Engr. | 9–16–77 | Victor G. Szebehely<br>Charles A. Sorber |
| 40. | Paul D. and Betty Robertson Meek and American Petrofina Foundation Prof. in ChE | 12–11–81 | William J. Koros |
| 41. | Paul D. and Betty Robertson Meek Centennial Prof. in ChE | 12–11–81 | Thomas F. Edgar |
| 42. | Paul D. and Betty Robertson Meek Centennial Prof. in Engr. (Matching) | 12–11–81 | José M. Roesset |
| 43. | Robert L. Parker, Sr., Centennial Prof. in Engr. (Matching) | 4–08–82 | Lee E. Baker |
| 44. | Harry H. Power Prof. in Engr. | 8–14–81 | Jason L. Speyer |
| 45. | Ashley H. Priddy Centennial Prof. in Engr. | 8–12–83 | Stephen G. Wright |
| 46. | RepublicBank Corp. Centennial Prof. in PE (Matching) | 8–12–82 | Open |
| 47. | Gerard A. Rohlich Regents' Prof. in CE * | 8–10–84 | Open |
| 48. | E. P. Schoch Prof. in Engr. | 12–04–70 | John J. McKetta, Jr.<br>H. Grady Rylander, Jr.<br>Robert P. Popovich |
| 49. | Bettie Margaret Smith Prof. in Engr. | 9–05–80 | John J. Bertin |
| 50. | Jewel McAlister Smith Prof. in Engr. | 4–10–81 | Hugo Steinfink |
| 51. | T. U. Taylor Prof. in Engr. | 9–20–68 | Phil M. Ferguson<br>Lymon C. Reese<br>David W. Fowler |
| 52. | Texas Atomic Energy Research Foundation Prof. in Engr. | 2–29–80 | Herbert H. Woodson<br>Edward J. Powers, Jr. |
| 53. | M. J. Thompson Regents' Prof. in AsE–EM | 8–10–84 | David G. Hull |
| 54. | Matthew Van Winkle Regents' Prof. in ChE | 8–10–84 | Open |
| 55. | C. T. Wells Prof. in Project Management | 7–26–79 | Richard L. Tucker |

**History of Holder (Cont'd)**

| Dept. | Date | Restrictions | Donor |
|-------|------|--------------|-------|
| PE | 1981– | PE | Atlantic Richfield Foundation |
| CE<br>ECE | 1977–81<br>1981– | Energy field | John J. McKetta, Jr. |
| AsE–EM<br>CE | 1978–83<br>1985–86 | None | Multiple individual donors |
| ChE | 1985– | ChE | American Petrofina Foundation and Paul D. and Betty Robertson Meek |
| ChE | 1983– | ChE | Paul D. and Betty Robertson Meek |
| CE | 1983– | None | University matching gift of Paul D. and Betty Robertson Meek |
| ECE | 1982– | None | University matching gift Robert L. Parker, Sr. |
| AsE–EM | 1982– | None | R. B. Trull |
| CE | 1985– | None | Sabine Corp. |
|  |  | PE | University matching gift of RepublicBank Corp. |
|  |  | CE |  |
| ChE<br>ME<br>ChE | 1970–81<br>1981–83<br>1983– | None | Engineering Foundation |
| AsE–EM | 1981– | None | Bettie Margaret Smith |
| ChE | 1981– | None | Bettie Margaret Smith |
| CE<br>CE<br>CE | 1969–73<br>1973–81<br>1981– | None | Engineering Foundation |
| ECE<br>" | 1980–82<br>1982– | None | Texas Atomic Energy Research Foundation |
| AsE–EM | 1985– | AsE–EM |  |
|  |  | ChE | University matching gift of Engineering Foundation |
| CE | 1982– | Project management | C. T. Wells |

| | Name of Professorship | Date of Regents' Acceptance | History of Holder Name |
|---|---|---|---|
| 56. | W. R. Woolrich Prof. in Engr. | 9–20–68 | Byron D. Tapley<br>Gary C. Vliet |
| 57. | Zarrow Centennial Prof. in Engr. (Matching) | 12–11–81 | Ned H. Burns |
| 58. | Zarrow Centennial Prof. in PE | 12–11–81 | Kenneth E. Gray |

*Not Fully Funded

## ENDOWED POSITIONS, SCHOLARSHIPS, AND FACILITIES IN THE COLLEGE OF ENGINEERING

| | Name of Teaching Fellowship | Date of Regents' Acceptance | History of Holder Name |
|---|---|---|---|
| 1. | Raymond F. Dawson Centennial Teaching Fellow. in Engr. (Matching) | 2–12–82 | Richard W. Miksad<br>Howard M. Liljestrand |
| 2. | Werner W. Dornberger Centennial Teaching Fellow in Engr. (Matching) | 2–12–82 | Steven I. Marcus<br>M. Ray Mercer |
| 3. | Engr. Foundation Centennial Teaching Fellow. in EE #1 | 6–11–82 | Jonathan W. Valvano |
| 4. | Engr. Foundation Centennial Teaching Fellow. in EE #2 * | 6–11–82 | W. Mack Grady |
| 5. | Engr. Foundation Centennial Teaching Fellow. in Engr. #1 (Matching) | 6–11–82 | Stelios Kyriakides |
| 6. | Engr. Foundation Centennial Teaching Fellow. in Engr. #2 (Matching) * | 6–11–82 | Roy R. Craig, Jr. |
| 7. | George H. Fancher Centennial Teaching Fellow. in PE (Matching) | 12–03–82 | A. Daniel Hill |
| 8. | Phil M. Ferguson Centennial Teaching Fellow. in CE | 2–12–82 | Karl H. Frank |
| 9. | Fluor Centennial Teaching Fellow. in Engr. #1 * | 12–08–83 | Keith P. Johnston<br>Open |
| 10. | Fluor Centennial Teaching Fellow. in Engr. #2 (Matching) * | 12–08–83 | David B. Ashley |
| 11. | John A. Focht Centennial Teaching Fellow. in CE | 2–12–82 | Charles A. Sorber<br>Richard E. Klingner |
| 12. | General Motors Foundation Teaching Fellow. in EE (Matching) | 8–12–83 | Dean P. Neikirk |
| 13. | General Motors Foundation Centennial Teaching Fellow. in ME | 8–12–83 | Ilene J. Busch–Vishniac |
| 14. | Gulf Oil Foundation Centennial Teaching Fellow. in ChE | 6–17–83 | Keith P. Johnston |

**History of Holder (Cont'd)**

| Dept. | Date | Restrictions | Donor |
|---|---|---|---|
| AsE–EM<br>ME | 1974–84<br>1985– | None | Engineering Foundation |
| CE | 1983– | None | University matching gift of the Zarrow families |
| PE | 1982– | PE | Zarrow families |

**History of Holder (Cont'd)**

| Dept. | Date | Restrictions | Donor |
|---|---|---|---|
| CE<br>CE | 1982–85<br>1985– | None | University matching gift of Warren S. Bellows Construction Corp. |
| ECE<br>" | 1982–84<br>1984– | None | University matching gift of Warren S. Bellows Construction Corp. |
| ECE | 1983– | ECE | Anonymous corporate donor |
| ECE | 1985– | ECE | |
| AsE–EM | 1983– | None | University matching gift anonymous corporate donor |
| AsE–EM | 1985– | None | |
| PE | 1984– | PE | University matching gift of George H. Fancher |
| CE | 1982– | CE | Warren S. Bellows Construction Corp. |
| ChE | 1984–85 | ChE, CE, ECE, or ME | Fluor Engineers, Inc. |
| CE | 1985– | ChE, CE, ECE, or ME | University matching gift Fluor Engineers, Inc. |
| CE<br>" | 1982–84<br>1984– | CE | Warren S. Bellows Construction Corp. |
| ECE | 1985– | ECE | University matching gift of General Motors Foundation |
| ME | 1985– | ME | General Motors Foundation |
| ChE | 1985– | ChE | Gulf Oil Foundation |

|     | Name of Teaching Fellowship | Date of Regents' Acceptance | History of Holder Name |
| --- | --- | --- | --- |
| 15. | Gulf Oil Foundation Centennial Teaching Fellow. in PE | 6–17–83 | Mark A. Miller |
| 16. | Carroll D. Simmons Centennial Teaching Fellow. in Engr. (Matching) | 2–12–82 | Gary L. Wise<br>John A. Pearce |
| 17. | J. Neils Thompson Centennial Teaching Fellow. in CE | 2–12–82 | C. Michael Walton<br>Stephen G. Wright<br>Calin M. Popescu |

*Not Fully Funded

## ENDOWED POSITIONS, SCHOLARSHIPS, AND FACILITIES IN THE COLLEGE OF ENGINEERING

|     | Name of Fellowship | Date of Regents' Acceptance | History of Holder Name |
| --- | --- | --- | --- |
| 1. | Leland Barclay Fellow. in Engr. | 8–10–84 | Ramon L. Carrasquillo |
| 2. | Myron L. Begeman Fellow. in Engr. (Matching) | 8–10–84 | Joseph J. Beaman |
| 3. | George and Dawn L. Coleman Centennial Fellow. in Engr. (Matching) | 2–11–83 | Glenn Y. Masada |
| 4. | Carl J. Eckhardt Fellow. in ME (Matching) | 8–10–84 | Ronald D. Matthews |
| 5. | Gulf Oil Foundation Centennial Fellow. in Engr. #1 (Matching) | 6–17–83 | Kurt M. Marshek |
| 6. | Gulf Oil Foundation Centennial Fellow. in Engr. #2 (Matching) | 6–17–83 | Bob E. Schutz |
| 7. | William W. Hagerty Fellow. in Engr. (Matching) * | 8–10–84 | Ching–Hsie Yew |
| 8. | William H. Hartwig Fellow. in EE (Matching) | 8–10–84 | Chuan–Lin Wu |
| 9. | Pearlie Dashiell Henderson Centennial Fellow. in Engr. (Matching) | 2–11–83 | Polichronis D. Spanos<br>Randall J. Charbeneau |
| 10. | Frank W. Jessen Centennial Fellow. in PE (Matching) | 2–11–83 | Ekwere J. Peters |
| 11. | Frank A. Liddell, Jr., Centennial Fellow. in ChE | 8–12–82 | Gary T. Rochelle |
| 12. | J. Hugh and Betty Liedtke Centennial Fellow. in Engr. (Matching) | 2–11–83 | Alfred E. Traver |
| 13. | Banks McLaurin Fellow. in Engr. | 4–12–85 | Open |

**History of Holder (Cont'd)**

| Dept. | Date | Restrictions | Donor |
|---|---|---|---|
| PE | 1985– | PE | Gulf Oil Foundation |
| ECE<br>ECE | 1982–84<br>1984– | None | University matching gift of Warren S. Bellows Construction Corp. |
| CE<br>CE<br>CE | 1982–83<br>1983–84<br>1984– | CE | Warren S. Bellows Construction Corp. |

**History of Holder (Cont'd)**

| Dept. | Date | Restrictions | Donor |
|---|---|---|---|
| CE | 1985– | None | |
| ME | 1985– | None | |
| ME | 1983– | None | University matching gift of Cockrell Foundation |
| ME | 1985– | ME | |
| ME | 1985– | None | University matching gift of Gulf Oil Foundation |
| AsE–EM | 1985– | None | University matching gift of Gulf Oil Foundation |
| AsE–EM | 1985– | None | |
| ECE | 1985– | ECE | |
| AsE–EM<br>CE | 1983–84<br>1985– | None | University matching gift of Cockrell Foundation |
| PE | 1983– | PE | University matching gift of Friends of Alec |
| ChE | 1983– | ChE | Mr. and Mrs. Frank A. Liddell, Jr. |
| ME | 1983– | None | University matching gift of Cockrell Foundation |
| | | None | |

| | Name of Teaching Fellowship | Date of Regents' Acceptance | History of Holder Name |
|---|---|---|---|
| 14. | Laurence E. McMakin, Jr., Centennial Fellow. in ChE (Matching) | 8–12–82 | John G. Ekerdt |
| 15. | William J. Murray, Jr., Fellow. in Engr. #1 | 8–10–84 | George S. Dulikravich |
| 16. | William J. Murray, Jr., Fellow. in Engr. #2 | 8–10–84 | Kenneth R. Diller |
| 17. | William J. Murray, Jr., Fellow. in Engr. #3 (Matching) | 8–10–84 | Desmond F. Lawler |
| 18. | William J. Murray, Jr., Fellow. in Engr. #4 (Matching) | 8–10–84 | David E. Daniel, Jr. |
| 19. | Charlotte Maer Patton Centennial Fellow. in Engr. (Matching) | 2–11–83 | Kenneth R. Diller J. Wesley Barnes |
| 20. | Pioneer Corp. Faculty Fellow. in PE (Matching) * | 8–10–84 | Open |
| 21. | Roberta Woods Ray Centennial Fellow. in Engr. (Matching) | 2–11–83 | Larry W. Mays |
| 22. | Carl Ernest and Mattie Ann Muldrow Reistle, Jr., Centennial Fellow. in Engr. (Matching) | 2–11–83 | John D. Borcherding |
| 23. | Charles Elmer Rowe Fellow. in Engr. (Matching) * | 8–10–84 | David R. Maidment |
| 24. | Robert and Francis Stark Centennial Fellow. in Engr. (Matching) | 2–11–83 | Walter S. Reed |
| 25. | Sun Exploration and Production Co. Centennial Fellow. #1 in PE | 12–03–82 | Gary A. Pope T. William Thompson |
| 26. | Sun Exploration and Production Co. Centennial Fellow. #2 in PE (Matching) | 12–03–82 | Kamy Sepehrnoori |
| 27. | Texas Atomic Energy Research Foundation Centennial Fellow. in EE (Matching) | 8–12–83 | Miroslaw Malek |
| 28. | Eli H. and Ramona Thornton Centennial Fellow. in Engr. | 2–11–83 | Douglas R. Lloyd |
| 29. | N. Doug Williams Memorial Centennial Fellow. in Engr. (Matching) | 2–11–83 | Linda H. Hayes |
| 30. | Louis T. Yule Fellow. in Engr. | 4–12–85 | Wallace T. Fowler |

**History of Holder (Cont'd)**

| Dept. | Date | Restrictions | Donor |
|---|---|---|---|
| ChE | 1983– | ChE | University matching gift of Mr. and Mrs. Frank A. Liddell, Jr. |
| AsE–EM | 1985– | None | |
| ME | 1985– | None | |
| CE | 1985– | None | |
| CE | 1985– | None | |
| ME<br>ME | 1983–84<br>1984– | None<br><br>PE | University matching gift of Cockrell Foundation |
| CE | 1983– | None | University matching gift of Cockrell Foundation |
| CE | 1983– | None | University matching gift of Cockrell Foundation |
| CE | 1985– | None | |
| ME | 1983– | None | University matching gift of Cockrell Foundation |
| PE<br>" | 1983–84<br>1984– | PE | Sun Company, Inc. |
| PE | 1983– | PE | University matching gift of Sun Company, Inc. |
| ECE | 1983– | ECE | University matching gift of Texas Atomic Energy Research Foundation |
| ChE | 1983– | None | University matching gift of Cockrell Foundation |
| AsE–EM | 1983– | None | University matching gift of Cockrell Foundation |
| AsE–EM | 1985– | None | |

| | Name of Endowed Presidential Scholarship or Fellowship | Date of Regents' Acceptance |
|---|---|---|
| 1. | Nasser I. Al–Rashid Endowed Presidential Scholarship | 7–11–80 |
| 2. | Douglas and Gladys Bailey Centennial Endowed Presidential Scholarship in Engineering | 2–10–84 |
| 3. | George W. Bean Endowed Presidential Scholarship in Engineering | 4–11–86 |
| 4. | Henry Beckman Fund Endowed Presidential Scholarship | 6–06–86 |
| 5. | C. W. Besserer Memorial Endowed Presidential Scholarship in Mechanical Engineering | 2–15–85 |
| 6. | John E. Breen Endowed Presidential Scholarship in Civil Engineering | 4–11–86 |
| 7. | C. W. Cook Endowed Presidential Scholarship | 2–29–80 |
| 8. | Wilda & Raymond Dawson Endowed Presidential Scholarship in Civil Engineering | 4–11–86 |
| 9. | Dow Centennial Endowed Presidential Scholarship in Chemical Engineering | 12–03–82 |
| 10. | Dow Engineering Alumni Centennial Endowed Presidential Scholarship | 10–14–83 |
| 11. | Engineering Foundation Endowed Presidential Scholarship | 4–11–86 |
| 12. | W. H. Espey Memorial Endowed Presidential Scholarship for Civil Engineers in Environmental and Water Resources Engineering | 12–06–85 |
| 13. | Courtney J. Evers Centennial Endowed Presidential Scholarship in Chemical Engineering | 6–17–83 |
| 14. | Phil M. Ferguson Endowed Presidential Graduate Scholarship in Civil Engineering | 9–05–80 |
| 15. | John A. Focht Endowed Presidential Graduate Scholarship in Civil Engineering | 9–05–80 |
| 16. | John Arnold Focht and Fay Goss Focht Endowed Presidential Scholarship in Civil Engineering | 10–11–85 |
| 17. | Ben Davis Geeslin Endowed Presidential Scholarship | 2–14–86 |
| 18. | Marsha L. Hamby Endowed Presidential Scholarship | 4–13–84 |
| 19. | John B. Holmes Endowed Presidential Scholarship | 2–12–82 |
| 20. | Joe J. King Centennial Presidential Scholarship | 12–03–82 |
| 21. | R. A. McKetta Centennial Endowed Presidential Scholarship for Undergraduate Students in Chemical Engineering | 4–15–83 |
| 22. | Robin Bruce Moran Memorial Centennial Endowed Presidential Scholarship for Undergraduates in Chemical Engineering | 8–12–82 |
| 23. | Archie W. Straiton Endowed Presidential Scholarship | 7–26–79 |

| Dept. | Restrictions/Process — Other | Book Value of Endowment ($) |
|---|---|---|
| CE | Jr./Sr. Nomination by Dept. Committee to Dean. | 25,000.00 |
| None | Full–time undergraduate/graduate student. U.S. citizen, man/woman, with demonstrated financial need. Selection by College Committee. | 25,000.00 |
| None | Undergraduate or graduate student. Nomination by College Committee to Dean. | 25,000.00 |
| None | Graduate student conducting research in engineering related to conservation of resources. Nomination by College Committee to Dean. | 25,000.00 |
| ME | Minimum award of $2,000.00 per year per recipient. Nomination by Dept. Committee to Dean. | 31,392.14 |
| CE | Jr./Sr. or graduate. Nomination by Dept. Committee to Dean. | 25,000.00 |
| None | Jr./Sr. Interested in energy production. Selection by College Committee. | 30,587.27 |
| CE | Undergraduate or graduate student. Preference to geotechnical engineering. Nomination by Dept. Committee to Dean. | 25,000.00 |
| ChE | Undergraduate or graduate student. Nomination by Dept. Chairman to Dean. | 25,000.00 |
| ME, CE, EE, ChE | Undergraduate students. Nomination by Dept. Chairman to Dean. | 105,206.69 |
| None | Graduate student, U.S. citizen. Selection by College Committee. | 100,000.00 |
| CE | Graduate student, U.S. citizen, or resident alien. Prefer Texas resident. Nomination by Dept. to Dean. | 12,500.00 plus 12,500.00 pledged |
| ChE | Undergraduates. Nomination by Dept. Committee to Dean. | 31,000.00 |
| CE | Graduate student. Nomination by Dept. Committee to Dean. | 30,164.97 |
| CE | Graduate student. Nomination by Dept. Committee to Dean. | 25,000.00 |
| CE | Nomination by Dept. Committee to Dean. | 26,900.00 |
| CE | Undergraduate in Civil Engineering or graduate student in Environmental and Water Resources Engineering. Nomination by Dept. Committee to Dean. | 25,000.00 |
| CE | Jr./Sr. female. Nomination by Dept. Committee to Dean. | 25,975.00 |
| None | Jr./Sr. Selection by College Committee. | 25,000.00 |
| None | Selection by College Committee. | 25,000.00 |
| ChE | Undergraduates. Nomination by Dept. Committee to Dean. | 30,000.00 |
| ChE | Undergraduates. Nomination by Dept. Committee to Dean. | 30,000.00 |
| EE | Jr./Sr. Must have completed 30 semester hours at UT Austin. Nomination by Dept. Committee to Dean. | 28,140.00 |

| | Name of Endowed Presidential Scholarship or Fellowship | Date of Regents' Acceptance |
|---|---|---|
| 24. | T. U. Taylor Endowed Presidential Scholarship in Engineering | 9–05–80 |
| 25. | T. U. Taylor Foundation Endowed Presidential Scholarship in Engineering | 9–05–80 |
| 26. | M. J. Thompson Endowed Presidential Graduate Scholarship in Aerospace Engineering | 9–05–80 |
| 27. | Carl R. Trull Endowed Presidential Scholarship in Engineering | 8–14–81 |
| 28. | Trigg and Fannie E. Twichell Centennial Endowed Presidential Scholarship in Civil Engineering | 8–12–83 |
| 29. | Joe C. Walter, Jr., Endowed Presidential Scholarship Fund | 8–14–81 |
| 30. | Whiting Endowed Presidential Scholarship in Engineering | 6–06–86 |
| 31. | Neena M. Woolrich Endowed Presidential Scholarship Fund | 0––1973 |
| 32. | N. K. Wright Memorial Endowed Presidential Scholarship Fund | 4–08–82 |
| 33. | R. Earle Wright Endowed Presidential Scholarship in Engineering | 12–06–85 |

| | Name of Endowed Laboratory | Date of Regents' Acceptance | Location |
|---|---|---|---|
| 1. | Amoco Foundation Numerical Reservoir Simulation Laboratory | 12–06–85 | Chem. & Petr. Engr. Bldg. 3.132 |
| 2. | Atlantic Richfield Co. Centennial Endowed Automated Production Laboratory in Petroleum Engineering | 10–14–83 | Chem. & Petr. Engr. Bldg. 1.142 |
| 3. | Marilyn F. and Thomas J. Billings Core Preparation Laboratory | 6–14–85 | Chem. & Petr. Engr. Bldg. 1.146 |
| 4. | David C. Bonner Polymer Laboratory in Chemical Engineering | 12–07–79 | Chem. & Petr. Engr. Bldg. 3.464 |
| 5. | Robert Emmett Booker Undergraduate Fundamentals Laboratory | 10–11–85 | Chem. & Petr. Engr. Bldg. 1.420 |
| 6. | Conoco North American Production Enhanced Oil Recovery Laboratory | 4–11–86 | Chem. & Petr. Engr. Bldg. 4.180 |
| 7. | Dow Chemical Co. Foundation Polymer Laboratory | 6–06–86 | Chem. & Petr. Engr. Bldg. 3.432 |
| 8. | Dow Chemical Co. Foundation Process Control Laboratory | Pending 8–86 | Chem. & Petr. Engr. Bldg. 5.412 |

| | Restrictions/Process | Book Value of Endowment ($) |
|---|---|---|
| **Dept.** | **Other** | |
| CE & EE | Jr./Sr. Dept. alternates if only one available. Selection by College Committee. | 28,611.88 |
| None | Sr. who has worked by "sweat of brow" to finance education. Selection by College Committee. | 40,703.85 |
| AsE | Graduate student. Nomination by Dept. Committee to Dean. | 25,000.00 |
| None | Jr./Sr. Selection by College Committee. | 62,051.92 |
| CE | Graduate student with specialization in hydrology or open channel hydraulics. Nomination by Dept. Committee to Dean. | 30,000.00 |
| None | Jr./Sr./Graduate. Selection by College Committee. | 100,030.78 |
| None | Preference to petroleum engineering or related majors in energy production. Part-time employed. Selection by College Committee. | 25,686.56 |
| None | Jr./Sr. female. Selection by College Committee. | 26,749.42 |
| None | Graduates. Selection by College Committee. | 25,000.00 |
| None | Undergraduate or graduate student. U.S. citizen. Selection by College Committee. | 12,484.00 plus 12,516.00 pledged |

| | Restrictions | Book Value of Endowment ($) |
|---|---|---|
| **Dept.** | **Other** | |
| PE | To purchase, maintain, and improve equipment and for activities and facilities necessary for the research and teaching functions associated with the designated laboratory | 25,000 plus 25,000 pledged* (not endowed) |
| PE | Support for special teaching and research aids | 25,000 |
| PE | To maintain and improve equipment and for activities and facilities necessary for the research and teaching functions associated with the designated laboratory | 10,000 plus 40,000 pledged* |
| ChE | General lab support | 25,800 |
| ChE | To maintain and improve equipment and for activities and facilities necessary for the research and teaching functions associated with the designated laboratory | 18,000 plus 7,000 pledged* |
| PE | To maintain and improve equipment and to support the research and teaching functions of the laboratory | 50,000 |
| ChE | To maintain and improve equipment and for activities and facilities necessary for the research and teaching functions associated with the designated laboratory | 12,500 plus 37,500 pledged* |
| ChE | To maintain and improve equipment and for activities and facilities necessary for the research and teaching functions associated with the designated laboratory | 25,000 plus 25,000 pledged* |

| | Name of Endowed Laboratory | Date of Regents' Acceptance | Location |
|---|---|---|---|
| 9. | Dresser Atlas Well Logging Laboratory | 4–13–84 | Chem. & Petr. Engr. Bldg. 3.136 |
| 10. | Eaton Industries Drilling Engineering Laboratory | 4–11–86 | Chem. & Petr. Engr. Bldg.1.116 |
| 11. | C. Shults Faulkner Catalyst Research and Development Laboratory | 8–10–84 | Chem. & Petr. Engr. Bldg. 4.460 |
| 12. | General Motors Foundation Centennial Automotive Research Laboratory | 8–12–83 | ETC II 1.012 |
| 13. | General Motors Foundation Centennial Combustion Sciences Research Laboratory | 8–12–83 | ETC II 7.152 |
| 14. | Kerr–McGee Petrophysics Laboratory | 6–14–85 | Chem. & Petr. Engr. Bldg. 1.108 |
| 15. | Leonardt F. Kreisle Senior Design Project Teaching Laboratory | 2–14–86 | ETC 4.110 |
| 16. | Myron George Kuhlman Polymer Processing Laboratory | 10–11–85 | Chem. & Petr. Engr. Bldg. 1.460 |
| 17. | Joe and Charleen Magliolo Laboratory for Polymer Engineering | 6–14–85 | Chem. & Petr. Engr. Bldg. |
| 18. | Marathon Oil Company Enhanced Oil Recovery Laboratory | 2–15–85 | Chem. & Petr. Engr. Bldg. 4.166 |
| 19. | Robert N. Miller Drilling Fluids Laboratory | 2–15–85 | Chem. & Petr. Engr. Bldg. 1.122 |
| 20. | Mobil Enhanced Oil Recovery Laboratory | 2–15–85 | Chem. & Petr. Engr. Bldg. 4.158 |
| 21. | Sun Exploration and Production Co. Advanced Petrophysics Laboratory | 8–10–84 | Chem. & Petr. Engr. Bldg. 4.138 |
| 22. | Tenneco Oil Advanced Petrophysics Laboratory | 2–15–85 | Chem. & Petr. Engr. Bldg. 4.136 |
| 23. | Herman J. Wetegrove Graduate Computation Laboratory | 10–12–84 | Chem. & Petr. Engr. Bldg. 3.148 |

*Not fully funded.

| Dept. | Restrictions Other | Book Value of Endowment ($) |
|---|---|---|
| PE | Support for teaching and research related to well logging | 50,000 |
| PE | To maintain and improve equipment and to support the research and teaching functions of the room | 10,000 plus 15,000 pledged* |
| ChE | To maintain and improve equipment and for activities and facilities necessary for the research and teaching functions associated with the laboratory | 36,000 plus 15,000 pledged* |
| ME | To maintain and improve equipment and for activities and facilities necessary for the research and teaching functions associated with the laboratory | 40,000 plus 10,000 pledged* |
| ME | To maintain and improve equipment and for activities and facilities necessary for the research and teaching functions associated with the laboratory | 50,000 pledged* |
| PE | To maintain and improve equipment and for activities and facilities necessary for the research and teaching functions associated with the designated laboratory | 12,500 plus 12,500 pledged* |
| ME | To maintain and improve equipment and for activities and facilities necessary for the research and teaching functions associated with the designated laboratory | 25,400 |
| ChE | To maintain and improve equipment and for activities and facilities necessary for the research and teaching functions associated with the designated laboratory | 12,500 plus 12,500 pledged* |
| ChE | To maintain and improve equipment and for activities and facilities necessary for the research and teaching functions associated with the designated laboratory | 15,000 plus 35,000 pledged* |
| PE | To maintain and improve equipment and for activities and facilities necessary for the research and teaching functions associated with the designated laboratory | 20,000 plus 30,000 pledged* |
| PE | To maintain and improve equipment and for activities and facilities necessary for the research and teaching functions associated with the designated laboratory | 22,500 plus 2,500 pledged* |
| PE | To maintain and improve equipment and for activities and facilities necessary for the research and teaching functions associated with the designated laboratory | 25,000 plus 25,000 pledged* (not endowed) |
| PE | To maintain and improve equipment and for activities and facilities necessary for the research and teaching functions associated with the laboratory | 25,000 |
| PE | To maintain and improve equipment and for activities and facilities necessary for the research and teaching functions associated with the laboratory | 17,000 plus 33,000 pledged* |
| PE | To maintain and improve equipment and for activities and facilities necessary for the research and teaching functions of the laboratory | 50,000 |

| | Name of Endowed Room | Date of Regents' Acceptance | Location |
|---|---|---|---|
| 1. | Alec Center for Creativity | 6-15-84 | ECJ 1.306 |
| 2. | R. C. Baker Foundation Seminar Room | 10-12-84 | Chem & Petr. Engr. Bldg. 2.202 |
| 3. | Folkert N. Brons Conference Room | 6-15-84 | Chem. & Petr. Engr. Bldg. 2.236 |
| 4. | Ben H. Caudle Classroom | 6-15-84 | Chem. & Petr. Engr. Bldg. 2.208 |
| 5. | Chemical Engineering Alumni Memorial Conference Room | 8-10-84 | Chem. & Petr. Engr. Bldg. 2.802G |
| 6. | Dresser Engineering Library Endowment | 2-29-80 | ECJ 1.306 |
| 7. | Thomas F. and Donna P. Edgar Computer Room | 10-11-85 | Chem. & Petr. Engr. Bldg. 2.706 |
| 8. | Edward H. Ellms Graduate Seminar Room | 6-06-86 | Chem. & Petr. Engr. Bldg. 2.222 |
| 9. | George H. Fancher, Jr., Study Hall | 2-15-85 | Chem. & Petr. Engr. Bldg. 3.180 |
| 10. | Himmelblau Graduate Research Conference Room | 6-15-84 | Chem. & Petr. Engr. Bldg. 4.446 |
| 11. | John E. Kasch Classroom | 4-11-86 | Chem. & Petr. Engr. Bldg. 2.216 |
| 12. | Joe D. Kubicek Memorial Room | 2-10-84 | ETC II 5.202 |
| 13. | John McKetta AIChE Student Chapter Room | 2-10-84 | Chem. & Petr. Engr. Bldg. 2.713 |
| 14. | John McKetta Student Study Hall | 2-10-84 | Chem. & Petr. Engr. Bldg. 2.802J |
| 15. | R. A. McKetta ChE Tutoring Room | 2-10-84 | Chem. & Petr. Engr. Bldg. 2.704 |
| 16. | Richard W. McKinney Engineering Library Endowment Fund | 5-30-80 | ECJ 1.300 |
| 17. | Sylvain J. G. Pirson Classroom | 6-15-84 | Chem. & Petr. Engr. Bldg. 2.204 |

| | Restrictions | Book Value of Endowment |
|---|---|---|
| **Dept.** | **Other** | **($)** |
| Engr. Lib. | Support special publications, furniture, and other support that would enhance professional creativity and idea development | 10,000.00 |
| PE | Support to maintain and improve equipment and for activities and facilities necessary for the research and teaching functions of the room | 10,000.00 |
| PE | Support to maintain and improve equipment and for activities and facilities necessary for the educational functions of the room | 10,000.00* |
| PE | Support to maintain and improve equipment and for activities and facilities necessary for the educational functions of the room | 10,000.00* |
| ChE | Support for room furnishings and functions of the room | 10,000.00 |
| Engr. Lib. | Purchase of library books and other literature for the John J. McKetta Collection | 100,000.00 |
| ChE | Support to maintain and improve equipment and for activities and facilities necessary for the research and teaching functions associated with the designated computer room | 10,002.00 |
| ChE | Support to maintain and improve equipment and for activities and facilities necessary for the research and teaching functions associated with the designated classroom | 10,000.00 |
| PE | Support to maintain and improve equipment and for activities and facilities necessary for the educational functions of the room | 10,000.00 |
| ChE | Support to maintain and improve equipment and for activities and facilities necessary for the educational functions of the room | 10,000.00* |
| ChE | Support to maintain and improve equipment and to support the research and teaching functions of the room | 10,000.00* |
| ME | Scholarship (annual) to needy student with scholarly achievement and leadership in one or more designated student engineering organizations | 11,205.44 |
| ChE | Support for equipment; support for the educational functions of the room | 10,000.00* |
| ChE | Support for equipment; support for the educational functions of the room | 10,000.00* |
| ChE | Support for equipment; support for the educational functions of the room | 10,000.00* |
| Engr. Lib. | Support for the purchase of library books and other literature for the John J. McKetta Collection; purchases recommended by Engineering Librarian and Library Committee and approved by the Dean | 100,000.00 |
| PE | Support to maintain and improve equipment and for activities and facilities necessary for the educational functions associated with the room | 10,000.00* |

| | Name of Endowed Room | Date of Regents' Acceptance | Location |
|---|---|---|---|
| 18. | Frederick Byron Plummer Tutorial Room | 2-15-85 | Chem. & Petr. Engr. Bldg. 3.156 |
| 19. | Venkat Rayer Centennial Room | 6-17-83 | ENS 615 |
| 20. | Arthur L. and Ruth Britton Smalley Classroom | 4-11-86 | Chem. & Petr. Engr. Bldg. 2.220 |
| 21. | Bettie Margaret Smith Centennial Room in EHE | 6-17-83 | ECJ 8.306 |
| 22. | Bettie Margaret Smith Centennial Room #2 | 6-17-83 | BRC, Bldg. 119, Room 42 |
| 23. | Sohio Petroleum Company Classroom | 8-10-84 | Chem. & Petr. Engr. Bldg. 2.206 |

*Not fully funded.

## COLLEGE OF ENGINEERING PHYSICAL PLANT, 1904–1985

| Building Name | Completed or Acquired (yr) | Space (sq ft) | Original Value ($) | Carrying Value ($) |
|---|---|---|---|---|
| **On Campus** | | | | |
| Old Engineering Building (now Dorothy Gebauer Student Services Building) | 1904 | 28,630 | 84,000 | 264,732 |
| Engineering Building (now T. U. Taylor Hall of Engineering) | 1929 1932, 1934 | 58,168 | 235,097 405,274 | 1,307,445 |
| Chemical Engineering Building (now E. P. Schoch Laboratory) | 1941 | 49,038 | 263,221 | 602,408 |
| Petroleum Engineering Building | 1941 | 49,481 | 270,696 | 423,226 |
| Engineering Laboratory Building (now W. R. Woolrich Laboratories) | 1959 | 78,071 | 1,361,698 | 1,443,677 |
| Engineering Science Building | 1963 | 210,369 | 3,787,089 | 3,985,059 |
| Ernest Cockrell, Jr., Hall | 1974 | 198,145 | 6,575,889 | 6,577,054 |
| Engineering Teaching Center #2 | 1983 | 224,664 | 18,505,585 | 19,074,543 |
| Chemical Engineering and Petroleum Engineering Building | 1985 | 124,000 | 19,695,044 | 19,695,044 |
| **Balcones Research Center** | | | | |
| BRC Building #5 (EM) | (1942)* 1949 | 36,082 | 57,340 | 73,870 |
| BRC Building #6 (CE) | (1942) 1949 | 24,392 | 101,652 | 101,652 |
| BRC Building #7 BRC Building #7a (ASE-EM) | (1942) 1949 (1942) 1949 | 9,311 1,200 | 23,200 4,000 | 23,200 4,000 |

| Dept. | Restrictions<br>Other | Book Value<br>of Endowment<br>($) |
|---|---|---|
| PE | Support to maintain and improve equipment and for activities and facilities necessary for the educational functions associated with the room | 10,000.00 |
| EE | Support graduate research related to cardiovascular functions in Biomedical Engineering | 10,000.00 |
| ChE | Support to maintain and improve equipment and to support the research and teaching functions of the room | 10,000.00 |
| CE | Support research activities in Environmental Health Engineering | 10,000.00 |
| CE | Support for Center for Research in Water Resources for developing publications, conferences, and research | 10,000.00 |
| PE | Support to maintain and improve equipment and for activities and facilities necessary for the educational functions of the classroom | 10,000.00 |

| Building Name | Completed or Acquired (yr) | Space (sq ft) | Original Value ($) | Carrying Value ($) |
|---|---|---|---|---|
| BRC Building #8b (CE) | (1942) 1949 | 294 | 2,370 | 2,370 |
| BRC Building #14 (EERL & ChE) | (1942) 1949 | 10,545 | 76,055 | 76,055 |
| BRC Building #16 (EERL) | (1942) 1949 | 15,386 | 94,793 | 94,793 |
| BRC Building #17 (CESE) | (1942) 1949 addition 1971 | 5,941 | 24,386 20,856 | 55,242 |
| BRC Building #24 BRC Building #24b (PMFSEL) | (1942) 1960 (1942) 1960 | 49,528 501 | 219,128 2,000 | 367,556 2,000 |
| BRC Building #26 BRC Building #26a (CESE) | (1942) 1949 (1942) 1949 | 1,600 360 | 11,830 | 11,830 4,320 |
| BRC Building #123 BRC Building #124 (ASE-EM) | 1971 1973 | 256 2,400 | 2,560 27,063 | 2,560 27,063 |
| BRC Building CES-CEM | 1985 | 103,114 | 8,491,152 | 8,491,152 |
| **Mt. Locke** | | | | |
| Mt. Locke Millimeter-Wave Observatory Control (A216) | 1974 | 657 | 45,541 | 62,266 |
| Mt. Locke Millimeter-Wave Observatory Dome Building | 1963 | 962 | 94,936 | 94,936 |

*Construction date

## FINANCIAL HISTORY* OF THE COLLEGE OF ENGINEERING

Operating Budget, 1884–1985, Exclusive of Endowment Income

| Fiscal Year | General Funds | | | Restricted Funds | | | Total |
|---|---|---|---|---|---|---|---|
| | Instruction | Research | Other | Instruction | Research | Other | |
| | $ | $ | $ | $ | $ | $ | $ |
| 1884 | no expenses specifically identified as "engineering" | | | | | | |
| 1885 | | | 218 | | | | 218 |
| | | | | | | | |
| 1886 | no expenses specifically identified as "engineering" | | | | | | |
| 1887 | no expenses specifically identified as "engineering" | | | | | | |
| 1888 | no expenses specifically identified as "engineering" | | | | | | |
| 1889 | 2,000 | | 42 | | | | 2,042 |
| 1890 | 2,000 | | | | | | 2,000 |
| | | | | | | | |
| 1891 | 2,000 | | 154 | | | | 2,154 |
| 1892 | 2,518 | | | | | | 2,518 |
| 1893 | 2,500 | | | | | | 2,500 |
| 1894 | 6,800 | | 12 | | | | 6,812 |
| 1895 | 2,500 | | | | | | 2,500 |
| | | | | | | | |
| 1896 | 2,800 | | | | | | 2,800 |
| 1897 | 2,800 | | 205 | | | | 3,005 |
| 1898 | 3,700 | | 94 | | | | 3,794 |
| 1899 | 3,700 | | 45 | | | | 3,745 |
| 1900 | 6,995 | | | | | | 6,995 |
| | | | | | | | |
| 1901 | 6,420 | | | | | | 6,420 |
| 1902 | 6,720 | | | | | | 6,720 |
| 1903 | 7,415 | | 1,148 | | | | 8,563 |
| 1904 | 13,131 | | | | | | 13,131 |
| 1905 | 38,429 | | 1,308 | | | | 39,737 |
| | | | | | | | |
| 1906 | 17,501 | | 301 | | | | 17,802 |
| 1907 | 17,434 | | | | | | 17,434 |
| 1908 | 19,208 | | | | | | 19,208 |
| 1909 | 19,716 | | | | | | 19,716 |
| 1910 | 20,874 | | 169 | | | | 21,043 |
| | | | | | | | |
| 1911 | 23,846 | | | | | | 23,846 |
| 1912 | 26,202 | | 72 | | | | 26,274 |
| 1913 | 31,806 | | | | | | 31,806 |
| 1914 | 36,133 | | | | | | 36,133 |
| 1915 | 39,071 | 2,411 | | | | | 41,482 |
| | | | | | | | |
| 1916 | 39,164 | 2,274 | | | | | 41,438 |
| 1917 | 42,351 | 4,622 | | | | | 46,973 |
| 1918 | 37,369 | 4,439 | | | | | 41,808 |
| 1919 | 46,318 | 3,792 | 720 | | | | 50,830 |
| 1920 | 54,940 | 6,976 | 878 | | | | 62,794 |
| | | | | | | | |
| 1921 | 90,391 | 6,843 | 1,635 | | | | 98,869 |
| 1922 | 74,531 | 9,377 | 2,920 | | | | 86,828 |
| 1923 | 79,655 | 12,683 | | | | | 92,338 |
| 1924 | 75,249 | 10,545 | | | | | 85,794 |
| 1925 | 77,668 | 11,496 | 1,750 | | | | 90,914 |
| | | | | | | | |
| 1926 | 90,770 | 13,692 | 1,697 | | | | 106,159 |
| 1927 | 108,896 | 13,713 | 2,880 | | | | 125,489 |
| 1928 | 105,047 | 13,156 | 3,100 | | | | 121,303 |
| 1929 | 99,988 | 6,873 | 3,097 | | | | 109,958 |
| 1930 | 102,907 | 8,837 | 3,499 | | | | 115,243 |

| Fiscal Year | General Funds | | | Restricted Funds | | | Total |
|---|---|---|---|---|---|---|---|
| | Instruction | Research | Other | Instruction | Research | Other | |
| | $ | $ | $ | $ | $ | $ | $ |
| 1931 | 112,178 | 9,081 | 3,503 | | | | 124,762 |
| 1932 | 107,050 | 7,636 | 3,316 | | | | 118,002 |
| 1933 | 106,783 | 7,918 | 3,279 | | | | 117,980 |
| 1934 | 79,602 | 6,560 | 5,638 | | | | 91,800 |
| 1935 | 78,218 | 5,019 | 6,164 | | | | 89,401 |
| 1936 | 105,129 | 6,191 | 6,510 | 0 | 0 | 0 | 117,830 |
| 1937 | 110,630 | 6,099 | 7,552 | 0 | 257 | 0 | 124,538 |
| 1938 | 143,269 | 9,639 | 9,754 | 0 | 0 | 0 | 162,662 |
| 1939 | 153,671 | 9,463 | 9,875 | 0 | 0 | 0 | 173,009 |
| 1940 | 170,178 | 15,941 | 11,151 | 0 | 517 | 0 | 197,787 |
| 1941 | 192,471 | 14,759 | 11,609 | 44,105 | 497 | 0 | 263,441 |
| 1942 | 221,564 | 19,104 | 14,491 | 5,700 | 39 | 0 | 260,898 |
| 1943 | 234,258 | 16,759 | 12,954 | 0 | 96 | 0 | 264,067 |
| 1944 | 292,177 | 13,582 | 17,356 | 0 | 1,787 | 0 | 324,902 |
| 1945 | 312,688 | 26,431 | 18,401 | 0 | 1,435 | 0 | 358,955 |
| 1946 | 324,796 | 16,241 | 23,558 | 0 | 3,431 | 0 | 368,026 |
| 1947 | 611,627 | 27,491 | 25,026 | 0 | 212,817 | 0 | 876,961 |
| 1948 | 745,801 | 27,305 | 29,253 | 0 | 196,979 | 0 | 999,338 |
| 1949 | 800,821 | 85,428 | 29,056 | 0 | 122,955 | 0 | 1,038,260 |
| 1950 | 794,938 | 96,759 | 3,393 | 0 | 93,068 | 0 | 988,158 |
| 1951 | 720,582 | 119,361 | 1,509 | 0 | 117,562 | 0 | 959,014 |
| 1952 | 605,318 | 116,923 | 1,317 | 0 | 99,918 | 0 | 823,476 |
| 1953 | 690,413 | 125,394 | 1,072 | 0 | 205,106 | 0 | 1,021,985 |
| 1954 | 655,667 | 131,521 | 783 | 0 | 239,358 | 0 | 1,027,329 |
| 1955 | 726,995 | 121,046 | 536 | 0 | 257,424 | 0 | 1,106,001 |
| 1956 | 850,995 | 144,923 | 1,599 | 0 | 341,681 | 4,878 | 1,344,076 |
| 1957 | 931,730 | 135,025 | 670 | 212 | 572,365 | 3,625 | 1,643,627 |
| 1958 | 1,162,206 | 145,226 | 1,400 | 794 | 365,476 | 794 | 1,675,896 |
| 1959 | 1,226,820 | 168,120 | 590 | 0 | 515,769 | 1,307 | 1,912,606 |
| 1960 | 1,284,338 | 277,920 | 1,753 | 0 | 622,709 | 9,219 | 2,195,939 |
| 1961 | 1,347,706 | 272,842 | 435 | 0 | 719,447 | 3,589 | 2,344,019 |
| 1962 | 1,451,260 | 276,546 | 1,823 | 47,843 | 967,604 | 2,858 | 2,747,934 |
| 1963 | 1,506,661 | 264,059 | 68,068 | 63,249 | 1,213,891 | 103 | 3,116,031 |
| 1964 | 1,667,321 | 308,612 | 1,027 | 68,514 | 947,975 | 8,699 | 3,002,148 |
| 1965 | 1,905,740 | 346,426 | 320 | 74,943 | 2,052,046 | 25,292 | 4,404,767 |
| 1966 | 2,289,713 | 370,256 | 772 | 102,321 | 2,398,055 | 29,199 | 5,190,316 |
| 1967 | 2,618,720 | 370,332 | 804 | 116,156 | 3,348,825 | 49,912 | 6,504,749 |
| 1968 | 3,015,159 | 398,580 | 796 | 232,961 | 3,321,672 | 62,439 | 7,031,607 |
| 1969 | 3,652,268 | 380,644 | 1,009 | 235,220 | 3,861,198 | 67,191 | 8,197,530 |
| 1970 | 4,089,230 | 353,542 | 894 | 311,618 | 4,295,208 | 55,880 | 9,106,372 |
| 1971 | 4,304,962 | 361,804 | 1,098 | 291,014 | 4,069,773 | 30,491 | 9,059,142 |
| 1972 | 4,564,721 | 327,606 | 831 | 263,875 | 4,186,116 | 26,079 | 9,369,228 |
| 1973 | 4,648,892 | 340,778 | 1,600 | 266,601 | 4,742,294 | 124,280 | 10,124,445 |
| 1974 | 4,907,199 | 428,724 | 1,113 | 266,671 | 5,373,294 | 148,542 | 11,125,543 |
| 1975 | 5,693,699 | 458,990 | 954 | 458,990 | 6,061,998 | 170,087 | 12,844,718 |
| 1976 | 6,363,646 | 759,576 | 2,358 | 520,141 | 6,344,010 | 185,193 | 14,174,924 |
| 1977 | 6,766,767 | 555,373 | 2,317 | 597,003 | 6,601,850 | 231,712 | 14,761,022 |
| 1978 | 7,019,755 | 835,761 | 1,454 | 766,038 | 7,176,079 | 258,462 | 16,057,549 |
| 1979 | 7,849,514 | 709,375 | 2,277 | 820,461 | 8,605,202 | 352,854 | 18,339,683 |
| 1980 | 9,114,768 | 528,433 | 16,780 | 1,085,979 | 8,606,103 | 518,523 | 19,870,586 |

| Fiscal | General Funds | | | Restricted Funds | | | |
|---|---|---|---|---|---|---|---|
| Year | Instruction | Research | Other | Instruction | Research | Other | Total |
| | $ | $ | $ | $ | $ | $ | $ |
| 1981 | 10,406,151 | 569,493 | 63,845 | 1,540,276 | 10,775,729 | 395,924 | 23,751,418 |
| 1982 | 12,327,430 | 1,075,011 | 55,584 | 2,463,569 | 10,780,873 | 484,265 | 27,186,732 |
| 1983 | 14,743,384 | 1,101,777 | 95,996 | 3,112,153 | 11,923,187 | 499,533 | 31,476,029 |
| 1984 | 16,219,211 | 1,224,009 | 91,798 | 3,245,931 | 14,611,956 | 467,963 | 35,860,868 |
| 1985** | 17,919,592 | 1,619,209 | 176,650 | 3,382,260 | 17,914,258 | 438,481 | 41,273,800 |
| 1986 | 19,801,149 | 2,142,214 | 239,184 | 3,524,315 | 21,962,880 | 412,172 | 48,082,614 |

*This history has three sources: For the period 1883 through 1930, *Biennial Reports of the Regents to the Legislature and Governor* were the source. From 1931 through 1940, *Reports of the Auditor* (annual) were sources. Beginning in 1941, the *Financial Report of The University of Texas and its Branches* was the source. Beginning in 1969, the title was *The University of Texas at Austin Financial Statements*. The earliest reported "disbursement" clearly identified as for engineering was $218.45 for "expenses for engineering room" on p. 42 of the *Report of the Regents* of December, 1886, to Governor John Ireland, for the year ending June 1, 1885.
**Budget for Fiscal Years 1985 and 1986 estimated. Fiscal Year 1986 began September 1, 1985, and ended August 31, 1986.

## COLLEGE OF ENGINEERING DISTINGUISHED GRADUATES, 1957–1986

| Year | Name | Degree(s) from College of Engineering |
|---|---|---|
| 1957 | †Julian Montgomery | BS CE 1912 |
| 1958 | †Eugene P. Schoch | BS CE 1894 |
| 1959 | †Gibb Gilchrist | BS CE 1909 |
| 1959 | Robert Rea Jackson | BS ChE 1923 |
| 1959 | Jerry McAfee | BS ChE 1937 |
| 1959 | †Pete J. Rempe | BS EE 1925 |
| 1960 | J. Leland Atwood | BS CE 1928 |
| 1960 | †Julian Hinds | BS CE 1908 |
| 1960 | John E. Kasch | BS ChE 1938, MS ChE 1939, PhD ChE 1943 |
| 1960 | †Elgin B. Robertson, Sr. | BS EE 1915 |
| 1961 | †Stuart E. Buckley | BS ChE 1932, MS ChE 1932 |
| 1961 | William C. Cawthon | MS ME 1947 |
| 1961 | †Henry Fink | BS EE 1908 |
| 1961 | †C. L. Orr | BS ME 1919 |
| 1962 | †Ernest Cockrell, Jr. | BS PE 1936, MS PE 1936 |
| 1962 | Dan M. Krausse | BS ChE 1947 |
| 1962 | Clarence H. Linder | BS EE 1924, MS EE 1928 |
| 1962 | O. Scott Petty | BS CE 1917 |
| 1962 | C. T. Wells, Jr. | BS ChE 1937, MS ChE 1937, PhD ChE 1939 |
| 1962 | Dan C. Williams | BS PE 1935 |
| 1963 | †Wayne F. Bowman | MS EM 1915 |
| 1963 | C. W. "Tex" Cook | BS EE 1930 |
| 1963 | George L. MacGregor | BS EE 1923 |
| 1963 | Guy T. McBride, Jr. | BS ChE 1940 |
| 1963 | †William J. Powell | BS CE 1905 |
| 1963 | John L. Tullis | BS EE 1933 |
| 1964 | †Bascom H. Caldwell | BS EE 1930, MS EE 1931 |
| 1964 | John A. Focht, Jr. | BS CE 1944 |
| 1964 | †Armour T. Granger | BS CE 1918 |
| 1964 | Charles F. Jones | BS ChE 1933, MS ChE 1934, PhD ChE 1937 |
| 1964 | Joe J. King | BS ME 1925 |
| 1964 | Arch C. Scurlock | BS ChE 1941 |
| 1964 | †Lowber D. Snow | BS CE 1914 |
| 1965 | †Harry Abeel Beckwith | BS CE 1911 |
| 1965 | Bob R. Dorsey | BS ChE 1940 |
| 1965 | Milton E. Eliot | BS CE 1935 |
| 1965 | †James Powers Exum | BS CE 1922 |
| 1965 | William B. Franklin | BS ChE 1930, MS ChE 1931 |
| 1965 | J. William Haun | BS ChE 1946, MS ChE 1948, PhD ChE 1950 |
| 1965 | William J. Murray, Jr. | BS PE 1936, MS PE 1937 |
| 1966 | Jerry W. Brougher | BS ME 1952 |
| 1966 | †Maurice N. Dannenbaum | BS ME 1919 |
| 1966 | William W. McLean | BS ChE 1940, MS ChE 1941 |

| Year | Name | Degree(s) from College of Engineering |
|------|------|----------------------------------------|
| 1966 | †H. H. Meier | BS ChE 1924, MS ChE 1927 |
| 1966 | Samuel C. Oliphant | BS PE 1938, MS PE 1941 |
| 1966 | †Elmer H. Schulz | BS EE 1935, MS EE 1936 |
| 1967 | Clarence J. Baldwin, Jr. | BS EE 1951, MS EE 1952 |
| 1967 | Maurice F. Granville | BS ChE 1937 |
| 1967 | †George P. Hill | BS ME 1922 |
| 1967 | Judson S. Swearingen | BS ChE 1929, MS ChE 1930 |
| 1968 | Z. D. Bonner | BS ChE 1941 |
| 1968 | John T. Files | BS ChE 1941, MS ChE 1942 |
| 1968 | †Walter W. McAllister, Sr. | BS EE 1910 |
| 1968 | Robert J. Phillips | BS ChE 1948 |
| 1968 | †Joe E. Ward | BS CE 1917 |
| 1968 | Frank P. Wood | BS EE 1939 |
| 1969 | †Melvin H. Gertz | BS ChE 1943, MS ChE 1944 |
| 1969 | Paul D. Meek | BS ChE 1953 |
| 1969 | Robert L. Parker, Sr. | BS PE 1944 |
| 1969 | Robert L. Purvin | BS ChE 1938 |
| 1969 | Fred S. Schwend | BS ChE 1939 |
| 1970 | Thomas D. Barrow | BS PE 1945 |
| 1970 | Alan L. Bean | BS ASE 1955 |
| 1970 | †Lawrence B. Jones | BS CE 1924 |
| 1971 | Kenneth E. Burg | BS EE 1926 |
| 1971 | Louis F. Davis | BS ME 1934 |
| 1971 | Claude R. Hocott | BS ChE 1933, MS ChE 1934, PhD ChE 1937 |
| 1972 | Phil M. Ferguson | BS CE 1922 |
| 1972 | George H. Meason | BS ChE 1940 |
| 1972 | Roy Tolk | BS EE 1938 |
| 1973 | †Joseph L. Franklin, Jr. | BS ChE 1929, MS ChE 1930 |
| 1973 | Jack S. Josey | BS PE 1939 |
| 1973 | Leonard A. Swanson | BS PE 1941 |
| 1973 | Robert V. West, Jr. | BS ChE 1942, MS ChE 1942, PhD ChE 1949 |
| 1974 | William A. Cunningham | BS ChE 1927, MS ChE 1929, PhD ChE 1941 |
| 1974 | Bannister L. DeBerry | BS CE 1937 |
| 1974 | Fred L. Ribe | BS EE 1944 |
| 1975 | Malcolm D. Abel | BS PE 1947 |
| 1975 | Edwin H. Blaschke | BS CE 1935 |
| 1975 | Fred I. Harmon | BS ChE 1946 |
| 1976 | Fraser H. Allen | BS PE 1939, MS PE 1943, PhD PE 1947 |
| 1976 | Perry G. Brittain | BS EE 1949 |
| 1976 | James R. Fair | PhD ChE 1955 |
| 1976 | Laurie W. Folmar | BS PE 1947 |
| 1977 | †Arthur A. Draeger | BS ChE 1932, MS ChE 1932 |
| 1977 | George A. Helland, Jr. | BS ME 1959 |
| 1977 | John H. Long | BS ARE 1937 |
| 1977 | Joseph C. Walter, Jr. | BS PE 1949 |
| 1978 | Warren S. Bellows, Jr. | BS CE 1939 |
| 1978 | Frank W. McBee, Jr. | BS ME 1947, MS ME 1950 |
| 1978 | John G. McMillian, Jr. | BS PE 1951 |
| 1978 | †Ashley H. Priddy | BS PE 1949 |
| 1978 | John W. Sheehan | PhD ChE 1948 |
| 1979 | Robert S. Braden | BS CE 1953 |
| 1979 | Felix W. Fenter | BS ASE 1953, MS ASE 1954, PhD ASE 1960 |
| 1979 | Charles B. Grant | BS PE 1942 |
| 1979 | L. R. Hellwig | BS ChE 1949, MS ChE 1951, PhD ChE 1955 |
| 1979 | †Harry Pistole | BS EE 1938 |
| 1980 | Nasser I. Al–Rashid | BS CE 1965, PhD CE 1970 |
| 1980 | Patrick O. Braden | BS ME 1954, MS ME 1961 |
| 1980 | Jesus Chavarria | BS PE 1948 |
| 1980 | T. Brockett Hudson | BS ChE 1947, MS ChE 1949 |
| 1980 | William G. Marquardt | BS EE 1941 |
| 1980 | Keating V. Zeppa | BS PE 1959 |
| 1981 | Ernest H. Cockrell | BS ES 1967 |
| 1981 | Arlen L. Edgar | BS PE 1957 |

| Year | Name | Degree(s) from College of Engineering |
|------|------|----------------------------------------|
| 1981 | Henry Groppe, Jr. | BS ChE 1946 |
| 1981 | Jack H. Herring | BS PE 1950 |
| 1981 | Robert C. Mathis | PhD EE 1963 |
| 1982 | H. Norman Abramson | PhD EM 1956 |
| 1982 | Robert L. Crippen | BS ASE 1960 |
| 1982 | Earnest F. Gloyna | MS CE 1949 |
| 1982 | Robert N. Miller | BS PE 1950 |
| 1982 | R. Earle Wright | BS PE 1942 |
| 1983 | Fred P. Bergeron | BS EE 1951 |
| 1983 | Curtis M. Klaerner | BS ChE 1942 |
| 1983 | William A. Moncrief, Jr. | BS PE 1942 |
| 1983 | C. A. Rundell, Jr. | BS ChE 1954 |
| 1984 | Ernest E. Ludwig | BS ChE 1941, MS ChE 1942 |
| 1984 | Calvin D. Sholtess | BS ME 1950 |
| 1984 | Archie W. Straiton | BS EE 1929, PhD EE 1939 |
| 1984 | Donald L. Wiley | BS ChE 1951 |
| 1984 | Jack Zarrow | BS PE 1947 |
| 1985 | Gerald P. D'Arcy | BS ME 1956, PhD ME 1973 |
| 1985 | Victor C. Eissler | BS PE 1951 |
| 1985 | Louis Garbrecht, Jr. | BS ChE 1944, MS ChE 1948 |
| 1985 | Lymon C. Reese | BS CE 1949, MS CE 1950 |
| 1986 | E. Oran Brigham | BS EE 1963, MS EE 1964, PhD EE 1967 |
| 1986 | A. Ray Dudley, Jr. | BS ChE 1948 |
| 1986 | William H. Espey, Jr. | BS CE 1960, MS CE 1963, PhD CE 1965 |
| 1986 | Joseph Magliolo, Jr. | BS ChE 1948, MS ChE 1949 |
| 1986 | L. Hudson Matlock | BS CE 1947, MS CE 1950 |

†Deceased

# INDEX

Page numbers in italics indicate photographs.

A

A. F. C.,
   Club, 192
   Knights of, 192
Adcock, Willis A., 111, 141, 172
Advanced Research Projects Agency, 80, 81
Advanced Transportation Studies, Council for,
   107, 139, 162
Aeronautical Research, Center for, 138, 150, 151
Aeronautical Sciences, Institute of the, 201
Aeronautics, National Committee on, 28
Aeronautics and Astronautics [formerly Aero-
   nautics], American Institute of, 204
Aerospace [formerly Aeronautical] Engineering,
   28–29, 31, 37, 102, 150
   Department of, 33, 43–44, 51, 54, 55, 58, 70,
      72, 73, 75, 81, 86, 96, 98, 251, 279, 281, 283,
      285, 287, 289
   and Engineering Mechanics, Department of,
      96, 107, 111, 123, 131, 133, 137, 152, 180,
      212, 251, 275, 277, 298–299
Aerospace Thin Shell Structures Laboratory,
   102, 151
Aggarwal, J. K., 141, 150, 169, 261, 282
Air School for Radio Operators, 28
Alamo Portland and Roman Cement Works, 8
Alec,
   Center for Creativity, 122
   Friends of, 114–117, 118, 287
   Order of, 198
   Sons of, 201

Allan, John J., III, 263
Alpha Alpha Gamma, 204
Alpha Chi Sigma, 204
Alpha Rho Chi, 204
American Meteorological Society, 76
Amstead, Billy H., 48, 49, 65, 69, 88, 89, 94, 95,
   103, 107, 114, 115, 247, 255
*Analog*, 84
Anderson, Charles A., 197
Antes, Leland L., 255
Applied Research Laboratory, 100, 149–150,
   150, 180, 182
Architectural Engineering, 32, 43
   Department of, 59, 72, 86, 97, 147, 251
Architectural Engineers, National [formerly
   American] Association of, 204
Architecture, 3, 22, 26, 30–31, 42, 43
   American Association of Collegiate Schools
      of, 30, 43
   Building, 36, 37, 40
   Department of, 30–31, 35–36, 42, 43, 59, 249
   Library, 47
   School of [1909–1921], 22, 26
   School of [1951– ], 59, 102, 204
Armstrong, Neal E., 139, 140, 162, 164, 264
Ashley, David B., 139, 159, 269, 284
Astronomy, Department of, 165
Atmospheric Research, National Center for, 165
Atmospheric Science Research Laboratory, 100
Austin Dam, 146
Austin Manual Training School, 24
Austin Oaks Project, 158

Automobile Mechanics, School of, 28, 29
Automotive Engineers, Society of, 205
Awards Day Convocation, 127, 201


B

Backus, Tom, 109, *117*, 130, *202*
Bacon, Rinaldo A., 254
Bailey, Richard E., 197
Baker, Lee E., 140, 178, 180, 266, 282
Baker, Margaret R., 88, 108, 141, 177, 262
Balcones Research Center, 55–56, 74, 75, 81,
    100, 101, 102, 123, 135, 137, 140, 141, 148,
    *149*, 158, 159, 164, 166, 177, 182, 211, 212,
    298–299
Bantel, Edward C. H., 19, 22–23, 31, 47, *71*,
    146, 186, 198, 247, 248, 252, 278
Barbarians, 187, 188
Barclay, Leland C., 31, 74, 253, 286
Barlow, Joel W., 138, 155, 265, 278
Barnes, J. Wesley, 142, 177, 266, 288
Barr, Ronald E., 141, 177, 267
Bartlett, Luis H., 44, 48, 52, 147, 255
Barton, Millard V., 49, 251, 255
Battle, William J., 17, 35
    Hall, 146
Baughman, Martin L., 118, 140, 167, 266
Beaman, Joseph J., 142, 177, 268, 286
Bean, Alan L., 127, *206*
Beard, Leo R., 111, 139, 140, 162, 164, 265
Becker, Eric B., 138, 152, 262
Becker, Michael F., 140, 168, 266
Beckman, Henry J., Foundation, 92, 278–279,
    290
Bedford, A. Marc, 112, 138, 152, 263
Beecherl, Louis A., 60, 143
Begeman, Myron L., 172, 249, 250, 253, 286
Beightler, Charles S., 142, 177, 259
Bellmont, Pig, 195
Bené, Robert W., 168, 263
Benedict, Harry Y., 187, 194, 196
Benish, Anthony A., 256
Benson, Leonard R., 254
Bergman, Theodore L., 142, 177
Berlin, University of, 4
Bertin, John J., 112, 138, 150–151, 262, 282
Bettis, Dale G., 264
Bio-Engineering Laboratory, 97
Biomedical engineering, 97, 134, 135, 139,
    141–142, 169, 172, 179–180
Bishoff, Kenneth B., 260
Black, Hulon, 59
Bluestein, Ed, 206
Boner, C. Paul, 54, 79, 180
Bonn, University of, 4
Bonner, Z. D., 118, 278–279

Borcherding, John D., 139, 159, 265, 288
Borgmann, Carl W., 78
Bostick, Frances X., 112, 140, 166, 169, 260
Bourell, David L., 141, 176, 268
Brackenridge, George Y., 34, 187
Brackenridge Hall, 36, 187, 191
Bradley, William F., 259
Breen, John E., 72, 94, 101, 111, 112, 139, 158,
    159, 260, 274, 282, 290
Breslau, University of, 4
Brittain, Perry G., 60, 143
Brock, James R., 139, 154, 259, 280
Broggs, Henry, 2
Brooks, Frederick E., 164, 165, 255
Broucke, Roger A., 138, 151, 152, 266
Broun, William L., 10
Brown, Earl I., 58
Brown, Howard E., 52, 147, 254
Brown, Kermit E., 112, 258
Brown, Newton H., 19, 22, 248, 252
Brown, S. Leroy, 28, 33
Bruns, Joe L., 69, 89, 99
Brussels, University of, 102
Bryant, Frank G., 257
Bryant, John M., 24, 27, 28–29, 32, 33, 34, 54,
    147, 248, 252
Buckman, A. Bruce, 140, 168, 266
Bucknall, Eric H., 258
Buffalo Bayou, Brazos, and Colorado Railroad, 8
Buffler, J. Robert, 254
Busch-Vishniac, Ilene J., 113, 142, 177, 284
Business, Graduate School of, 135
Business Administration, College of, 118, 136
Business Research, Bureau of, 49
Burleson Bells, 208
Burnett, John H., 7
Burns, Ned H., 89, 112, 139, 159, 195, 260, 284
Butcher, William, 139
Butler, William S., 264


C

California,
    Institute of Technology, 33, 77
    University of, 28, 59, 210
Calvit, Harry H., 262
Cambridge University, 3
Camp Mabry, 28
Cardullo, Forrest E., 24, 249, 252
Carey, Graham F., 138, 152, 154, 267
Carman, Clyde S., 89, 92, 98
Carrasquillo, Ramon, 113, 139, 159, 268, 286
Carron Ironworks, 2
Carruthers, William S., 191
Carter, William J., 76, 255
Caudle, Ben H., 74, 86, 88, 112, 142, 179, 250,

260, 282, 296

Centennial Endowed Teachers and Scholars
  Program, 122

Ceramic Engineering, 72
  Department of, 55, 56, 75, 250

Ceramics Kiln Laboratory, 156

Chance, Clayton W., 89, 90, 258

Chandy, Kanianthra M., 266

Charbeneau, Randall J., 140, 164, 267, 286

Charles II, 2

Chemical Engineering, 10, 11, 32, 38
  Department [formerly School] of, 24–26, 27,
    42, 43, 44–45, 54, 56, 72, 73, 74, 75, 81, 86,
    91, 96–97, 98, 102, 111, 112, 133–134,
    138–139, 143, 144, 148, 154–155, 179–180,
    213, 250, 299, 275, 277, 279, 281, 283, 285,
    287, 289, 291, 293, 295, 297, 299

Chemical Engineering and Petroleum Engineering Building, 121, 122, 123, 156, 292, 294, 296,
  298

Chemical Engineers, American Institute of, 42,
  69, 86, 155, 204

Chemistry, Department [formerly School] of,
  10, 26, 44, 155

Chi Epsilon, 204

Chulalongkorn University, Thailand, 60–61

Cincinatti, University of, 64

Civil Engineering, 2, 3, 4–5, 8–9, 10, 11, 14, 17,
  18, 20, 32, 43, 44, 58, 75, 80, 82, 212
  Department [formerly School] of, 22, 23–24,
    31, 36, 38, 42, 54, 56, 61, 72, 74, 81, 86, 87,
    88, 97, 98, 100–102, 105, 111, 134, 139, 143,
    144, 146, 147, 148, 155–164, 212, 213, 248,
    275, 277, 279, 281, 283, 285, 287, 289, 291,
    293, 298–299

Civil Engineers,
  American Society of, 5, 42, 106, 159, 186, 204,
    205
    Texas Section, 41
  Institution of, 3
  Society of, 3
  The University of Texas Society of, 186

Civilian Pilot Training, 51

Claire, Alexander Frederic, 187, 190–194, 197,
  201

Clark Field, 206

Clark, Lyle G., 73, 86, 138, 152, 251, 259

Clarke, Edith, 54, 256

Coates, Clarence L., 86, 92, 168, 248, 260, 72

Cockrell, Ernest, Jr., 60, 69, 79, 122, 276, 278

Cockrell, Ernest, Jr., Hall, 65, 121, 123, 134,
  194, 296, 298

Cockrell, Ernest H., 60, 143, 276

Cockrell Foundation, 122, 274–275, 276–277,
  279, 287, 289

Cogdell, John R., 140, 166, 262

Collins, Royal E., 180, 268, 276, 280

Colquitt, Oscar B., 34

Columbia University, 91

Commercial engineering, 31–32

Committee of 75, 66, 70

Computation Center, 75, 180, 187, 198

Computational Mechanics, Texas Institute for,
  138, 150, 152

Computer and Vision Research Center,
  140–141, 150, 169

Computer Science, Department of, 135, 169

Connally, John, 87, 98

Conner, Edward Coward, 190

Construction Industry Institute, 139, 150, 159

Continuing Engineering Studies, Office of
  [formerly Engineering Programs, then Engineering Institutes], 89, 98–99, 107, 132–133

Cook, Abner, 14

Cook, C. W. (Tex), 118, 206, 278–279, 290

Cooper, Hal B. H., 266

Cooper, Oscar H., 9, 14

Cooperative Engineering Education, 89, 99,
  130–131, 214

Cornell University, 18, 28, 146, 147

Corps de Ponts et Chausees, 2

Corpus Christi, 101

Correll, James A., 24, 35, 54, 248, 249, 252

Courtney, Thomas H., 263

Cragon, Harvey G., 111, 141, 172, 269, 274

Craig, Roy R., Jr., 112, 138, 151, 260, 284

Crain, Cullen M., 163, 165, 255,

Crawford, Melba M., 113

CRAY X-MP/24 supercomputer, 123, 154, 212

Crofton, Bouldin, 194

Crondstadt Docks, Russia, 3

Culberson, Charles A., 18

Cunningham, William A., 47, 48, 54, 60, 69, 74,
  75, 93, 100, 103, 154, 206, 250, 253, 278

Cunningham, William H., 106

Curtiss-Wright Engineering Cadette Program,
  51–52


D

Dallas, 146

Dalley, Joseph W., 257

Daniel, David E., Jr., 140, 156, 268, 288

Daniel, Price, 198

Darter, William C., 194

Dartmouth University, 5

Davis, Ed D., 109, 130

Davis, John H., 140, 166, 267

Dawson, Doug, 207

Dawson, Raymond F., 44, 48, 49, 61, 69, 147,
  155–156, 253, 284, 290

Defense Mapping, Committee on Education
  and Training for, 50

Defense Advanced Research Projects Agency, 80
Defense Research Laboratory, 54, 55, 72, 100, 150, 180
Degler, Howard E., 31, 33, 147, 249, 253
Delaware, University of, 64, 84
Delta Nu Alpha, 204
Detroit, University of, 118
Development Board, 99, 122
Diller, Kenneth R., 135, 141, 180, 265, 288
Dingle, William W., 257
Dolling, David S., 150
Dorfman, Myron H., 136, 141, 142, 147, 175, 177, 250, 266, 276, 280
Dornberger, Werner W., 49, 59, 204, 251, 253, 284
Dorsey, Bob R., 60, 118, 143, *207*, 278–279
Dougal, Arwin A., 72–73, 74, 88, 91, 103, 166, 167–168, 260
Doughtie, Venton L., 51, 73, 80, 172, 195, 249, 250, 253
Draper, E. Linn, 173, 264
Drawing, 74
    Department of, 22, 36, 58, 75, 86, 249
    School of, 22
Drexel Institute, 74, 84, 86
Driskill Hotel, 185, 189, 192
Duesterhoeft, William C., 92, 109, 112, 140, 167, 195, 255, 280
Duke University, 58
Dulikravich, George S., 288
Duncombe, Raynor L., 138, 151, 152, 266
DUNGS, 208


E


Eads, James B., 5
Earth Sciences and Engineering, Center for, 102, 142, 150, 178, 179, 299
Eckenfelder, W. Wesley, Jr., 164, 261
Eckerdt, John G., 138, 148, 155, 268, 288
Eckhardt, Carl J., Jr., 194, 198, 203, 208, 253, 286
Ecole des Mines, 2
Ecole des Ponts et Chausees, 2
Ecole Polytechnique, 2
Economic Geology, Bureau of [formerly Economic Geology and Technology], 24–25, 33, 35, 48, 49, 147, 148
Eddy, Amos, 261
Edgar, Thomas F., *109*, 130, 131, 133, 134, 138, 155, 179, 250, 264, 282, 296
Education, American Council on, 93, 129, 144
Education, College of, 118
Electrical and Computer Engineering [formerly Electrical Engineering], 10, 11, 18, 19, 20, 22, 24, 32, 38, 44, 54–55, 57, 82, 97, 299

Department [formerly School] of, 19, 22, 24, 42, 43, 44, 54, 72–73, 74, 75, 81, 86, 91–92, 97, 98, 100, 111, 123, 125, 131, 134–135, 140–141, 144, 164–172, 179–180, 212, 213, 248, 275, 277, 279, 281, 283, 285, 287, 289, 291, 293, 299
Electrical Engineering Research Laboratory, 54–55, 57, 82, 100, 140, 150, 164–166, 169, 299
Electrical Engineers, American Institute of, 10, 42, 204
Electromechanics and Energy Building, 123, 299
Electromechanics, Center for, 123, 141, 150, *171*, 173, 299
Electronics Research Center, 140, 148, 150, 166, 168–169
Eliezer, Zwy, 142, 176, 177, 266
Elkins, Lincoln F., 111
Ellingson, Olaf, 249
Endress, George A., 22, 29, 249
Energy Research Institute, 118,
Energy Studies, Center for, 108, 123, 134, 141, 142, 150, 173, 176, 177, 182, 299
Engineer, 93–94, *95*, 102
Engineer-In-Training examinations, 125
*Engineering*, 110
Engineering Association, 186
*Engineering Brief Case*, 103
Engineering Building [1904], 20, *21*, 33, 188, 298
Engineering Career Assistance Center [formerly the Placement Office], 47–48, 69, 89, 107, 108, 130, 214
Engineering, College [formerly Department] of [see also separate listings for programs and research centers],
    administration, 22–23, 30, 43–44, 47–49, 67–69, 74–75, 86, 89, 92, 106–108, 131, 247–251
    advisory council to the dean, 66, 75, 85
    annual report, 83–84, 110–111
    budget, 38, 48, 54, 61, 66, 69–70, 78, 80, 84, 86, 88, 90–91, 99, 113–116, 137, 144, 145, 146, 148–149, 214–216, 300–302
    computational facilities, 75, 102–103, 123, 152, 153, 154, 212
    degrees granted, 38, 61, 82, 125, 126, 127, 144, 145, 270–273
    departmental visiting committees, 46, 69, 72, 91, 133, 215
    Distinguished Graduates, 107, 127, 182, 208, 302–304
    endowments, 92, 109, 118–120, 122–123, 144, 195, 216, 274–299
    enrollment, 11–12, 17, 19, 20, 29, 30, 34, 38, 44–45, 50, 51, 52, 56, 58, 59, 61, 66–67, 74, 77, 78, 82–83, 85, 88, 93–94, 98, 99, 106–107, 123–126, 128, 129, 136, 144–145,

212–213
   foreign students, 48, 129, 130, 212
   management, 131–132, 133, 137
   minorities, 94, 128–130, 131, 144, 205, 213
   women, 51–52, 94, 127–128, 131, 213
   establishment, 14, 16–18, 20
   extension courses, 28–29, 50–51, 93, 94, 132
   faculty, 70, 77, 78, 79, 86–88, 112, 113, 211,
      252–269
   graduate education, 22, 26, 30, 32–33, 37, 42,
      43, 44, 46, 52–53, 55, 56, 58, 63, 72, 73–74,
      75, 77, 78–80, 82, 83, 97, 98, 100, 125, 130,
      131–132, 133, 134, 135, 136, 144, 145–146,
      148
   honors programs, 82–83, 94–95
   planning document, 110, 210
   publications, 49, 83–84, 110–112
   research, 48, 54–56, 66, 69, 72, 77, 81–82,
      86–87, 99–103, 106, 137–142, 144,
      145–183, 213, 214
   rivalry with School of Law, 188–194, 205
   sports, 205
   student financial aid, 78–80, 82, 91, 130, 144,
      195, 214, 290–293
   summer school, 19, 43
Engineering College Research Association, 42,
   48
Engineering Counselor, Office of, 107, 108
Engineering Data Processing Center, 75
Engineering education,
   American Civil War, 5, 7, 16
   American Revolution, 4
   American Society for, 42, 59, 76, 89, 90, 94,
      98, 110
   modern origins of,
      France, 1–2, 3, 4
      Germany, 3–4
      Great Britain, 2–3, 4
      Texas, 1, 6–10
      United States, 1, 3, 4–6
   research, 4, 48, 54–56, 210
   Society for the Promotion of, 30, 42
   through apprenticeship, 1, 2, 3
   World War I, 25, 26–30
   World War II, 54, 148
Engineering Exposition, 198–199
Engineering Foundation, 59–60, 66, 69–70, 75,
   77–78, 79, 81, 82, 83–84, 90–91, 92, 93–94,
   99, 102, 103, 107, 109, 112, 113, 114–116, 118,
   119, 120, 122, 143, 182, 196, 197, 215, 277,
   278, 279, 281, 282, 284, 285, 290
Engineering Management Society, 204
Engineering Mechanics, 54, 64
   Department of [see also Aerospace Engineer-
      ing and Engineering Mechanics, Depart-
      ment of], 58, 70, 72, 73, 251
   Research Laboratory, 138, 152, 158

Engineering, National Academy of, 72, 90, 99,
   103, 106, 111, 112, 123, 134, 137, 138, 139,
   140, 141, 142, 144, 152, 154, 155, 156, 158,
   162, 164, 166, 172, 177, 179,
Engineering Power Show, 196–197, 204
Engineering Research, 111
Engineering Research, Bureau of, 43, 48–49, 52,
   55, 69, 75, 97, 99–100, 103, 107, 108, 114, 137,
   145–146, 148, 149, 162, 169, 173, 176, 182,
   213, 214
Engineering Scholars [formerly Engineering Fel-
   lows], 82–83, 125, 127, 128
Engineering Scholarships, Office of, 109, 195
Engineering science, 58, 63, 65, 75–77, 89, 96,
   136–137
Engineering, Science, and Management War
   Training, 50–51
Engineering Science Building, 80, 81, 89, 91,
   102, 123, 174, 194, 298
Engineering-Science News, 50
Engineering Science, Society of, 204
Engineering Students' Association, 47, 197
Engineering Teaching, Bureau of, 90, 110, 107,
   214
Engineering Teaching Center II, 121, 123, 198,
   294, 296, 298
Engineering Teaching Effectiveness Colloquia,
   90
Engineers, American Association of, 204
Engineers' Ball, 194, 198
Engineers' Banquet, 29, 185–186, 201
Engineers' Club, 186
Engineers' Graduate Club, 201
Engineers' Joint Council, 88–89
Engineers' Loan Fund, 109, 195
Engineers, National Academy of, of Mexico, 106
Engineers' Reception, 186
Engines Test Laboratory, 172
Engines Research Laboratory, 172
Enhanced Oil and Gas Recovery Research, Cen-
   ter for, 142, 150
Ensminger, Richard R., 112, 261
Environmental Engineering, American Acad-
   emy of, 106,
Environmental Health Engineering Laboratory,
   80, 82, 101, 106, 140, 162
Eppes, Bill G., 258
Equal Opportunity in Engineering, 107, 109,
   129–130, 202, 213
Eta Kappa Nu, 93, 201
Ettlinger, Hyman J., 33
Everett, Raymond, 204, 252
Ewing, Benjamin B., 162, 256
Experimental Aerodynamics Laboratory, 150
Experimental Science Building, 75
Extension, Division of, 132
Eyres, Walter L., 28

**F**

Fair, James R., 111, 133, 138, 155, 268, 274, 276
Fairey, Thomas E., 197
Fancher, George H., 54, 55, 177, 250, 254, 278–279, 284–285, 296
Fannin, Bob M., 108, 140, 165, 257
Ferguson, James E., 23, 187, 192
Ferguson, Phil M., 31, 54, 72, 88, 92, 111, 112, 158, 248, 253, 278–279, 282, 284, 290
Ferguson, Phil M., Structural Engineering Laboratory [formerly the Civil Engineering Structures Research Laboratory], 72, 101, 139, 158–159, 161, 211–212, 299
Files, John T., 60, 143
Fililula Band, 185
Finch, Stanley P., 23, 32, 35, 44, 48, 54, 147, 186, 248, 252, 278
Fine, Morris, 276
Flake, Robert H., 136, 140, 167, 262
Flawn, Peter T., 106, 122, 131
Florida, University of, 78
Focht, John A., 25, 31, 46, 47, 69, 71, 89, 147, 194, 195, 247, 248, 253, 284, 290
Fonken, Gerhard J., 109
Ford, Davis L., 164
Ford Foundation, 78–79, 92, 279
Forsgard, Lee William, 190
Fowler, David W., 112, 139, 159, 162, 261, 282
Fowler, Wallace T., 110, 112, 138, 151, 153, 261, 288
Frank, D. A., 205
Frank, Karl H., 139, 159, 266, 284
Franklin, William B., 60
Franzolino, Anthony L., 108, 130
Fritz, Harry, 184, 192
Fruh, E. Gus, 164, 262, 278
Fulton, Robert, 5
Furlong, Richard W., 139, 159, 259, 278
Fusion Engineering, Center for, 108, 122, 140, 150, 172, 176
Fusion Research, Center for, 172
Fusion Studies, Institute for, 172


**G**

Gafford, Burns N., 54, 72, 86, 248, 252, 280
Gage, Stephen J., 98, 261
Galbraith, Ralph A., 54, 254
Garrett, Jerry, 197
Gas Research Institute, 177
Gatlin, Carl, 73, 74, 86, 250, 259
General Dynamics Award for Excellence in Engineering Teaching, 89–90, 99, 112–113, 127
Georgia Institute of Technology, 78

Geotechnical Engineering Center, 113, 139, 150, 156–158
German, John P., 255
Gertz, Melvin H., 60, 143, 276
Gideon, Samuel E., 26, 27, 28, 252
Giesecke, Frederic E., 22, 26, 30, 32, 35, 147, 249, 252
Gill, Joe, 191
Gill, Murray, 191
Glee Club, 207
Gloyna, Earnest F., 54, 56, 72, 74, 80, 82, 88, 101, 103, 104, 105, 106, 108, 109, 110, 111, 112, 114, 115, 118, 127, 131, 139, 140, 162, 164, 185, 201, 205, 247, 256, 276, 280
Goldsmith, Goldwin W., 30, 249, 253
Gonzalez, Mario J., Jr., 108, 248, 269
Goodenough, John B., 111, 142, 177, 269, 274
Gory Goo Roos, 187
Gottingen, University of, 10
Government Sponsored Research Office, 79
Graduate Engineering Council, 108, 201, 205
Graduate Research Internship Program, 130–131
Graduate Studies, School of, 30, 31, 32–33, 66, 98
Grady, W. Mack, 140, 167, 284
Granberry, C. Read, 44, 55, 147, 164–165, 253
Granger, Armour T., 252
Graves, Quinton B., 56, 254
Gray, Kenneth E., 86, 92, 102, 136, 142, 150, 179, 250, 260, 280, 284
Great Depression, 22, 30, 33, 37, 39, 46, 49
Greene, O. K., 191
Greer, Dewitt C., 87, 92, 263, 280
Gregg, William D., 262
Griffis, William K., 255
Griffith, Dean E., 89, 99, 132
Griswold, John, 44, 154, 254
Guernsey, Roscoe, 254
Guggenheim Foundation, 33
Gulf Universities Research Corporation, 100
Gunter, Edmund, 2


**H**

Hackerman, Norman, 86, 89, 90, 92, 102, 106
Hagerty, William W., 48, 58, 64–65, 66, 67–70, 73, 74, 75, 76–77, 80, 81, 84, 86, 91, 96, 114, 115, 125, 196, 247, 259, 286
Haliburton Education Foundation, 92, 280–281
Halton, John C., 115
Hamilton, Mark F., 142, 177
Hamlin, Edwin W., 54, 164, 165, 254
Hampton, Loyd D., 150, 182
Harbourt, Cyrus O., 112
Hargis, John, 129

Harper, Henry W., 32
Harris, Harwell T., 59
Harris, Roy, 136
Hartwig, William H., 84, 99, 168, 257, 286
Harvard University, 5, 210
Haupt, Herman, 5
Haurwitz, Bernard, 261
Hayes, Linda J., 113, 138, 152, *153*, 267, 288
Haywood, Marcel, 129
Healey, Anthony J., 265
Health, National Institute of, 63, 80, 164
Helwig, William F., 253
Herman, Robert, 111, 139, 162, 268, 280
Hertel, Nolan E., 141, 176, 268
Heyt, John W., 173
Hickey Quartet, 190
Higher Education, Texas Commission on, 57
High-Performance Computing, Center for, 123, 212
Highway Research, Center for, 100–101, 139, 159–160
Hill, A. Daniel, 179, 284
Himmelblau, David M., 80, 133, 138, 154, 250, 258, 278, 296
Hixson, Elmer L., 140, 167, 258
Hoberock, Lawrence L., 263
Hocott, Billy and Claude R., Distinguished Engineering Research Award, 112
Hocott, Claude R., 111, 112, 142, 179, 254
Hogg, James S., 18
Holley, A. L., 5
Holley, Edward R., 140, 164, 268, 278
Hollingsworth, Paul, 114
Holmes, James R., 254
Hougen, Joel O., 92, 154, 262
Hough, Eldred W., *41*, 257
Houston, David F., 20, 22
Houston, University of, 144
Howell, John R., 135, 142, 176, 267, 278
Hudson, W. R., 47
Hudson, William R., 103, 107, 139, 162, 247, 261, 280
Hull, David G., 138, 152, 262, 282
Hume, John, 60
Humenick, Michael J., 264
Hunnicutt, William H. P., 11, 12
Huston-Tillotson College, 93, 132

I
Illinois, University of, 28, 30, 59
Industrial Associates, 77–78, 89, 92, 99, 116
Industrial Chemistry, Bureau of [formerly the Division of Chemistry], 24–25, 49, 52, 55, 56, 148
Industrial engineering, 58

Industrial Revolution, 2
Inman, Bobby R., 60, *143*
Iota Sigma Pi, 204
Itoh, Tatsuo, 140, 150, 166, 169, 267, 280

J

J Hall, 29
Jacoby's Beer Garden, 191, 208
James, Hinton, 5
Jefferson, Nellie, 51
Jehn, Kenneth H., 58, 100, 165, 256
Jensen, Paul A., 142, 177, 262, 280
Jessen, Frank W., *41*, 257, 280, 286
Jirsa, James O., 139, 150, 158–159, 265, 278
Johns Hopkins University, 105
Johnson, C. Philip, 139, 159, 264
Johnson, Franklin B., 72, 86, 155, 251, 258
Johnson, James A., 99
Johnson, Lyndon B., 55, 158
Johnston, Keith P., 138, 155, 284
Jones, Charles F., 60
Jones, Cy, 191
Jones, Jerold W., 142, 176, 265
Jones, Lawrence B., 60
Jones-Lindzey report, 134, 144
Jordan, Bryce, 106, 131
Jordan, Louis, 27, 206
Josey, Jack S., *206*, 280–281
*Journal of Architecture, Engineering, and Industry*, 49
*Journal of Engineering and Industrial Research*, 49
Juricic, Davor, 136, 141, 177, 268

K

Kasch, John E., 60, 143, *203*, 296
Katz, Donald L., 78
Keller Personalized System of Instruction, 110
Kelly Field, San Antonio, 29
Kennedy, Thomas W., 107, 108, *109*, 139, 162, 247, 261, 278
Kent, Harry L., Jr., 61, 73, 112, 250, 254, 280
King, Joe J., 60, 92, 115, 118, *206*, 280–281, 290
Professional Engineering Achievement Award, 127
King's College, 3, 4
Klein, Dale E., 135, 141, 174, 267
Klingner, Richard, 139, 159, 267, 284
Knapp, Roy M., 265
Kobe, Kenneth A., 54, *87*, 154, 250, 255, 281
Koen, Billy V., 110, 141, 176, 263
Konecci, Eugene B., 96, 262
Korean War, 52

Koros, William J., 138, 154, 269, 282
Koschmieder, E. Lothar, 140, 164, 263
Kosciuszko, Thaddeus, 4
Kowarski, Lew, 263
Kreisle, Leonardt F., 75, 89, 90, 94, 108, 112, 194, 195, 198, 208, 255, 294
Krezdorn, Roy R., 255
Kuehne, Hugo F., 22, 26, 249
Kweehee Club, 186, 192
Kyriakides, Stelios, 138, 151, 152, 268, 284


L


LaCoste, Lucien J. B., 180
LaGrone, Afred H., 100, 165, 258
Lainiotis, Demetrios G., 262
Lake, Larry W., 142, 150, 179, 268, 280
Lamb, J. Parker, Jr., 82, 107, *109*, 112, 133, 135, 138, 150, 151, 173, 247, 250, 251, 260, 278
Lamont, Norman, 258
Land Grant Association, 48
Lane, Alvin V., 11–12, 14
Lanham, William T., 20
Lasdon, Leon S., 267
Lawhon, Ruth W., 52
Lawler, Desmond F., 140, 164, 268, 288
Lawrence, Abbot, 5
Learned Societies, American Council of, 143
Lebeaux, Jacob M., 256
Ledbetter, Joe O., 164, 259
Lee, Clyde E., 101, 139, 159, 259, 278
Leipziger-Pearce, Hugo, 254
Lenhart, Jack, 75, 254
Lerner, Bernard J., 257
Lesso, William G., 110, 132, 142, 177, 247, 262, 278
Liberal Arts, College of, 94, 120, 132
Liljestrand, Howard M., 140, 164, 268, 284
Linder, Clarence L., 60
Linvill, William, 118
Lipovski, Gerald J., 172, 266
Little Campus [formerly the Blind Institute], 29, 35
Livesay, Henry G., 249
Lloyd, Douglas R., 138, 155, 269, 288
Locy, Jack J., 120, 122, 182
Loehr, Raymond C., 111, 140, 164, 269, 274
Long, Wayne E., 61, 173, 257
Longhorn Band, 207–208
Longhorn Hall of Fame, 206
Louisiana State University, 10
Lowenberg, Edwin C., 259
Lower Colorado River Authority, 164

M

MacFarlane, Alexander, 10, 11
MacGregor, George L., 60, 73
Machemehl, Randy B., 139, 162, 267
Mack, Lawrence R., 138, 152, 260
Magruder, John B., 6
Mahmassani, Hani S., 139, 162
Maidment, David R., 140, 164, 269, 288
Main Building, 8, 14, 17, 20, *21*, 36, 208
Malek, Miroslaw, 172, 267, 288
Malina, Joseph F., Jr., 80, 82, *109*, 134, 139, 162, 164, 248, 259, 278
Mallet, John W., 10–11
Mansbendel, Peter, 192
Mansbendel, Peter, Jr., 89
Marcus, Harris L., 135, 141, 150, 176, 266, 280
Marcus, Stephen I., 140, 169, 266, 284
Marshek, Kurt M., 142, 176, 177, 269, 286
Martin, Norman M., 266
Masada, Glenn Y., 142, 176, 286
Masch, Frank D., 162, 260
Massachusetts Institute of Technology, 5, 22, 26, 28, 30, 44, 58, 75, 77, 91, 162, 172, 210
Materials Science and Engineering, Center for, 141, 150, 171, 176–177
Mathematics, Department [formerly School] of, 10, 33
Matlock, L. Hudson, 134, 156, 158, 248, 257
Matthews, Ronald D., 142, 176, 268, 286
Maxey, Margaret M., 113, 118, 120, 269, 276
Mays, Larry W., 140, 164, 267, 288
McBee, Frank W., Jr., 118, 182
McClain, Peggy Jean, 83
McClung, James D., 256
McClure, Paul F., *109*, 114–115
McCrocklin, Andrew J., 255
McCullough, B. Franklin, 139, 150, 162, 264, 278
McFarland, James D., 22, 58–59, 86, *109*, 147, 195, 196, 249, 253
McGuire, Noel C., 256
McKetta, John J., Jr., 47, 54, 60, 64, *65*, 72, 73, 80, 85–86, *87*, 88, 89, 90, 92, 93, 94, 96, 98, 99, 103, 111, 112, 114, 115, 122, 125, 154, 247, 250, 256, 276, 280, 282–283, 296
McKinney, Chester M., 182
McKinney, Richard W., Engineering Library, 46–47, 80, 122, 193, 194, 212, 296–297
McLaurin, Banks L., 31, 58, 191, 194, 195, 248, 251, 253, 286
McMath, Hugh L., 59, 249, 253
McNeill, Walter H., 22, 59, 249, 252
Mechanical Engineering, 3, 8–9, 10, 24, 28, 29,

30, 32, 38, 43, 44, 82, 208, 299
  Department [formerly School] of, 24, 29–30,
    31, 33, 36, 42, 51, 54, 58, 73–74, 81, 86, 98,
    102, 111, 135, 141, 143–144, 147–148, 169,
    172–177, 180, 213, 249, 275, 279, 281, 283,
    285, 287, 289, 291, 295, 297
  Laboratory, 36, 208
  Propulsion Laboratory, 82, 173
  Thermal Systems Laboratory, 173
Mechanical Engineers,
  American Society of, 10, 40, 42, 204
  Institution of, 3
Meek, Paul D., 60, 143, 282–283
Megathemollipod, 194
Memorial Stadium, 206, 208
Mercer, M. Ray, 140, 143, 167, 284
Meteorology, 28, 55, 58, 75, 100, 165
Mexico, 93, 106
Meyer, Alvin H., 139, 162
Meyer, Warren A., 255
Mezes, Sidney W., 23, 32
Michigan, University of, 5, 24, 33, 64, 73, 76,
  78, 86
Microelectronics and Computer Technology
  Corporation, 135, 140, 141
Microelectronics Research Center, 140, 150, 167,
  169, 170
Miksad, Richard W., 139, 140, 157, 164, 266, 284
Military Aeronautics, School of, 28–29, 33
Military engineering, 2, 9
Military Engineers, American Institute of, 201
Military Physics Research Laboratory, 100, 180
Miller, John D., 195
Miller, Mark A., 286
Mills, W. Charles, 197
Mining and Metallurgical Engineers, American
  Society of, 35, 42
Mining Engineering, 3, 18, 19, 20, 22
  School of, 19, 22, 248
Mining Engineers, American Institute of, 204
Mining, Metallurgical, and Petroleum Engi-
  neers, American Institute of, 204
Minnesota, University of, 64
Missouri, University of, 6
Moncrief, Jack, 179
Moncure, Leah, 52, 53
Moody, Dan, 192
Moore, Joe, 184, 192
Moore, Walter L., 64, 72, 86, 88, 159, 162, 248,
  256
Moree, Calvin, 202
Morehouse College, 129
Morgan, Carl W., 89, 90, 108, 109, 112, 130, 162,
  195, 256

Morrill Act, 5, 48
Mount Locke Millimeter-Wave Observatory, 100,
  165–166, 299
Munich, University of, 4
Municipal Research and Reference, Bureau of,
  147
Murchison, Clint W., Sr., Chair of Free Enter-
  prise, 111, 113, 118, 120, 276
Murray, William J., Jr., 60, 69, 79, 288


N

Nacozy, Paul E., 138, 152, 263
Nagle, James, 12
Napier, John, 2
Nash, James P., 147
Nation, Carry, 187–188
National Aeronautics and Space Administra-
  tion, 64, 69, 73, 80, 90, 99, 102, 133, 151, 165
National Architect Accrediting Board, 30
National Defense Education Act, 90
National Defense Program, 50
National Engineers' Week, 201
National Environmental Development Associa-
  tion, 106
National Oceanographic and Atmospheric Ad-
  ministration, 151
National Research Council, 84, 143
National Science Foundation, 48, 63, 72, 75,
  79–80, 81, 88, 90, 100, 138, 139, 140, 142, 143,
  144, 149, 151, 155, 159, 164, 165, 166, 167,
  169, 177
Natural Sciences, College of, 120
Neff, Pat M., 34
Neikirk, Dean P., 140, 169, 284
Nelson, Priscilla, 113, 139
Newcomen, Thomas, 2
Newton, William N., 255
Nexus, 111
Nobel Prize for Chemistry, 87, 102, 111, 112
North, Eliphalet, 5
North Carolina State University, 78
North Carolina, University of, 5
Norwich University, 4
Nuclear Engineering, 58, 73–74, 98
  Teaching Laboratory, 141, 174, 176
Nuclear Radiation Laboratory, 173
Nuclear Reactor Laboratory, 73–74


O

Oberkampf, William L., 173, 264

O'Connor, James T., 139, 159
Oden, J. Tinsley, 138, 150, 152, 265, 280
O'Donnell, Peter, 122
Ohio State University, 28
Olson, R. W., 60
Olson, Roy E., 139, 157, 264, 280
Omega Chi Epsilon, 204
Operation FEW, 94
Operation Gopher, 198, *199*
Oughtred, William, 2


P


Painter, Theophilus S., 28, 55
Panton, Ronald L., 142, 176, 265
Parker, Denny, 19
Parker, Robert L., Sr., 60, 118, 143, *206*,
    282–283
Partridge, Alden, 4
Paul, Donald R., 112, 133, 138, 150, 154, 155,
    250, 263, 276, 280
Pearce, John A., 140, 286
Pease, Elisha M., 16
Pence, Forrest K., 56, 250, 254
Penn Field, 28
Peregrinus, 189–190, 197
Permanent University Fund, 16–18, 20, 34–35
Perronet, Jean Randolphe, 2
Perry, Ervin S., 88, 93, 261
Peters, Ekwere J., 113, 142, 177, 268, 286
Petroleum Club, 204
Petroleum Engineering [formerly Petroleum
    Production
    Engineering], 38, 55–56, 98, 102
    Building, *45*, 46, 80, 123, 298
    Department of, 33, 42, 43, 44–45, 54, 58, 69,
        74, 81, 86, 91, 111, 136, 142, 177–179, 180,
        213, 250, 275, 277, 279, 281, 283, 285, 287,
        289, 293, 295, 297, 299
Petroleum Engineers, Society of, 204
Pharmacy, Department of, 155
Phi Lambda Upsilon, 204
Phillips, William B., 19, 248, 252
Physics, Department [formerly School] of, 10,
    11, 28, 33, 81, 92, 102, 111, 112, 168, 180, 182
Pi Epsilon, 204
Pi Epsilon Tau, 204
Pi Sigma Pi, 110, 130, *202*, 205
Pi Tau Sigma, 201–202
Pirson, Sylvain J. G., 258, 296
Pittsburgh, University of, 107
*Placement Manual*, 108
Plasma Dynamics Laboratory, 72
Plass, Harold J., Jr., 251, 257
Plummer, Frederick B., 33, 250, 253, 298
Podio, Augusto L., 88, 142, 179, 263, 280

Pollard, James J., 61, 72, 251, 256
Polymer Research, Center for, 138, 150, 155
Pope, Gary A., *109*, 136, 142, 179, 250, 267, 280,
    288
Popescue, Calin M., 139, 159, 266, 286
Popovich, Robert P., 134, 139, 179, 265, 282
Porter, John W., 138, 152, 261
Potter, A. A., 43
Powell, Major W. J., 194
Power, Harry H., *41*, 54, 250, 254, 282
Powers, Edward J., Jr., *109*, 112, 135, 140, 150,
    168, 248, 261, 280, 282
Prairie View A&M University, 93, 129
Prather, William L., 19, 20, 187
Priddy, Ashley H., 118, 282
Prigogine, Ilya, 87, 102, 111, 112, 263
Professional Development, Engineering Council
    for, 40, 42, 44, 56, 57, 59, 63, 65–66, 67, 70,
    84, 93, 96, 99
Professional Engineers,
    National Society of, 41, 52, 113
    Texas Society of, 41, 82, 88, 112, 196, 204,
        205, 212
Psychology, Department of, 102
Ptah, 195
Public Affairs, Lyndon Baines Johnson School
    of, 118, 132
Purdue University, 43


Q


Quartermaster Research and Engineering Com-
    mand, 158


R


Rainey, Homer P., 44, 50
Ralls, Kenneth M., 112, 141, 176, 263
Ramamoorthy, Chittoor V., 263
Ramsey, Joseph W., 20, 24, 27, 54, 248, 252
Ramshorn, 195–196, 201
    Association, 196, 197, 201
    Club, 196
    Society, 196, 204
Ransom, Harry H., 66–67, 73, 78, 81, 89, 90, 93
Rase, Howard F., 72, 86, 88, 94, 97, 112, 132,
    138, 154, 250, 257, 278
Rathbun, Kenneth C., 82, 173, 258
Regents' Endowed Teachers and Scholars Pro-
    gram, 122
Reed, Walter S., 136, 141, 177, 265, 288
Reeder, W. Thomas, *109*
Reese, Lymon C., 72, 86, 88, 107, 111, 112, 132,
    134, 139, 150, 156, 162, 247, 248, 258, 274, 282
Rensselaer Polytechnic Institute, 4, 19, 186

Research and Development, Balcones Institute
   for, 137
Research Applied to National Needs, 137
Research Laboratory in Ceramics, 56
Research Triangle, North Carolina, 210
Rice, William Marshall, University, 77
Richardson, Phillip C., 263
Ripperger, Eugene A., 97, 138, 152, 156, 158,
   180, 256
Roberts, Oran M., 8, 13
Robottom, Jack, 130
Rochelle, Gary T., 155, 267, 286
Roebuck, John, 2
Roesset, José M., 139, 157, 268, 292
Rogers, Lorene L., 106
Rohlich, Gerard A., 111, 164, 265, 278, 282
Rolfe, Walter T., 30, 249, 253
Root, Paul J., 258
Roth, Charles H., Jr., 112, 140, 169, 260
Rowe, Charles E., 19, 22, 28, 35, 47, 147, 195,
   247, 248, 249, 252, 288
Royal Military Academy,
   in Great Britain, 4
   in Poland, 4
Royal Society, 2, 10
Ruffini, F. E., 14
Rundell, Herbert A., 258
Runge, Thomas M., 180, 263
Runnels, Hardin R., 7, 9
Rusticusses, 187
Rylander, H. Grady, Jr., 109, 112, 135, 141, 173,
   195, 250, 256, 280, 282
Rylander, H. Grady, III, 140, 180


S

Saint Patrick, 191
San Antonio, 8, 29, 94
San Jacinto Monument, 156
Sandberg, Irwin W., 111, 141, 172, 269, 274
Santa Rita Number One, 35, 208
Santee Canal, South Carolina, 5
Scanlan, Jack A., 73, 256
Schechter, Robert S., 111, 112, 133, 136, 142,
   154, 179, 250, 258, 274, 276, 278
Schmidt, Philip S., 112, 129, 142, 176, 264
Schoch, E. P., Laboratories, 45, 46, 123, 298
Schoch, Eugene P., 24–25, 33, 42, 44, 49, 52, 57,
   118, 148, 154, 162, 204, 207–208, 250, 252, 282
Schutz, Bob E., 138, 151, 264, 286
Science, National Academy of, 102
Sciences, Academy of, of Venzuela, 106
Scott, Arthur C., 19, 22, 248, 252
Seaman, John N., 256
Seamans, Robert C., 123
Sellards, Elias H., 33

Separations Research Program, 138, 155, 157
Sepehnoori, Kamy, 142, 177, 269, 288
Shallene, Wilbert E., 256
Sheehan, John W., 60, 143
Sheffield, J. E., 4
Short, Byron E., 49, 54, 58, 73, 88, 147, 172, 247,
   249, 253
Shurtz, Robert F., 256
Shutts, William H., 257
Siegel, Ernest M., 164
Sigma Gamma Tau, 204
Silberberg, Irwin H., 142, 177
Silicon Valley, 210
Sill, Fort, Oklahoma, 29
Simmons, Charles M., 60, 143
Sims, Orland Lecompte, 190
Sipes, Teresa Gail, 128
Skull and Bones, 187
Sladek, K. J., 168
Sloan, Alfred P., Foundation, 110
Slonneger, Robert D., 257
Smeaton, John, 2–3
Smerdon, Ernest T., 111, 140, 150, 162, 164, 269
Smith, Ashbel, 10
Smith, Bettie Margaret, 205, 276–277, 282–283,
   298
Smith, Harold W., 100, 112, 163, 165, 166, 169,
   140, 256
Smith, Preston, 87
Smith, Richard T., 259
Smokey, 208
Snow, Lowber D., 205
Social Sciences Research Council, 143
Sorber, Charles A., 107, 109, 132, 140, 202, 248,
   268, 282, 284
South Carolina Railroad, 6
Southern Interstate Nuclear Board, 98
Southwest Placement Association, 48
Space Research and Applications, Center for,
   138, 151–152
Spanos, Polichronis D., 267, 286
Speece, Richard E., 264
Spence, David W., 12
Speyer, Jason L., 112, 138, 152, 267, 282
Sphinx Club, 204
Splawn, Walter M. W., 32, 44
Spurr, Stephen H., 106, 141
Staley, Raymond C., 257
Stanford University, 33, 75, 118, 210
Staph, Horace E., 255
Stark, John P., 141, 176, 261
Statistical Mechanics, Center for, 87, 102
Stearman, Ronald O., 102, 138, 152, 262
Steel Construction, American Institute of, 80
Steel, Ernest W., 54, 56, 60, 162, 248, 257
Steinfink, Hugo, 139, 154, 259, 282

Steinmark, Freddie, 206
Stephenson, Charles, *178*
Stern, Morris, 138, 151, 262
Steyer, Carl C., 258
Stice, James E., 90, 94, 110, 112, 263, 280
Stokoe, Kenneth H., II, 139, 157, 265, 278
Stone, Robert L., 56, 156, 250, 257
Storey, Lawrence J., 16
Straiton, Archie W., 54, 60, 82, 86, 88, 100, 111, 118, 134, 164, 165, 166, 248, 255, 290
Strategic Defense Initiative, 141, 174
Streetman, Ben G., 135, 140, 150, 169, 269, 274, 27
Structural Mechanics Research Laboratory, 72, 102, 158
Structures Fatigue Research Laboratory, 82, 159
Student Affairs, Office of, 214
Student Architects, Association of, 204
Student Army Training Corps, 27
Student Engineering Council, 108, 127, 194, 196, 197–201, 205
    Engineering Leadership Service Award, 200–201
Suren, George A., 23
Swanson, Donald S., 261
Swearingen, Judson S., 254, 276
Szebehely, Victor G., 112, 133, 138, 151–152, 251, 263, 274
Szygenda, Stephen A., 110, 111, 150, 183, 266, 276, 282


T

Tapley, Byron D., 72, 73, 86, 88, 92, 133, 138, 150, 151, 251, 259, 276, 284
Tasch, Al F., Jr., 141, 269, 274
Tau Beta Pi, 201
Tau Sigma Delta, 204
Taylor, Herbert L., 262
Taylor T-Room, 123, 198
Taylor, T. U., Hall of Engineering, 36, *37*, 40, 73, 75, 123, 135, 147, 186, 198, 298
Taylor, T. U., Foundation, 195
Taylor, Thomas U., 11, 13–14, *15*, 17, 18, 20, 22, 23, 24, 27, 30, 31, 32, 35, 37–38, 40, 41, 46, 92, 108, 114, 115, 118, 146, 162, 185–186, 187, 188–189, 192, *193*, 194, 195–196, 198, 205, 247, 248, 249, 252, 282, 292
Taylor's Bandits, 189
Tchernev, Dimiter I., 263
Teasdale, Arthur R., 256
TECEM Club, 191
Technology Development and Transfer, Center for, 120, 122, 146, 182, 213–214
Telford, Thomas, 3
Tennessee, University of, 40, 51

Tennessee Valley Authority, 40, 48
Terrell, Alexander W., 9
Tesar, Delbert, 136, 142, 177, 269, 274
Texas
    Academy of, 87
    Agricultural and Mechanical University, 6, 9, 12, 16, 17, 19, 20, 22, 26, 30, 31, 55, 125, 137, 177, 208
    Atomic Energy Advisory Committee, 98
    Atomic Energy Research Foundation, 73, 92, 172, 282–283, 288–289
    Engineering Registration Act, 41
    Highway Commission, 87
    Highways and Public Transportation, Department of, 23, 100, 105, 147, 158, 163
    Industrial and Commercial Resources Council, 49
    Memorial Museum, 194
    Petroleum Research Committee, 55–56, 142, 177
    Railgun, 174
    Railroad Commission, 55, 177
    Reconfigurable Architecture Computer, 141, 170, 172
    State Lunatic Asylum, 147
    Technological College, 105
    The University of,
        at Arlington, 92–93
        at Austin, [see also separate listings for subdivisions, buildings, and programs]
            centennial, 197, 209–211
            Distinguished Alumni, *206–207*, 208
            establishment, 6–10
            honor system, 195
            seal, 208
        at El Paso, 19, 92–93
        at San Antonio, 108, 110, 132, 180
        in the Permian Basin, 103, 132
    Water Development Board, 165
Theta Xi, 186–187
Thomas, Ian B., 112
Thompson, Edward W., 266
Thompson, Ernest O., 55, 177
Thompson, J. Neils, 44, 55, 81, 88, 100, 102, 112, 137, 148, 156, 158, 206, 255, 286
Thompson, Milton J., 51, 54, 70, 86, 150, 251, 255, 282, 292
Thompson, T. William, 267, 288
Thurston, George B., 135, 141–142, 180, 264
TOKAMAK, 92, 172, 173
Tolbert, Charles W. 100, 165
Toombs, Alf, 185, 188, 191, 192
Toprac, A. Anthony, 82, 158, 159, 198, 257
Townes, Charles Evans, 188–189, 191
Trachtenberg, Isaac, 139, 155
Tracor, Inc., 114, 182

Transportation Research, Center for, 139, 163
Traver, Alfred E., 142, 177, 286
Treat, Burnett F., 253
TRIGA Mark I thermal fission reactor, 73–74, 98, 135, 174, 176
Trudaine, D. C., 2
Trull, Robert B., 276–277
T-Square Club, 186
Tucker, Richard L., 139, 159, 267, 282
Tullis, John L., 60
Tulsa, University of, 74
Turnbow, James W., 112, 257
Turpin, Robert D., 257
Tyler, Richard G., 23, 27, 31, 147, 252

U

Udden, Johann A., 35
Uncle Nasty's, 208
Union College, 5
Union Theological Seminary, 118
United States
    Air Force, Department of the, 102, 151, 165, 166
    Army, Department of the, 100, 105, 165, 166
    Army Signal Corps 24, 28
    Atomic Energy Commission, 73, 80, 98, 158, 164, 174
    Defense, Department of, 168, 182
        Atomic Support Agency, 158
        Joint Services Electronics Program, 63, 86, 91–92, 140, 166–168, 179
    Energy, Department of, 142, 172, 177
    Environmental Protection Agency, 106
    Geological Survey, 13, 146
    Housing and Urban Development, Department of, 102, 158
    International Cooperation Administration, 60
    Military Academy, West Point, 4, 6
    Navy, Department of the, 165, 166, 180
        V–12 Flight Training Group, 51
    Transportation, Department of, 163
University College, 3
University Excellence Program, 66, 77, 78
University of Texas Engineer, The, 49
University Power Plant, 24, 33, 36, 146
Upthegrove, William R., 86, 88, 250, 261

V

Vallance, Alexander, 33, 249, 252
Valvano, Jonathan W., 140, 284
Vanderbilt University, 6
van Rensberg, Willem C. J., 136, 142, 269, 278
van Rensselaer, Stephen, 4

Van Winkle, Matthew, 72, 87, 92, 154, 250, 257, 278, 282
Vaughn, Glenn, 184, 192
Vector, 111, 198
Venezuela, 93, 106
Villanova University, 64
Vinson, Robert E., 28
Virginia Military Institute, 6
Virginia, University of, 6, 10, 13, 14, 195
Vliet, Gary C., 142, 176, 265, 284
Vogel, Wolfhard, 166
Vogt, Fred B., 97, 134, 139, 264
Volterra, Enrico G., 80, 251, 258

W

Wagner, Edward J., 259
Wagner, Gerald, 264
Wagner, Louis C., 186, 195, 249
    Scholarship Fund, 82
Wagner, Norman K., 140, 164, 262
Wagner, Terry J., 140, 169, 261
Walls, H. Alan, 142, 177, 261
Walser, Rodger M., 140, 168, 264, 280
Walton, C. Michael, 139, 162, 265, 286
War Research Laboratory, 180
Ward, Joe E., 192
Warner, Robert W., 54, 248, 254
Washington, George, 4
Washington and Lee University, 6
Washington University, St. Louis, 6, 204
Water Pollution Control Federation, 106
Water Resources, Center for Research in, 82, 101–102, 106, 139, 150, 163, 164, 212
Watt, James, 3
Watt, John R., 255
Weaver, Hal C., 24, 27, 28–29, 31, 33, 35, 36, 147, 249, 252
    Power Plant, 147
Webb, Walter P., 208
Weiss, E. Joseph, 56, 156, 250, 257
Welch, Ashley J., 140, 179, 261, 278
Welch, Ruby, 47
Weldon, William F., 135, 141, 150, 173
Westkaemper, John C., 112, 138, 151, 257
Wheat, Dan L., 113, 139, 159
Wheat, Harovel, 113
White, Robert L., 35, 36, 248, 252
Whitney, F. L., 28
Wilkov, Melvin A., 261
Williamson, Thomas, 6
Wilson, Logan R., 65, 66, 69, 70, 73, 74, 84, 129
Winston, George T., 18
Wisconsin, University of, 40
Wise, Gary L., 140, 168, 267, 286
Wissler, Eugene H., 74, 86, 97, 107, 112, 132,

133, 138, 154, 247, 250, 258, 278
Womack, Baxter F., 140, 167, 260
Women Engineers, Society of, 128, *202*,
   204–205
Women Student Architects and Engineers, So-
   ciety of, 204–205
Wood, Frank P., 107, 137
Woodson, Herbert H., 108, 111, 112, 135, 140,
   141, 150, 167, 172, 173, *179*, 182, 248, 265,
   274, 282
W. R. Woolrich Laboratories [formerly the Engi-
   neering Laboratories Building], 77, 80, 81, *83*,
   *91*, 123, 298
Woolrich, Willis R., 19, 39–*41*, 42, 43, 44, 46,
   47, 48, 50, 51, 52, 54, 59–61, 75, 76, 80, 92,
   99, 114, 147, 156, 1776, 185, 194, 196, 197,
   198, 247, 254, 284
Wooten, Thomas D., 18
World of Engineering, 130, 204
World War I, 27–30, 186, 192
World War II, 33, 44, 46, 50–54, 148

Wright, Marvin, Engineering Athlete Award,
   207
Wright, R. Earle, 60, 118, 143, 292
Wright, Stephen G., 139, 157, 264, 282, 286
Wu, Chuan-lin, 141, 172, 269, 286


Y

Yale University, 5, 54
Yew, Ching-Hsie, 138, 151, 260, 286
Young, Dana, 54, 58, 251, 255
Youngblood, William A., 259
Yuan, Shao W., 259
Yura, Joseph A., 112, 139, 158, 159, 262, 278


Z

Zapalac, William F., Jr., 207
Zoology, School of, 28